SEXUAL DIMORPHISM

SEXUAL DIMORPHISM

IN THE

ANIMAL KINGDOM

A THEORY OF THE EVOLUTION OF SECONDARY SEXUAL CHARACTERS

BY

J. T. CUNNINGHAM, M.A.

FORMERLY FELLOW OF UNIVERSITY COLLEGE, OXFORD; AUTHOR OF 'MARKETABLE
MARINE FISHES OF THE BRITISH ISLANDS.'

WITH THIRTY-TWO ILLUSTRATIONS

LONDON
ADAM AND CHARLES BLACK
1900

PREFACE

IT must be admitted that my discussion of Sexual Dimorphism in this work is incomplete, and this in two senses. In the first place, evidence of the kind I have endeavoured to collect is in many cases wanting, and has yet to be obtained in the future. The absence of such information is partly due to the difficulty of obtaining it, to the want of opportunities, and partly to the neglect of opportunities and to the absence of any special efforts to obtain it. It is not my intention by such an assertion to throw the blame upon collectors and field naturalists. Their methods of work are naturally adapted to the ends they have in view, and so long as the minute study of habits and conditions of life is generally regarded as of little importance, so long will the collection of specimens and the discovery of species be considered the chief objects of a zoological expedition. It is strange that even from the point of view of selection more attention has not been devoted since Darwin's time to the study of the particular functions or utilities of special characters. When we desire to know fully the irritations and stimulations produced on living tissues by the special habits of the animal, and how its special organs or characters are affected when they come into action, it is clear that the detailed study of the habits of the living animal becomes still more important. A zoological expedition, provided only with notebooks and drawing materials, and strictly forbidden to kill, preserve, or bring home a single specimen, might obtain results of the greatest value to science.

It is surprising that our scientific menageries have not added more to our knowledge in the direction to which I refer. It is true that many interesting and valuable observations have been made, but as the description of the behaviour of a living animal adds so much less to a man's reputation than an anatomical or systematic research, the study of habits makes slow progress.

If the incompleteness of my work in this sense should appear to be a reason for deferring its publication, I would plead a hope that in its present state it may stimulate and suggest investigations, which are not likely to be undertaken until the importance of their object is realised.

But I cannot claim that my book contains all the information that has been recorded, or that I have fully considered that information. The reason of this is that, owing to the pressure of other duties, I was unable to devote more time to it. If I had not published it now as it is, it might never have been published at all—a contingency which, whatever my fellow-zoologists may think, I at least could not accept with equanimity.

Incomplete as it is, the book would have been much more so but for the generous aid of many able friends. Mr. E. W. L. Holt supplied me with valuable material for the Chapter on Fishes, and also assisted by superintending the preparation of some of the illustrations. Mr. Rupert Vallentin allowed me to make use of the unique photographs from the living elephant seal which he took with his own camera in the Falkland Islands. To Dr. Hans Gadow I am deeply indebted for much information and many suggestions, especially in reference to the Chapters on Mammals and Birds. In fact, without Dr. Gadow's advice and influence the book would probably never have appeared. Dr. A. G. Butler, Mr. G. A. Boulenger, F.R.S., and other members of the Staff did everything in their power to facilitate my work at the Natural History Museum. To these friends, and also to the artists who have supplied the figures, Miss S. A. Willis, Mr. H. Grönvold, and Mr. E. Knight, I have much pleasure in recording my gratitude.

Apart from these contributions the book consists very largely of facts and descriptions taken from zoological literature, and few of the facts are based on my own observations. It is, indeed, for the most part, a compilation, and the only part of it for which the author is specially responsible is the theory, which by many will probably be considered the least valuable part. Such an opinion may be really correct. I would only ask that the theory I have tried to elaborate shall not be condemned and rejected merely because it is in opposition to the views which have the sanction of authority. Mr. Arthur Balfour has maintained, with much ingenuity, that authority is the surest foundation of belief. However it may be in matters theological, history proves that, in matters intellectual, authority is merely an obstacle to progress, and that the only sound foundation for belief is reason. I appeal to reason, and if my arguments are ultimately proved to be unsound, no one will regret their demolition less than myself.

J. T. CUNNINGHAM.

PENZANCE, *Nov.* 1899.

CONTENTS

INTRODUCTION

CHAPTER I

MAMMALS

CHAPTER II

BIRDS

CHAPTER III

REPTILES AND AMPHIBIA

CHAPTER IV

FISHES

CHAPTER V

INSECTS

CHAPTER VI

CRUSTACEA

CHAPTER VII

MOLLUSCA, CHÆTOPODA, AND LOWER SUB-KINGDOMS

SEXUAL DIMORPHISM

INTRODUCTION

IN investigating the history, and attempting to discover the causes, of the evolution of the animal kingdom, it is of great importance that we should have a correct conception, and a logical analysis of the phenomena to be explained, the phenomena of animal structure. In the first place structural differences divide animals into groups which are separated in different degrees in relation to reproduction and descent. This is the natural result of descent with modification. The degree of difference between separate groups will depend on the time during which modification in different directions has taken place, and the rate at which the changes have been produced. The ultimate groups are those which we call species, or in some cases the smaller subdivisions which we call varieties. The individuals of a species are united in the great majority of cases not merely by a great degree of resemblance to one another in structure, but by the fact that they consist of males and females which unite together in the process of sexual reproduction, while the individuals of one species do not interbreed as a rule with those of others. Groups of species are united together by resemblances of less degree into genera, genera into families, families into classes and orders, and finally the classes into the great sub-kingdoms. The first class of structural peculiarities, then, are those which

1

distinguish kinships of animals from one another, the special characters by which we classify animals.

The individuals generated by two parents of the same species are in many cases similar to those parents and to one another, with the exception of those irregular and generally slight differences which we call individual variations. But in other cases we find that the individuals generated by the same two parents differ greatly either from their parents or from one another, so that the species includes two or more well-marked forms or types, intermediate forms being more or less exceptional. The different forms may be sexually perfect, or may reproduce without sexual union, or may be quite sterile. When they are sexually perfect they unite in sexual intercourse and reproduce the same distinct types, which although constantly mingled in the fertilised ova, separate spontaneously in each successive generation, like oil and water after agitation.

This is the well-known phenomenon of polymorphism. One of the most frequent cases of this is sexual dimorphism, the occurrence of characters peculiar to the males on the one hand, to the females on the other. Another important instance is the distinction of several classes of individuals in social insects, such as workers and queens, or workers, soldiers and fertile forms.

Thirdly, we have to consider the important fact that the structure of the individual is not constant throughout its existence, but that in many cases there is a more or less complicated metamorphosis, the difference between the two states of the same individual at different periods of life being often greater than that between individuals of distinct orders or classes.

These three categories, which we may entitle diversity, polymorphism, and metamorphosis, include all the phenomena of structure in the animal kingdom. The other classes of facts distinguished by Darwinian writers concern the history and relations of these phenomena of structure. Palæontology gives us evidence concerning the history of structure in past epochs of time, while variation in nature and under artificial conditions shows us changes taking place at the present time.

Accepting the conclusion that all changes of structure have occurred in the course of the natural succession of generations, the problem before students of animal evolution at the present time is to discover the causes which have produced these three kinds of structural difference in animals.

We may consider first the peculiarities which distinguish animals of different and separate lines of descent, or pedigrees. These are conveniently termed diagnostic characters, and include all those by which the groups of various degrees are distinguished for the purpose of classification. Thus we have specific characters, generic characters, ordinal characters, and so on to the higher and more general subdivisions called sub-kingdoms or phyla.

Animal structure is not, like the shapes of crystals, entirely a matter of abstract form. Animals are living creatures, and life depends upon relations between the organism and the surrounding world.

The essentials of animal existence are the acquisition of food, the escape from enemies, and the generation of offspring. Under different conditions these objects are attained in different ways. In the most familiar animals we observe in the bodily structure striking and complicated mechanisms for attaining them. Such co-ordinated structural adjustments are called adaptations. The study of the modes in which the structure of the bodies of animals enables them to maintain their existence leads to two great questions:—
(1) Is everything in structure essential or advantageous to

the maintenance of life? (2) What is the cause by which adaptations are produced?

Every one knows that the theory of natural selection is based upon the conception of adaptation. It insists upon the observed facts of the small differences among individuals of the same species, competition in the struggle for existence, and individual heredity; and draws the inference that among a number of different and competing individuals, those which are more perfectly adapted to the conditions succeed in maintaining life, and producing offspring, while the rest fail. But if there are diagnostic and hereditary peculiarities which are in no way essential or advantageous to the maintenance of life, then these remain untouched by the argument. Weismann in constructing a theory of variation which excluded the inheritance of acquired characters, and attributed all constant and hereditary structure to selection, maintained that every detail of structure was adaptive, was, if not essential, at any rate advantageous, to the maintenance of life or the accomplishment of reproduction. He adduced the peculiarities of the whale as an illustration of this. But such an argument is quite inadequate. The whale is a specialised animal maintaining its life under special conditions, and it is by no means obvious that all the characters of other animals are equally adaptive, and further, there is, properly speaking, no animal which can be correctly called the whale without further definition. There are many species of whale, and the question of the adaptive importance of *specific* peculiarities is not discussed by Weismann. We thus arrive at a subject of enormous extent, namely the determination of the significance, in relation to the maintenance of the individual or of the race, of all the structural peculiarities by which the subdivisions of the animal kingdom are distinguished from one another; a subject which may be briefly described as the extent of adaptation in diagnostic characters.

It is not my intention to deal with the whole of this subject at present. I will merely mention one or two special cases which are included in it. We may consider characters diagnostic of a kinship of any degree, from the most general to the most particular, from the sub-kingdom to the species or even the variety. We must remember that the subject is not exhausted by multiplying cases of adaptation, which are numerous enough throughout the animal kingdom. We must take care to include all the characters which are really constant, hereditary, and peculiar, and enquire whether they are all adaptive. On the present occasion I will content myself with taking the most general and the most special cases of kinships, namely the sub-kingdom and the species.

The principal sub kingdoms or phyla of animals are the Coelenterata, the Echinodermata, the Chætopoda, the Mollusca, the Arthropoda, and the Vertebrata. In the first two the general plan of the body exhibits radial symmetry, in the last four the body is bilaterally symmetrical. It may be maintained that in animals which are free and active, and move in one direction in search of food, bilateral symmetry is an advantage, favouring regular and definite movements. But on the other hand, why should the starfish and the sea-urchin consist of five similar parts arranged regularly round a central axis? These animals are free and active and yet are not bilaterally symmetrical. It might be suggested that they obtain their food in such a manner that it is of greater advantage to them to be able to move with any part of the body foremost, than with always the same part foremost. But this would not explain why the generative organs are also situated in radially symmetrical positions. It might be urged that this was merely a consequence of the general structure of the body. But this is exactly what I wish to maintain. All the peculiarities are intelligible if we regard them as consequences of the conditions of life and growth.

It is known from embryological and palæontological evidence that free echinoderms are descended from animals which grow like lilies at the end of fixed stalks, and such fixed animals grow equally in the directions of a number of radii. We are not justified in assuming that many other modes of growth were possible and that radial symmetry has been selected from a number of indefinite variations because it was the most advantageous. On the other hand, we are justified in concluding that the general plan of the echinoderm body has been determined by the sessile condition of life, the growth taking place equally in a number of directions from the fixed centre, because the supply of nourishment and the impacts of external forces are equal along those directions.

The Cœlenterata, such as hydroids, sea-anemones, and coral polyps, are also characterised by radial symmetry, and are also fixed, and the same arguments apply to them.

In the Mollusca we have essentially unsegmented animals provided with an incomplete calcareous investment. In one large tribe of Mollusca, the Gasteropoda, the shell and body are twisted into a spiral. There is good reason to suspect that the twisting of the shell during growth has mechanically caused the torsion of the principal organs, intestine, nerve-cord and heart, of the Gasteropod body. But no Darwinian has succeeded in proving that the torsion is in any way advantageous in the struggle for existence.

The typical and primitive Vertebrate is the fish, from which the terrestrial forms have been derived. The characteristic vertebrate structures, axial skeletal rod, pharyngeal gill-slits, fins, etc., are all adaptations in the defined sense. But we need not be surprised to find that the diagnostic structural features are here more obviously adaptational than in other phyla, because the vertebrate gets its food by active motion, and the whole body is an elaborate locomotive mechanism. But it does not follow, because in one phylum the individual body is organised to act as a single mechanism, that the same degree of organisation obtains in the individuals of all phyla. The more correct reasoning, it seems to me, is to start from the idea of units of protoplasm growing wherever food was available, and to recognise that there are definite ascertainable principles of growth, such as, that stimulation of certain kinds by external forces causes growth to take certain directions, and that new growth has a tendency, inherent in the processes of life, to resemble old growths in form. Similarity of parts is thus but a phenomenon of the same kind as heredity, and the characteristic forms of the various sub-kingdoms are not the most useful selected out of a number that occurred, but are the definite and only possible results of the expansion of growing organisms under different conditions. The laws of growth and the effects of conditions are not fully known, but it is possible to investigate them.

We will next briefly consider the extent of adaptation or utility in the peculiarities which distinguish species. The conception of species has played a very important part in the history of zoological science. Darwin, as we know, called his theory a theory of the origin of species. If distinct species of animals were not separately created, how did they arise? Darwin's answer was, by natural selection or the survival of the fittest. In artificial breeding man preserves and keeps separate those individuals which have certain characters either useful or agreeable to him, and so forms numerous breeds out of one stock, or modifies one stock to a great degree from its original condition. In nature the struggle for existence and the survival of the fittest are alleged to produce similar results. One set of individuals survives by reason of one slight advantage, another of another. According to this view the primary and essential differences between species must be differences of adaptation.

But when we examine and compare species we find that they are distinguished by characters, many of which are not obviously adaptive, and it is open to question in many cases whether any of the specific peculiarities are adaptations. Darwin's remark on this subject is as follows : "In looking at many small points of difference between species which, as far as our ignorance permits us to judge, seem quite unimportant, we must not forget that climate, food, etc., have no doubt produced some effect. It is also necessary to bear in mind that, owing to the law of correlation, when one part varies, and the variations are accumulated through natural selection, other modifications, often of the most unexpected nature, will ensue." Darwin himself, then, was obliged to admit that many specific characters were not adaptive, so far as he could discover.

As an example specially familiar to myself I will refer to the flat fishes.

The Plaice, Flounder, and Dab, are three species of the same genus, whose habits and life-histories are fairly well known, and whose structural peculiarities have been minutely investigated. The Dab is principally characterised by the presence of well-developed ctenoid or spinulated scales all over both sides of the body, and by the semi-circular curve of the lateral line above the pectoral fin.

In the Plaice we see conspicuous red spots; the scales are for the most part smooth, cycloid, and reduced, the lateral line is straight, and the bony ridge behind the eyes is elevated into five tubercles.

In the Flounder we find another condition of the scales, some are smooth and reduced in size as in the Plaice, while others are enlarged and developed beyond the condition seen in the Dab. Along the bases of the marginal fins there are series of these enlarged scales, which form thorny tubercles, and there are others along the lateral line. Other peculiarities are the smooth ridge behind the eyes and the small number of the fin-rays.

In other respects these three species of fish are much alike. There are differences in their habits and life-histories. The flounder lives in estuaries and rivers, only descending to the sea in the spawning season. The plaice and dab are almost invariably found together. The plaice feeds mostly on molluscs, the dab chiefly on crustacea, worms, and echinoderms. The young plaice congregate near shore, while young dabs are found at various depths. The plaice begins to spawn earlier in the year than the dab.

Now it is quite impossible, at any rate up to the present time, to find the slightest indication that the specific characters of these three species are useful in relation to the slight differences of life-history. We cannot find that the rough tubercles of the flounder are useful to it because it lives in rivers or for any other reason ; we know of no advantage which the plaice derives from its red spots, its smooth scales, or the bony tubercles on its head. Nor can we find any indication that these peculiarities are correlated with adaptive differences. The only adaptive difference at present clear is that the plaice has blunter teeth in its throat than the other species, and that these are suitable for crushing the shells of the bivalves on which the plaice feeds. But we know of no connection between this and the other characters. The theory, then, that these specific peculiarities are due to the natural selection of indefinite variations is unsupported by any evidence.

How then are we to explain such specific characters ? It seems to me we are forced to regard them as the necessary consequences of growth and the conditions of life. It is evident enough that differences of habit and the extension of a species into different regions will necessarily lead to its subdivision into groups between which little or no inter-

breeding takes place. The individuals which lived in
estuaries would breed together, and not with those that lived
always in the sea. Thus any modification produced in the
one group would remain confined to that group, and by
interbreeding within that group would be transmitted to all its
members. It is difficult in the present state of our knowledge
to say how modifications of the kinds here in question are
determined. There are indications that continuous modification takes place in successive generations without any direct
stimulus that can be detected. We must remember that the
development of the individual is the growth and multiplication of groups of differentiated cells. This development is
controlled partly by heredity, partly by surrounding conditions, but the development of every part and every organ
is to some extent independent. The facts indicate that a
particular part or organ may, for some unknown reason,
obtain increased nourishment and develop with increased
vigour, or, on the contrary, may show diminished vigour, and
that the change may be progressive in successive generations.
It would seem that ultimately the effect must be due to
external conditions acting upon the properties of living
matter. But the action is evidently very indirect, and the
processes involved are so complicated and so recondite that
at present we know nothing about them. We have indications of the influence of external conditions in the differences
in the same species in different geographical areas. Thus the
flounder in the Mediterranean has scarcely any tubercles,
while in the Baltic and Arctic regions they are excessively
developed, so that nearly the whole skin is covered with
them. Whether this is due to the cold or not we do not
know, but it is a fact that the plaice also shows greater
roughness of the scales in the north than in the south. The
difficulty is that this effect of northern latitudes is not
observed in fishes of all families, and we have to face the

problem how it is that the same change of conditions produces
different effects in different cases.   It is possible, however,
to investigate the subject by observation and experiment.
The selection theory does not explain the origin of specific
characters, it only supposes that the variations when they
appeared were selected because of some advantage they conferred.   We are not compelled to accept this view because
we cannot explain the origin ourselves.   We also suppose
that the variations occurred, and being either indifferent, or
not sufficiently harmful to cause the death of the individual,
were transmitted to the progeny.   They would thus become
common to the species, but could not be transferred to other
species, because species do not breed together.   The first step
in the differentiation of species, therefore, is the existence of
barriers to interbreeding.   The view that specific characters
are of some use or significance in the struggle for existence is
in a vast number of cases unsupported by any evidence.

Having thus indicated the reasons for rejecting the conclusion that all distinguishing characters are adaptive or
advantageous, we may proceed to consider the origin of
adaptations.

It may be truly said that no animal is without adaptations; it must be provided with some means by which the
essentials of life are secured, but these means may be exceedingly simple or exceedingly complex.   But there is another
idea implied in the conception of adaptation, the idea of
unity in diversity, of parts essentially similar being modified
in different animals for different purposes, being adapted in
many cases for purposes quite different from that which they
originally served, as in the case of the fore-leg becoming in
birds the wing.   It is possible to trace such modifications
and more or less disguised homologies without any reference
to the doctrine of evolution.   The principle of descent with
modification gives the explanation of the phenomenon.   The

unity of plan is due to heredity, the divergence of detail
to adaptation under different conditions. But we must
pursue the investigation further and endeavour to discover
how the modification is effected. It may be asked, since we
admit that adaptation is such a prevalent phenomenon in
the animal kingdom, even if it is not universal and exclusive,
what other explanation of it is required than natural selection ? In reply to this I would urge in the first place that
natural selection implies and assumes the appearance of
variations, of slight modifications, by virtue of which certain
individuals differ from their brethren and from their parents,
in fact from all pre-existing individuals. The real explanation of evolution therefore lies in the explanation of individual variations. We admit that they occur, but how and
why ?

Darwin held that the use or disuse of organs and the
direct action of conditions caused modifications of individuals
in definite directions, and that these modifications were
hereditary in some degree. Now, if once we admit this,
selection becomes a secondary and subordinate factor. For
if a new set of conditions, or a change of habits, caused a
hereditary change of structure in all the individuals exposed
to it, continuous modification would take place even if all the
individuals generated survived, or if those which were killed
were taken at random without selection. A later school of
evolutionists have maintained that the effects of habits or
conditions on the individual are not inherited, and therefore
not cumulative. According to this view only those variations are hereditary which arise in the germ, in the internal
constitution of the egg; such variations are supposed to be
numerous and to take place in all possible directions, and
natural selection is supposed to pick out from among them
those which are advantageous, and so accumulate them. I
do not propose here to discuss the various theories of

heredity. The question of the possibility of the transmission of acquired characters, of the determination of congenital modifications by the direct influence of conditions, is a very important one, and has been much discussed. But I wish to draw attention to a mode of considering the subject which is generally neglected, namely the inductive method. The doctrine of evolution is an induction from the facts of zoology; in my opinion conclusions concerning the method and the causes of evolution can also be obtained as inductions from a sufficiently wide survey of the phenomena.

Every one will admit without hesitation that all variations must be due to causes. But according to the selectionists the conditions of life are never the causes of hereditary variations. On this view, therefore, no modification which is hereditary can have any essential or necessary relation to the requirements of life. The fitness of a structure or structural mechanism for its function is thus originally accidental. For example, the long legs of wading birds are suitable for their habit of wading, but the habit of wading did not make the legs long. Some individuals had longer legs than others, and those which had the longest survived because the length of their legs enabled them to wade.

Romanes maintained with much truth that natural selection was a theory of the origin of adaptations, not necessarily of the origin of species, but it is further necessary to realise that it originates adaptations only in the sense of preserving and combining the variations or modifications which occur, and which happen to be advantageous. It may be said to combine only in the sense of causing different variations in the parents to be transmitted together to the offspring, and of allowing new variations to occur only in the individuals which have survived.

It may be admitted that the first step of a modification or organ having occurred, there is nothing impossible in the conception of its progressive development by the process of selection. It is a matter of observation that any character may be somewhat more or somewhat less developed in individual offspring than in the parents. If the major variations only survive, there will be in the course of generations a definite increase of the character. Different characters leading to survival in different individuals may be combined in the offspring as the result of sexual union.

But there are two difficulties which generally become evident in applying this explanation to particular cases. Firstly, the difficulty of believing that ordinary differences between individuals of the same species are sufficient to form the starting-point on which selection could act, in producing an adaptation of an extraordinary kind; secondly, the impossibility of proving that the changes produced in the individual organism directly by a change of habits or conditions of life had nothing to do with the process of evolution. We know that functional exercise, and external stimulation or irritation do produce great modifications of structure, by causing local growth or local absorption. Constant exercise of special muscles causes enlargement not only of the muscles but of the bones to which they are attached. Broken bones which are not set are known to form new " joints " for themselves at the point of fracture, and these abnormal articulations resemble to a remarkable degree the natural articulations. Friction of the epidermis causes it to become horny, and the absence of friction causes it to become thin and soft.

A special adaptation necessarily implies special habits and special stimulations. These must produce, at least in the individual, corresponding modifications of structure. The peculiarities of special adaptations are generally of the same kind as the modifications which would result from the direct action of the special conditions. The natural conclusion is that the peculiarities in question are the effects of the special conditions accumulated by heredity. The only reason for rejecting this conclusion is the belief that the direct effects of conditions are not inherited. But this is only a belief, not an established truth.

Now it is possible by actual observation to ascertain what evidence there is that variations which might by natural selection be combined into the adaptations we see, do occur apart from the special habits or conditions to which the adaptations are related. The variations that occur constantly in the form of individual differences have been minutely investigated in the past few years by statistical methods with the aid of the higher mathematics. The greater the difference the more rarely it occurs, and occasionally striking abnormalities are observed, the character of which points to definite principles of symmetry and repetition in development. But it is not proved that, without change of conditions, variations occur which could, by selection, give rise to such special adaptations as abound in the animal kingdom. For example the power of partial or complete flight by means of a membranous fold of skin has been evolved in many independent cases in the vertebrate sub-kingdom, in the extinct pterodactyle reptiles, in bats, in flying squirrels, and in flying marsupials. But the variations in the condition of the skin, in animals that do not fly or take long leaps through the air, are not such as to justify the belief that these variations would make any difference in the struggle for existence when long leaps became necessary. Unless the differences were great enough to cause the comparative success of certain individuals and the comparative failure of others, the process of natural selection could not commence. On the other hand, the very condition which the principle of natural selection in this case implies, the necessity or advantage of long leaps or incipient flight, involves the practice of new and special actions and movements. Such new habits must have had some effect in modifying the muscles, bones, and skin, and on the *hypothesis* that these effects in time became hereditary the evolution becomes intelligible. Thus it seems to me much more probable that the new conditions produced the successive steps of modification directly, than that they merely selected variations already in existence.

To consider another example. There is a fish which has its eyes in a very remarkable condition. Spectacles for human eyes are sometimes made, in which the upper half has a curvature different from that of the lower. The fish to which I refer, the *Anableps*, which lives in the estuaries of Brazil and Guiana, does not wear spectacles, but actually has its eyes made in two parts, the upper half of the lens having a different curvature from that of the lower. The pupil is also divided into two by prolongations from the iris. This fish is in the habit of swimming at the surface with its eyes half out of water, and the upper half of the eye is adapted for vision in air; the lower half for vision under water. Now, however various the individual variations in fishes' eyes, there is no evidence that variations, which could by selection give rise to this curious condition, occur in other species of fish. It seems to me that we have no reason to suppose that the required variations ever occurred until the ancestors of *Anableps* took to swimming with their eyes half out of water. A similar argument applies to many other cases of special adaptation, and the logical conclusion is that the habits and conditions determined the modification.

The question, however, of the origin and causes of adaptations cannot be considered apart from the phenomena of development and metamorphosis in the individual. In order to consider how the evolution of an existing structure is to be explained, we must know how it arises in individual development. In the initial form of every animal, that is in the fertilised ovum, there is no visible evidence of any of the organs and characters of later life. These arise by the multiplication of cells and differentiation of tissues. We must consider, therefore, whether their development affords evidence of the manner and causes of their evolution.

Now the embryos of the higher vertebrates all exhibit certain characters in common, in the presence of gill-arches and gill-slits, and in the origin of the limbs as bud-like outgrowths. The great embryologist of the beginning of this century, Von Baer, whose studies were directed principally to the higher vertebrates, formulated the generalisation that animals of different classes resembled each other closely in the earlier stages of their development, and diverged more and more as they progressed towards their final form. This remains true of the higher classes of vertebrates, reptiles, birds, and mammals. When the doctrine of evolution became paramount, and it was seen that the comparative anatomy of the higher vertebrates obviously pointed to their common derivation from ancestors which were essentially fishes, the resemblance in the structure of the embryos was attributed to the retention in these embryos of the essential characters of the fish. The generalisation of Von Baer was therefore changed into another, to wit, that in development the individual passed successively through the stages of its ancestors to arrive at its present final condition. Haeckel gave great publicity to this doctrine, calling it the biogenetic law, and formulating it in the terms that ontogeny, or the development of the individual, is a repetition of phylogeny, or the evolution of the race. The late Professor Milnes Marshall still further popularised and established the principle by embodying it in another phrase, namely, that the individual in development was compelled to climb its own genealogical tree.

A more comprehensive and more accurate study of the

facts of development throughout the animal kingdom has shown that this law is by no means universal. It is true in regard to a certain number of facts in the development of the higher vertebrates, but it is not the whole truth about them, and it is contradicted by a great many other facts even in the development of reptiles, birds, and mammals. For example, snakes are characterised by the absence of limbs. In some snakes rudiments of the hind limbs are present in the adult condition, but in no snake has any trace of the fore limbs been discovered in any embryonic stage. Yet we cannot doubt that the ancestors of snakes possessed two pairs of limbs. Again, there can be no doubt that the wing of the bird has been evolved from a limb with five digits like that of many reptiles, but the wing contains only three digits, and the most complete embryological investigation has only succeeded in discovering small and very doubtful rudiments of the lost two. The ancestors of birds had teeth, but no trace of teeth has been found in the embryo. In the horse, again, there are traces of the 2nd and 4th metacarpals and metatarsals in the limbs of the adult, but examination of the development has shown that only the merest vestiges of the 2nd and 4th digits are ever formed, and of the 1st and 5th none at all.

Balfour has expressed the general results of observation in the statement that ancestral stages are liable to be omitted from embryonic development by abbreviation, to be obscured or replaced by new characters in free larval development. He also suggested that the retention of the branchial arches and clefts in the embryos of higher vertebrates was due to the fact that these structures were functional in the larval stage of the amphibian ancestors of these vertebrates after they had become rudimentary in the adults, and that the limbs in snakes had completely disappeared because there was no such advantage in their retention at a particular stage.

Mr. Sedgwick has lately elaborated this last suggestion into the general theory that ancestral characters are only retained in the embryo when the ancestral condition was once a larval condition, which has more recently become embryonic, in consequence of the retention of the larva in the egg, or within the body of the mother, until after its metamorphosis.

There are numerous instances of the truth of Mr. Sedgwick's theory, but it is not a general theory of individual development. The general truth is that when the habits and conditions are different at different periods of the individual life, then and to a proportionate degree will the structure of the individual be different during those periods. It may be said that this is merely another way of stating the principle of adaptation as the result of natural selection, the most advantageous variations being selected at each stage of life separately. But my contention is that we have no evidence that the necessary variations ever occurred until the particular habits and conditions produced them. If it is difficult to believe that the modifications were independent of external conditions, when we compare different adaptations in different individuals, it is still more difficult when we compare successive stages of the same individual, and follow in actual progress the changes of structure and function corresponding with change of habits and conditions. To my mind the phenomena of metamorphosis can only be explained as due to the heredity of modifications of growth originally caused directly in the individual by changed conditions which introduced new irritations, new stimulations, and changes of function.

This matter again can only be studied in particular instances. The most familiar case is that of the frog and other amphibia. We can have no doubt that the air-breathing amphibia were evolved from fishes, though we may not be able to say exactly what kind of fishes. We have, however, various transitional or intermediate forms in the lower amphibia and the dipnoi or lung-fishes, which breathe air to some extent. Now how can we conceive the conversion of a single individual fish into an air-breathing creature apart from the change of conditions, the breathing of air? It is true that the blood can and does secrete gases, oxygen or other, into a closed air-bladder, but the structural arrangements connected with the action of lungs cannot be conceived apart from the respiration of atmospheric air. We know of plenty of cases in which, the water being scarce or foul, fish have become capable of breathing air in one way or another, but we have no evidence of the occurrence of variations in adult life tending towards air-breathing structures in fishes which are never exposed to the air. We do not find them, for instance, in fishes that live on the sea-bottom or in the ocean-abysses. When the fish is exposed to the air at a late stage of its life, then its structure undergoes modification, and it is converted into a lung-fish breathing both air and water, or into an amphibian that retains its gills throughout life. Afterwards such a form spreads into places where water is still scarcer and it becomes still more modified, so as to breathe air altogether, and to crawl about on land.

But at the same time the young aquatic stage or larva is being modified. If we suppose that the tadpole resembles the ancestor of the frog, it follows that that ancestor was destitute of paired limbs and of fin-rays; and that the terrestrial form of limb, transversely jointed into three segments, and divided at the extremity into five digits, was not evolved from the fin of a fish, but was a new organ. Such a view is very improbable and by no means inevitable. It is much more reasonable to suppose that the terrestrial limb was evolved by the modification of the fin of a fish. The tadpole has lost its limbs, because in this temporary stage of life their use has been abandoned. It does not sustain itself in the water, but fixes itself to plants by means of its suckers, and moves from one place to another by violent strokes of its tail. Its habits have been almost as much altered as those of the frog, and its structure has been determined by its habits. Thus from an ancestral fish has been evolved a creature passing by a well-marked metamorphosis from a larval aquatic stage to an adult terrestrial stage, and in each of those stages it has become very different from its ancestors.

The original reptiles were derived from the amphibia by a change in the character of their eggs, which acquired large yolks and were enclosed in tough shells. Within the shell the larva was retained, never being set free in the water, and thus for the first time terrestrial vertebrates became entirely independent of a liquid medium. The embryo in the later evolution of terrestrial vertebrates has undergone various modifications, but the condition in which we find it at the present day is the original larval condition of the amphibian ancestor, except so far as it has been modified by the conditions of development within the eggshell or the uterus. Thus the course of development in the higher vertebrates is not to be explained by the law of recapitulation, according to which transient embryonic stages represent ancestral structures, but by the fact that the embryonic stage is a larval stage which passes through its metamorphosis before hatching or birth. The larval stage and the metamorphosis were originally determined by the temporary conditions of life in the individual, and the persistence of certain larval characters in the embryo is due to the fact that there has been nothing in the conditions of embryonic life to change them.

Let us turn now to another instance, namely the transformation of the flat-fishes. Perhaps it will be thought that

there can be no excuse for throwing doubt upon the accepted
doctrine that the larva of these fish, swimming upright in
the water with an eye on each side of its head, repeats in
individual development the condition of the ancestor. But
a more careful study of the facts shows that this doctrine is
erroneous, or at least only partially true, and it must be
modified to agree with the state of knowledge at the present
time. A brief summary of the facts will be sufficient to
prove this.

The flounder, when first hatched, is a minute larva not
quite one-eighth of an inch in length. The right and left
sides are perfectly similar to one another, and it swims
vertically in the water. But it has no fin-rays, and no
bones: a continuous fin-membrane passes along the edge of
the back round the end of the tail. The conversion of this
larval form into the fully developed flounder takes place
when it is from two to three months old, and about half an
inch long. When the bones and fin-rays begin to develop
the left eye rises first to the edge of the head, and then
passes completely over to the right side. At the same time,
the little fish begins to lie on its side on the ground, and
loses the power of sustaining itself in the water. With
slight differences in details, the development and metamorphosis of other species of flat-fish are similar. The early
condition of the flat-fish, therefore, is not that of any fully-
developed fish at all, but of a fish larva without bones or
fin-rays. It is in all respects similar to the larvae of other
marine fishes; for instance, to that of the mackerel or that of
the cod. When the bones begin to develop, the eye begins
to become asymmetrical, and we have not the ancestor, but
the flat-fish. We do not know at present whether the
elongated fins along the dorsal and ventral edges had the
same form in the ancestor; we have reason to believe they
had not so great an extent, yet they are developed directly,

not by gradual increase. The true reading of the matter, therefore, is not that the ancestral condition is repeated, but that the *larval* condition of the ancestor is retained, because the larva is still hatched, and still lives in the same way ; but the structure after metamorphosis is different, because the fish has acquired different habits. On the theory of natural selection, we must suppose that those individuals have been selected whose eyes were most symmetrical in the larval stage, and most asymmetrical in the adult condition. But we have no evidence that among symmetrical fishes individuals occasionally occur in which one eye moves up towards the edge of the head during growth. Even if slight variations of such a character were proved to exist it would be difficult to believe that they would be great enough to make any difference to the fate of the individuals possessing them when the fish took to lying on the ground. The theory of independent variation and selection as applied to flat-fishes is unsupported by evidence, while the conclusion that the metamorphosis of these fishes is the direct result of the change of conditions is in harmony with all that we know of the effect of physical conditions on individual organisms.

In these two cases, that of the frog and that of the flat-fish, the larval condition is either unmodified or less modified from the ancestral condition than the adult. But in numerous other cases the larva has been modified in adaptation to new conditions, while the adult has remained nearly the same. This is particularly conspicuous in many insects. I will not discuss at length the question of the tracheal gills of aquatic larvae, for although they are probably secondary adaptations, there are some who regard them as representing an ancestral series of organs, from some of which the wings were derived. But if this be the case, the entire absence of wings and tracheal gills in the terrestrial larvae shows that the latter by no means recapitulate the ancestral history.

Again, if the legs on the abdomen of the caterpillar behind the three pairs of thoracic legs are in any way related to the abdominal appendages of the ancestor, it is all the more certain that the maggots of the flies, or of the ants, bees, and wasps, having no legs at all, cannot resemble the ancestor. In such cases, the structure of the larva corresponds to its mode of life, and is much more different from any possible ancestor than is the adult. The individual does not here climb its own genealogical tree, unless it may be said to begin at the top and climb downwards. As for the origin of the modifications in the young stages, we have no evidence that their appearance was independent of the conditions: the fact that the special structure only lasts as long as the special larval habits last, suggests strongly enough the direct dependence of the modifications on the conditions of life.

I may possibly in the future be able to undertake a more detailed study of the evidence concerning the action of the external conditions of life in producing the differences of structure in different kinships of animals, and in different stages of the individual life. But the present work is devoted especially to the consideration of the commonest case of Polymorphism, namely, Sexual Dimorphism, and the general aspects of this subject are to be exhibited in the remainder of this Introduction.

Darwin's theory of Sexual Selection is a logical corollary of his more general theory of Natural Selection. The facts on which it is based cannot be denied. Fierce combats between mature male animals for the possession of the females are known to occur in large numbers of species. The average result of such struggles must be the victory of those individuals best provided with weapons, and with the strength and skill to use them. Rivalry of another kind in the endeavour to please the female and win her admiration and consent, is displayed abundantly in the higher vertebrates generally.

Special decorations or peculiarities in the external appearance or appendages of the body are seen to have no significance except in courtship, and it is not unreasonable to infer that the individuals best endowed with beauty or melodiousness of voice succeed oftenest, and impress their qualities on the next generation more than their less fortunate fellows. Assuming, then, that differences in the degree of development of such peculiarities occur among the males in each generation, and that the best succeed in producing most offspring, transmitting their advantages in various degrees to their male progeny, the progressive evolution of such characters is the necessary consequence.

The theory, however, has not been universally accepted by followers of Darwin. Mr. A. R. Wallace has been a vigorous and consistent opponent of it. His objections are clearly summarised and criticised by Romanes in his *Darwin and after Darwin,* vol. i. 1892. One of them is, that the supposed action of sexual selection would, if it occurred, be wholly neutralised by the action of natural selection; for unless the most highly-ornamented males preferred by the females are also the most fitted for the other conditions of life, they will be eliminated in the general struggle for existence, and the chances must be small that the otherwise best fitted males should be likewise the most highly-ornamented, unless there is a natural correlation between embellishment and general perfection, which Mr. Wallace maintains to be the case. Now this objection is not a very powerful one, for it was obvious from the first that the female could only exercise her choice among the individuals which had survived in the struggle for existence, and Darwin's theory simply maintains that after a male has succeeded in getting a living and escaping his enemies, he must compete for the possession of a mate before he can leave progeny.

Another objection of Mr. Wallace's is that each bird finds a mate under all circumstances; in other words, that failure to please one female does not imply failure to please all. But, nevertheless, it would seem probable, especially in polygamous animals, that some males are fathers on a much larger scale than others.

Again, he considers it very improbable that through thousands of generations all the females of a species should always have had the same taste with regard to every detail in the nuptial adornment of their mates. This is certainly a valid objection, or at least appears to be so. The criticism of Mr. Romanes is that it is not very safe to infer what sentiments may be in the mind of a hen. We have evidence that the preferences of females with regard to male attractions are very conservative in our own species, but it is certainly difficult to conceive that the female Argus pheasant should have the power or the opportunity of appreciating minute differences in the perfection of the ocelli on the wing-feathers of the male.

Mr. Wallace argues that the principal cause of the greater brilliancy of male animals in general, and of male birds in particular, is, that they do not stand so much in need of protection by concealment as the females do. Therefore natural selection is more active in repressing in the female those bright colours which are normally produced in both sexes by general laws. More than this, natural selection promotes the development of heightened colour in the males, because this is correlated with health and vigour, and the healthy and vigorous males are preserved by natural selection.

With regard to the display which, according to Mr. Romanes, is the strongest of all Mr. Darwin's arguments in favour of sexual selection, Mr. Wallace says that there is no evidence that the females are in any way affected by it. On these points I cannot agree with either Romanes or Wallace. I do not consider that the display is the strongest argument in favour of Darwin's theory, and I think the effect on the females is perfectly obvious. Wallace argues that the display and gestures of the male, in the case of birds, for example, may be due to general excitement, pointing out that moveable feathers are habitually erected under the influence of anger and rivalry to make the bird look more formidable in the eyes of antagonists. The display and erection of organs or appendages present only in the males according to this argument is no proof of competition or of selection on the part of the females, no proof that the most adorned males accomplish the act of reproduction while the least ornamented fail to beget offspring.

The more brilliant colour and excessive development of certain feathers or other appendages, being due according to Wallace to the exuberant health and vigour of the males, the question arises how is it that the more vigorous development does not extend equally to all parts and appendages of the body, instead of being confined, as it is very precisely, to particular parts or appendages? To explain this fact Wallace adopts the theory expounded by Mr. Alfred Tyler in his book on *Coloration of Animals and Plants* (1886). Mr. Tyler maintained that diversified coloration follows the chief lines of structure and changes at points, such as the joints, where function changes. Mr. Wallace maintains that the enlarged plumes of male birds are situated at points where the nerves and blood-vessels converge. Thus, in his book entitled *Darwinism* he states that Mr. Beddard examined for him the anatomical relations of the roots of the great tufts of golden feathers in the bird of paradise, and found that they were situated just above the point where the arteries and nerves for the supply of the pectoral muscles leave the interior of the body. But, as Professor Lloyd

Morgan has already pointed out, there is no physiological reason why the growth of feathers should be connected with the proximity of main arteries and nerves. We have no reason to suppose that the large supply of blood for the pectoral muscles overflows into the skin and causes the feathers of the breast to sprout luxuriantly as does the grass round a spring of water. And, moreover, if it were so, the special plumes ought to be equally developed in the females, and indeed all birds ought to possess plumes on the breast similar to those of the male bird of paradise, since in all the position of the nerves and blood-vessels is the same.

In so far as it attributes the evolution of secondary sexual peculiarities to supposed general physiological principles, and not to selection from indefinite individual variations, Wallace's explanation resembles these views of evolution which are distinguished as Lamarckian. This is only one out of several subjects on which Mr. Wallace is Lamarckian without knowing it, and apparently in spite of himself. Although he independently invented the theory of natural selection he does not admit the action of that principle in the case of the mental and moral characteristics of man, or of a special kind of selection in relation to sex. Not that Mr. Wallace has ever acknowledged himself to be a Lamarckian. He probably has a strong prejudice against the epithet, but that may be because, like many others, he has to some extent misunderstood the position of the Lamarckians, and has not realised the similarity between his own views and theirs.

The views which I am about to support are also of the kind called Lamarckian, but they are by no means the same as those of Mr. Wallace on the subject under consideration. I attribute the evolution of secondary sexual characters to alleged physiological principles of growth and modification, but these principles are quite different from those suggested by Mr. Wallace, and I believe they are principles founded on

sufficient evidence, whereas, after careful consideration, I can
find no evidence of any necessary or general connection
between health and vigour, or anatomical features, and the
special peculiarities in which one sex differs from the other.
Other suggestions or theories which have been propounded
in explanation of the evolution of secondary sexual characters
appear to be merely ingenious variations of the idea of selection. Stolzmann [1] has maintained that among birds the males
are more numerous than the females, which of course is one
of the main points in Darwin's theory. According to Stolzmann the fact is a necessary consequence of the defective
or scanty nourishment of the eggs. The female devoting her
energies and labour to the work of nest-building takes less
food and performs more work than she otherwise would, and
consequently the nutrition of the eggs is less generous.
Scantily-nourished eggs produce males rather than females,
and the majority of birds' eggs being scantily nourished,
males are in a majority among the young produced. It is
obvious that this argument does not deserve serious attention.
It is certain that birds' eggs, as compared for instance with
those of fishes, amphibia, or mammals, are supplied with an
enormous quantity of the most nutritious food-yolk, and it is
difficult under these circumstances to understand what is
meant by the assertion that they are badly nourished.

However, to continue Stolzmann's argument, the excess
of male birds is pernicious to the species, not only on account
of their interference with the females during the performance
of their maternal duties, but also because they occupy
valuable space and lessen the supplies of food. Anything
therefore tending to lessen the undue excess of males would
be seized upon and perpetuated by natural selection. Hence
the gaudy colours, crests and spurs, and pugnacious habits
of the males. The bright colours render them visible not

[1] *Proc. Zool. Soc.* 1885.

only to each other but to hawks and other enemies; their long plumes diminish their powers of escape; their constant fights tend to diminish their numbers, while their dances and rival singing are merely distractions which protect the females against their too constant attentions.

A very little reflection is enough to show that these curious and ingenious suggestions are of no real assistance towards the solution of the problem. As far as individual selection within the species is concerned, the males with the special peculiarities most highly developed must according to the theory be the first to be exterminated, and therefore it is impossible to understand how such peculiarities could ever make much progress in evolution. The theory is founded on the argument that the decimation of the males is for the good of the species, which merely means that those species in which the males are most conspicuous, and exposed to the most numerous perils, will flourish most. But how are we to conceive of the evolution of a species which is at the same time characterised by the greatest development of peculiarities in the males and the greatest destruction of males on account of those very peculiarities. The two processes supposed are in direct opposition, and logically the result would be nothing. There is no variation of species apart from individuals, and according to the assumptions made by Stolzmann, the individuals in the species with the greatest development of the required characters would not transmit their peculiarities.

The fundamental objection to Darwin's theory of sexual selection, or to any other selection theory, is that it does not account for the origin of the variations which it assumes. Those who consider the process of selection as the most important factor, maintain, and rightly maintain, that individual variations do actually occur, and they are either not inclined to analyse the problem further, or they support some theory which professes to explain the indefinite variation, or variability, on which selection acts. Now there are two almost universal peculiarities of secondary sexual characters on which the theory of sexual selection throws no light whatever: (1) the characters do not begin to appear in the individual until it is nearly adult and sexually mature, in other words they appear when, or a little before, the animal begins to breed; (2) they are inherited only by the sex which possesses them.

If it were a mere question of the occurrence of individual variations, and a preference by the female sex, there would be no reason whatever why variations occurring at the beginning of life should not be selected. The theory merely supposes that each female has a number of candidates for her favour which are not all alike. Now let us suppose that a single cock-bird, a peacock for example, began to develop its special tail as soon as it developed its other feathers, and had a well-developed tail of the characteristic kind as soon as it was fledged. When it became sexually mature its special plumage would be perfect, while that of its fellows of the same age was only partially developed, for in the ordinary case males are mature before the development of their secondary characters is completed. According to the theory of sexual selection, then, the young male in which precocious development of the special plumage occurred would be preferred to others of the same age in which the development was later, and the result in a few generations would be that the peculiarities of the males would appear as soon as the permanent feathers appeared. The selection of course does not take place until maturity is reached and mating occurs, but the selection has nothing to do with the production of the variations, and the time at which selection takes place cannot determine the time at which the modifications occur in the individual.

Secondly, why should the individual peculiarities in the

male selected not be transmitted to his female offspring as well as to the male? It is true Darwin believes that this has occurred in some instances, but why does it not occur always? This is a phenomenon with which selection has nothing to do. Wallace maintains that the females require to have dull colours, and to be inconspicuous, in order to escape the notice of enemies when sitting on their nests. But selection, whether of dull-coloured females by the conditions of life, or of brilliant and ornamented males by female fastidiousness, only assumes, and does not explain, the inheritance of special characters by one sex and not by the other.

It is with these two special peculiarities of secondary sexual characters that my own arguments are chiefly concerned, and I will therefore consider here what attempts have hitherto been made to explain them.

It cannot be said that Darwin succeeded in explaining the phenomena. In the extent and accuracy of his knowledge, and the perfect impartiality and devotion to truth with which he collected and examined the evidence bearing upon the general problems of structure and evolution, Darwin surpassed all his predecessors and contemporaries. His detailed and careful examination of the problems of evolution in general, and of sexual dimorphism in particular, was a great and noble work. His treatises form the foundation of our present knowledge on these subjects. But we do not honour him most by maintaining his doctrines and conclusions without change. There is no finality in knowledge. It is perfectly true that some new views may be in the wrong direction, may be retrogressive, but progress, further investigation of causes, is always possible, and it is no proof of the unsoundness of new conclusions that they go beyond or differ from those of any authority, however great.

Darwin's chief conclusion concerning the peculiarities of secondary sexual characters which I have mentioned, is that there is a connection between them. He found that it was a general rule that characters were inherited in the offspring at the same age at which they appeared in the parents, and that when characters appeared in one sex late in life they were generally inherited only by the same sex. He attributed this to the fact that the sexes do not differ much in constitution until the power of reproduction is gained, while after that the differerence is great. In support of this he cites the well-known contrast between ordinary species of deer and the Reindeer. In the latter both sexes bear antlers, although those of the female are considerably smaller, and the antlers commence to appear in both sexes within four or five weeks after birth ; in other deer the male alone bears antlers, and they begin to appear at periods varying from nine months to twelve or more after birth. It must be remembered, however, that reindeer as well as other deer shed and renew their antlers every year, and even in the reindeer the full size and branching is not attained till after several years. Darwin, however, concludes that one, though not the sole, cause of characters being exclusively inherited by one sex, is their development at a late age. How far this is a sufficient explanation I shall discuss in the following pages, but it is clear without further discussion that it is not an explanation of the origin of the variations themselves. Darwin does not attribute the latter to any definite causes, merely pointing out that secondary sexual characters are highly variable, and therefore afford plenty of opportunity for selection.

Later investigators have offered various suggestions as to the origin of the variations in question, for the most part attributing them to " constitutional " differences between the sexes, and basing their views largely on the fact that, as a general rule, it is the males that have been modified, while the females exhibit the original condition. Thus the American zoologist, W. K. Brooks (1883), attempted to explain

unisexual variation and heredity by a modification of Darwin's
"provisional hypothesis" of gemmules. According to this
hypothesis, gemmules of infinitesimal size were given off by
all the organs and tissues of the body, and were accumulated
in the reproductive cells. It was the property of these
gemmules to develop again the organs and tissues from which
they were derived in the parents. Brooks suggested that the
male gemmules were more prone to variation than the female,
and therefore when they developed in a male individual they
gave rise to variations. The male, therefore, had a special
tendency to variation, while the female kept up the general
constancy of the species; thus he attempted to explain why
it is that often in allied species the females are much alike,
while the males are very different.

St. George Mivart regards the beauty of males and their
other peculiarities as the direct expressions of an internal
force.

This view of the unisexual characters as due to internal
constitutional causes has been elaborated by Messrs. Patrick
Geddes and Arthur Thomson.[1] They argue that, essentially
and constitutionally, males incline to activity, females to
passivity ; that the physiological processes in the female
tissues tend to the passive accumulation of nourishment
and to growth, while in the male they tend to the active
production of movement and energy. When there is a
difference the female is in many insects and lower animals
large and stationary, the male small, agile, and often short-
lived. The details of secondary characters are due to the
abundance of diverse excretory products produced by the
more intense physiological changes in the tissues of the male.
To quote the words of these authors : " So brilliancy of colour,
exuberance of hair and feathers, activity of scent glands, and
even the development of weapons, are not and cannot be

[1] *Evolution of Sex*, 1889.

explained by sexual selection, but in origin and continued development are outcrops of a male as opposed to a female constitution." The male element of reproduction, the spermatozoon, is an extremely minute, microscopic particle, shaped like a tadpole, and moving with great activity in a liquid medium by means of the lashings of its tail; the egg is a large mass of living substance or plasm charged with nutriment, thousands or millions of times as large as the spermatozoon, and showing no movement at all except slight internal contractions and slow changes. Geddes and Thomson regard the male animal as, so to speak, made up of spermatozoa. They consider every cell in the body of the male as partaking of the active, spendthrift character of the spermatozoon, while the female tissues and the female animal as a whole are, like the egg, inert, receptive, vegetative.

It is obvious enough that none of these suggestions are of any assistance in explaining the details of the unisexual peculiarities; they do not explain why the male constitution of the stag is exhibited in the antlers on its head, in the peacock in the feathers of its tail. With regard to size, the authors admit that the superiority of the males in many mammals and birds is an objection to their theory. They hold that the apparent exceptions are the natural result of the increased stress of external activity which is thrown upon the shoulders of the males when their mates are incapacitated by incubation or pregnancy, and they point to the strengthening influence of the combats between males, and to the large supplies of nourishment which the females give up to their offspring.

Eimer also states, as one of the general principles of the origin of variations, that where new characters appear, the males, and especially the vigorous old males, acquire them first; that the females, on the contrary, remain always at a more juvenile, lower stage, and that the males transmit these new characters to the species. He calls this the law of male preponderance.

For my own part, I am inclined to doubt whether there is any essential or constitutional difference between the sexes with regard to the tendency to variation. In vast numbers of species the individuals of opposite sexes are so much alike that it is difficult to distinguish them without examination of the generative organs. Examples of this fact among mammals are furnished by the mouse, the cat, hyæna, rabbit, hare, and many others. Among birds examples are very abundant. Darwin found that there were six classes into which birds could be divided according to the differences and similarities in the characters of the sexes. In two of these classes the adult male resembles the adult female, examples of which condition are afforded by the robin, the kingfisher, many parrots, crows and rooks, and the hedge-warbler. In fishes the sexes are more often alike than different, and among the lower animals special peculiarities in the males are by no means universally present.

Cases in which the exceptional characters, conspicuous or extraordinary peculiarities, are confined to the females, though less common than the opposite condition, are not wanting, as in the species of *Turnix* among birds mentioned by Darwin.

On the other hand, in either sex unisexual characters have, as a general rule, some function or importance in the special habits or conditions of life of the sex in which they occur. The antlers of stags are certainly fighting weapons, and are habitually employed by every healthy stag in combat with his fellows. The special plumes of male birds are habitually erected and displayed in courtship. The melody of singing birds is intended for the ears of their mates, and the note of the male bell-bird, the call-notes of birds in general, are love-notes. So far there can be no doubt that Darwin was perfectly right and his opponents all wrong.

The facts being so, there is rivalry, combat, and competition, and there must be selection. But the important truth, which appears to have been generally overlooked, is that in the case of each special organ its special employment subjects it to special, usually mechanical, irritation or stimulation, to which other organs of the body are not subjected. Every naturalist and every physiologist admits that in the individual any irritation or stimulation regularly repeated produces some definite physiological effect, some local and special change of tissue in the way of either growth or absorption, enlargement or decrease, or change of shape. Thus not only hypothetically at some former time, but actually at present in every individual, the unisexual organs or appendages are subjected in their functional activity to special strains, contacts, and pressures, that is, to stimulation, which must and does have some physiological effect on their development and mode of growth. This argument will, of course, be received with more or less courteous contempt, because it is held by the majority that any effects on the individual, any "acquired characters," are not inherited, and therefore have nothing to do with the evolution of characters which are constant in species, and evidently hereditary. I do not propose here to attempt to prove that acquired characters are inherited. My object is merely to point out how remarkably the multitudinous facts all agree with the hypothesis that secondary sexual characters are due to the inheritance of acquired characters.

We have seen that the attempts that have been made to explain the restriction of such characters not only to one sex, but to the period of maturity in the individual and often to one period of the year, have not been successful. The true explanation in my opinion is, *that heredity causes the development of acquired characters for the most part only in that period of life and in that class of individuals in which they were originally acquired.* Heredity, according to my conception of it, whatever its mechanism, is a tendency in the new individual to pass successively through the same stages of growth as its parent. That which is inherited is not a state, but a process. Unisexual characters consist, in general, in modifications of growth in particular parts of the body, very often in excessive growth or hypertrophy. They may, in fact, in many cases, be correctly described as excrescences, and these excrescences are as truly the result in the first instance of mechanical or other irritation, as a corn in the human epidermis. But the irritation and the consequent hypertrophy or proliferation have been in every generation inseparably associated with a certain condition of the organism, that condition, namely, in which the testes, or the ovaries in certain cases, were mature and active.

If there were no question of inheritance in the matter, and the secondary sexual character were produced *de novo* by certain stimulations applied only in one sex when the animal began to breed, then we should have no cause to wonder why such characters were confined to one sex and to one period of life in that sex. The reason would be that the stimulations only acted on the individuals of the one sex at that period. The characters would be acquired characters confined to the individuals which acquired them, and not appearing until the actions and influences to which they were due came into operation.

But it is evident enough that the development of the characters at the present stage of evolution takes place by heredity, even though the usual irritations are partly or entirely wanting. The modifications of growth which in each generation have been produced in a certain phase of individual development, occur of their own accord when that phase is reached or approached. In the more familiar cases the phase in question is the functional activity of the testes, and the physiological condition associated therewith.

The activity of the testes does not leave the rest of the body unaffected. On the contrary, it is associated with a nervous exaltation which again influences the activities of all the other organs. It was during this condition that the secondary characters were originally produced. The special processes of growth occur in subsequent generations by heredity, *when the body is in the same condition, not otherwise.* Thus we understand why it is that the antlers of the stag do not develop in the female, and fail to develop perfectly in the stag which is castrated. In either of these cases the animal fails to reach the condition of body in which alone the local hypertrophy can occur. On the other hand, it is not to be doubted that the female inherits the tendency to produce antlers. This is necessarily the case because the female individual, like the male, arises from the union of male and female germ-cells. It is also proved to be the case by the fact that the female often transmits to her progeny peculiarities in the secondary sexual characters of her own father, and even occasionally, when old and no longer fertile, develops to some extent such characters herself.

The known phenomena of the frequent development of male characters in aged females, and of the suppression of the male characters in castrated males, compelled Weismann to admit the presence of both male and female determinants, not merely in the germ, but in the somatic cells of each individual. He considered that thus under certain circumstances the latent set of determinants might become active and manifest their effects. But he does not thus surmount the difficulty presented to his theory. The question is, why should the absence of the testes or the sterility of the ovaries affect the activity of determinants in somatic cells? According to Weismann's conceptions the behaviour of the somatic cells is determined solely by the germ from which they sprang, and in that case they cannot be affected by the presence or absence of the germ-cells which are to give rise to the *following generation*. It is conceivable that the activity of one or the other set of determinants in somatic tissues should be called forth by external stimuli, such as temperature or irritation, the determinants themselves arising only in the germ. But it is not conceivable, on Weismann's hypothesis, that the removal of the testes in the young animal should affect the behaviour of the determinants for the antlers in later life, for according to the hypothesis there is no continuity between the testes and the somatic cells. And it is obvious that if the removal of the testes can affect the development of tissues in the head, the development of the latter may affect the properties of the testes. To my thinking, the suppression of male characters in consequence of castration is in itself sufficient to disprove the theory of the absolute continuity of the germ-plasm, and its absolute independence of the somatic cells. If, as Weismann supposed, the germ-cells were entirely unaffected in their essential properties by the history and circumstances of the body in which they were contained, it is impossible to conceive how the removal of the generative organs could affect the development of the tissues of that body.

Another interesting point which gives remarkable support to the view here advocated is that the existence of secondary sexual characters is, in many cases, not merely limited to the period of mature life, but actually to that part of the year in which the reproductive organs are active, that is to the breeding season. It is a familiar fact that this is the case with the antlers of the stags, which drop off in the early part of the year and are developed again in summer. The rutting season of stags occurs in autumn, and it is only during this season that they consort with the females and engage in fights with other stags. If the antlers were originally outgrowths of bone produced by the pressure of the heads of the fighting stags against each other during the rutting season, and afterwards developed constantly by the strains of the antlers of the combatants against each other, then the hereditary tendency to the periodic annual growth of the antlers would be an intelligible fact. It cannot be too strongly emphasised that hitherto no attempt has been made to give an explanation of such facts as these. The theory that I advocate does explain them, while on all other theories of evolution the occurrence of the variations is merely assumed, and no reason for the peculiar modes and times of their occurrence is even offered. I believe I may claim that my theory is, in its special details, new and original. The theory of the inheritance of acquired characters is, of course, old, and regarded by many as even extinct. But so far as I know I have not been anticipated in my elaboration of this theory into the form in which I present it, namely, *that the direct effects of regularly recurrent stimulations are sooner or later developed by heredity, but only in association with the physiological conditions under which they were originally produced*, and that this is the explanation of the limitation of particular modifications, not merely to particular species or kinships, but to particular periods in the life of the individual, to a particular sex, and even to a particular season of the year in that sex.

It may be objected to my argument that I have not proved that particular stimulations actually produce the effects I attribute to them, and still less that any such effects are ever inherited. Such an objection would show a complete misunderstanding of my object in this work and my method of reasoning. Experimental investigations of the direct effects of stimulations have been made and published, by myself among many others.[1] That stimulations do produce local

---

[1] See *Coloration of Pleuronectidæ*, Cunningham and MacMunn. *Phil. Trans.*, 1890.

modifications in the growth of living tissues is enough for
my present purpose. I make no attempt in the present work
to give an account of our knowledge on this subject. With
regard to the question of the inheritance of such effects, it
may be true that at present we have no direct or experimental
proof of its occurrence, or not sufficient proof. But on
the other hand its impossibility has not been established,
and my argument is merely that the hypothesis of
such inheritance as I have formulated it, affords the only
sufficient explanation of the phenomena which I pass in
review.

Weismann in one of his essays maintains that the inheritance of acquired characters being theoretically impossible,
a theory of the selection of variations arising in and from the
germ is our only hope of escape from a supernatural explanation of evolution. I maintain, on the contrary, that theories
of selection being found on application to the facts to be
insufficient for their explanation, and the theory of the
inheritance of acquired characters being found to harmonise
with the facts, we are logically bound to believe that such
inheritance does take place, at any rate until some other
explanation can be found. I do not concern myself with the
question how such inheritance can be produced, *it is a fact
that the modifications with which I have to deal are hereditary,
and my object is to produce inductive evidence that they were
determined by special stimulations.*

I proceed, therefore, to examine the most important
examples of secondary sexual characters in detail, taking the
chief divisions of the animal kingdom in systematic order.
In this survey I shall endeavour to show that in every case
the development of the special character is associated with
special habits or conditions that necessarily involve stimulations closely corresponding to the character in question, and
absent where the character is absent; also that there is

no evidence of the origin of the character or its elements apart from the incidence of these stimulations. Doubtless there are many errors and many deficiencies in my explana- tions. It is a subject in which much research is required, and I should be much gratified if my suggestions tended in some degree to promote such research.

All characters or peculiarities confined to one sex only may be called unisexual characters. These may be primarily divided into three classes according to their function, their relation to the habits and conditions of life of the animals possessing them :—

(1) Weapons, organs or characters which are employed in combats with other males for the exclusive possession of the females.

(2) Allurements, organs or characters whose function is to attract the female, physiologically speaking, to excite the sexual instinct in the female. With these may be included organs or structures whose function is to seize or hold the female.

(3) Unisexual characters which are not related directly to sexual reproduction at all, but are related to the different conditions of life to which the different sexes are exposed. These may be, and perhaps are, in all cases indirectly related to sexual reproduction, since the different modes of life of the two sexes correspond to the different parts they perform in reproduction, the one sex taking care of the eggs and the other not, for instance.

In the body of the work the various classes of animals will be considered in order, and an attempt made to describe the functions performed by the unisexual characters in the life of the animal, and to ascertain the particular modes in which the habits and actions of the animal give rise to the various stimulations to which the development of the particular characters is attributed.

In obtaining the facts for consideration I have taken Darwin's work on Sexual Selection as the basis of my researches, for the obvious reason that it is by far the most complete and detailed collection of such facts available to the naturalist.

CHAPTER I

MAMMALS

PRIMATES. — The male gorilla differs considerably from the female. Darwin says it is believed to be polygamous, and cites this as evidence in favour of the occurrence of sexual selection. There is a great difference in the skull between the two sexes, the peculiarity in the male being chiefly related to the great development of canine teeth. Male gorillas fight much, and the canine teeth are their chief weapons. Granting that the use of the teeth gradually increases their size, and that the general exertion of muscles has an inherited effect, the unisexual characters of the male gorilla in canines, size, and strength are explained. The sagittal crest is strongly marked in the male, absent in the female, and this is connected with the great extension of the attachment of the temporal muscle in the male, one of the chief muscles which are employed in biting. Another peculiarity of the male gorilla is his voice, and he is furnished with a laryngeal sac, as likewise is the male orang. Here there is no difficulty in tracing the direct effects of exertion : the pressure of the air would cause the distension of the larynx into a sac.

In all the anthropoid apes the male is larger and stronger than the female, with larger canine teeth. In the Orang the beard is confined to the male, but in the Gorilla and Chimpanzee, no great development of beard occurs in either sex.

The discussion of the sexual differences in Man is best undertaken here, as it does not seem possible to explain all of them as due to conditions which have arisen since he diverged from ape-like ancestors. With regard to the greater size and bodily and mental power of man as compared with woman, there seems no difficulty in explaining these peculiarities as directly due to differences in habits. Such differences evidently existed in the ape-like progenitors as well as throughout the evolution of civilised man. Among the wild ancestors, the males gained their superior size and strength by fighting for the females with one another, and throughout the subsequent evolution the males have led the more active, energetic, and pugnacious existence. Almost from the earliest stage of man's evolution, as in the most primitive savages in historical times, the women have been in the habit of attending to the requirements of the family home, while the men, before they tilled the land or possessed domesticated cattle, were engaged in hunting and warfare. Among the African negroes the labours of agriculture seem to be left entirely to the women, but the exertions and fatigues of warfare are still confined to the men. In more civilised nations the contrast between the part played by men and that performed by women in providing for their own existence or that of the family is sufficiently obvious. At the same time the degree of difference between men and women varies considerably in different nations and races. Among western nations the freedom and energy of women is much more encouraged than in those commonly called oriental, and it is not difficult to foresee that in the evolution of society which is now going on in England, the assimilation of the habits of women to those of men, will result in considerable diminution of the average difference between the sexes in mental and bodily powers.

From the zoological point of view, however, it is more important to consider differences in particular characters between man and woman. The most conspicuous of such differences is the presence of beard and moustache in man and their almost entire absence in woman. This difference is most developed in the Aryan and Semitic races, in others it is less conspicuous. As the beard is confined to the male orang, it is probable enough that it was derived by ourselves from the ape-like ancestor. Darwin believed that the beard in the quadrumana, in some confined to, or more developed in the males, in others equally developed in both sexes, was first acquired by the males as an ornament, through sexual selection. But he points out that where the beard is a male unisexual character it is not fully developed until sexual maturity is attained. In my opinion, as maintained in the Introduction, this is an indication that some stimulation is at work which only comes into action with sexual maturity. There is little reason to believe that among wild apes the females would choose a mate for the sake of his more handsome beard. As the keepers of the Zoological Gardens informed Darwin that many monkeys attack each other by the throat, it is, I think, not impossible that the growth of the beard was originally excited by the stimulus caused by such attacks, the hair of the throat and around the mouth being regularly moved and pulled by the adversary's jaws and teeth, or perhaps by the hands. The evidence, I admit, is very slender, but further observation of the natural habits of the orang and other quadrumana might strengthen it. Such a result is, at all events, not impossible in apes whose face and throat were already hairy. It may be asked in reference to the mandrill described below, why I have there attributed a totally different condition to similar attacks. The reply to which is that in the mandrill the snout is long, and the wounds of the adversary's teeth in that species are supposed to be inflicted on the skin of the sides of the snout, which was already nearly or quite hairless.

It is a curious fact that the greatest resemblances to the beard in the Caucasian races, and to the long hair of women, are to be found, not among the anthropoid apes, but in two species of the Platyrhini or American apes, whose dentition differs from that of man.[1] Pithecia Satanas, the Couxia, has a magnificent beard much larger in the male than in the female, while in another species, the Yarké, the head of the female is adorned with elongated hair. It would be of great importance to know whether the habits of these two species are such as to involve any special stimulation of the hair follicles on the chin in the one case, on the head in the other.

The majority of anthropologists agree in the conclusion that all the races of man are descended from a single species. The most important characters of man as distinguished from apes are the erect attitude, the more developed brain and skull, the specialised hand, and the faculty of speech. It appears *prima facie* very improbable that all these characters were evolved independently in descendants of more than one species of anthropoid ape. But, on the other hand, similarities of almost if not quite equal importance are common not merely to the species but to the genera of anthropoid apes. The Gorilla, Orang, and Gibbon resemble one another in the characters adapting them to an arboreal existence much in the same way as the main races of man resemble one another in the human peculiarities mentioned above. Yet no one suggests that the former are races of one species. There is certainly some foundation for the supposition which has been suggested by some anthropologists, that the Negro is more closely allied to the Gorilla than to the Caucasian race of man. It is conceivable that distinct species of ape in former geological periods gave rise independently to the

---

[1] See *Man and Apes*, by St. George Mivart, London, 1873, p. 59.

erect social beings which constituted the principal races of mankind. This might be suggested as the origin of the three principal human races—the Caucasian, the Negroid, and the Mongolian. In this case the Gorilla and Chimpanzee may be descended from the same stem as the Negro, or from a species closely allied to the simian ancestor of the Negro. It is well known that the gorilla in his young immature condition resembles the negro more than he does when adult, and this renders it possible that the gorilla has diverged from man in the course of his evolution. On this theory the fact that the beard, moustache, and whiskers are fully developed in the Caucasian race and not in the others would be explained by the fact that the simian ancestor of this race had them, while the ancestral forms of the other two races were almost destitute of them. The Orang might be a somewhat degenerate existing descendant of the simian ancestor of the Caucasian type, or, at any rate, might be allied to the ancestral form which has long been extinct. "The forehead of the orang is high and erect, not retreating like that of the chimpanzee. The end of the nose, further removed from the eyes than is generally the case in the chimpanzee, is not so broad as it is in the latter animal and in the gorilla."[1] Whether there is any reason to suggest a corresponding affinity for the Mongolian type I am unable to say.

The above speculations arise from the idea that the special development of the beard, etc., as a secondary sexual character is due to the stimulation of the growth of the hair by teeth or hands in the combats of mature males. It is unlikely that men should fight in the way suggested after they had reached even the stage of evolution known to us in the lowest existing savages, for then they seem always to fight with weapons. The fact, however, that even among civilised nations fighting of men with hands and teeth is not unknown, and that

[1] Hartmann, *Anthropoid Apes*, Internat. Sci. Series, London, 1885, p. 37.

4

women sometimes fight by tearing one another's hair, must
not be forgotten. If there is any truth in the view that the
special growth of the beard is due to such causes as I have
suggested, then it is reasonable to suppose that those causes
have been in action in the ancestors of the Caucasian race
more than in those of the other two races. It is not impossible, if primitive man was derived from a single ancestral
species, that in the earlier stages of his evolution he may have
developed different habits in different races, and that in one
race the hair of the face was stimulated in the fights of the
men, in others not. What is wanted is evidence concerning
the influence of mechanical irritation of the hair follicles on
the growth of the hair. The Primates generally are distinguished among all the Mammalia for the extraordinary
variety of special developments of hair about the head and
on other parts of the body, and it would be of great interest
to know whether these special growths were generally associated with special mechanical stimulations due to particular
habits. At present observations on the habits of the various
species in their natural state necessary for such an inquiry
appear to be wanting.

If we suppose that the beard and moustache so well
developed in the white or Caucasian race are derived from
the original single ancestral species of man, it follows that in
most other races, except the Papuans, Australians, and
Fijians, the beards have very much diminished, or almost
disappeared. There seems to be very little if any evidence
that this can have been caused by sexual selection on the
part of the women. It seems necessary to attribute it to
spontaneous variation without selection. It is important,
however, to notice that there are indications of the influence
of climatic conditions in causing modification of the beard
and hair in definite directions. In the North American
Indians the beard is rudimentary, and in the present in-

habitants of the country descended from European colonists
the beard has become lank and scanty.

It does not necessarily follow, because a character such as
the beard in man shows great variations in individuals and
allied races, that therefore its evolution or origin is sufficiently explained by the occurrence of such variations and
the process of selection. On the contrary, I believe that
such marked variation is often an indication that the
character is merely persisting under the influence of
heredity alone, the definite stimulation which gave rise to it
having ceased to act. This is, in my opinion, the explanation of the long-horned and hornless breeds of domesticated
cattle, and the great differences in the development of the
secondary male characters in breeds of domestic poultry.

Whatever doubts may arise concerning the origin of the
beard and moustache, it seems tolerably certain that the hair
of the body in both sexes, and on the face in woman, has
become rudimentary since the first differentiation of the
human species. In connection with this modification, we
have also to consider the fact that children of both sexes are
more hairless than adults.

In seeking the possible causes of the loss of hair, we
naturally consider other cases of hairless animals. In the
first place, we find nakedness characteristic of certain permanently aquatic animals, namely, the Cetacea and Sirenia.
It is possible that the loss of hair in these is really due to
the influence of the water, but this seems to be inconsistent
with the fact that seals and otters have such well-developed
fur. However, seals and otters are aquatic carnivora, whose
near allies have thick fur, and they are not permanently
immersed in water, but spend a considerable portion of
their time on land. The hippopotamus is hairless, and the
elephant and rhinoceros nearly so. The fact that the extinct
mammoth and woolly rhinoceros of the glacial epoch were

provided with fur indicates that the loss of hair in the existing forms has been due to the heat of a tropical climate.
According to Quatrefages, extremes of climate have had
marked effects on the development of hair in certain races of
domestic animals. On cold and lofty plateaux in the Andes
pigs which have run wild have, after some generations,
developed a kind of wool. In the warm valleys of the Mag-
dalena the wool of sheep becomes detached in flakes and is
replaced by a short, stiff, and shining hair. In the burning
plains of Mariquita, again, the cattle have become hairless.

Important as these indications of the influence of tropical
heat may be, it is evident that all animals are not hairless in
the tropics. The skins of some orders, e.g. Ungulata, may bo
affected, and others, e.g. Carnivora, not. As Darwin says, the
fact that apes and monkeys in the tropics are well clothed
with hair is opposed to the supposition that man became
naked through the action of the sun, and so likewise is the
fact that he has long hair on the head, and, in the male sex,
hair on the face.

Darwin suggests that woman first became deprived of
hair for ornamental purposes by means of sexual selection.
We have, however, no reason for assuming that primitive
men preferred the women who had least hair. It seems to
me much more probable that the true cause of the loss of
hair was the wearing of clothes. It is true that some
savages wear little or no clothes in their present state, but if
we have reason to believe that all human races are descended
from a single primitive species, we may conclude that the
habit of covering the body is very ancient, and possibly is
derived from the single primitive human race. The erect
attitude and some skill of hand, when this organ was released
from the function of supporting the body or aiding in
progression, would lead at a very early stage to the wearing
of some kind of clothes, whether for protection, warmth,

or ornament. In all communities the women pay more attention to clothes than men, and this agrees with the fact that women, as a rule, have less hair.

We have, however, to explain, if we can, the fact that hair in both sexes is almost entirely absent in childhood, and appears more especially on the pubes at puberty. If the diminution of the hair is attributed to the wearing of clothes, it may be objected that in many savage races the children are allowed to run naked and only the mature are clothed. This objection, however, loses some of its force when we consider the treatment of babies. Swaddling clothes are a very general and probably a very ancient institution, and many primitive races, such as the American Indians, use portable cradles, in which the infants are closely swathed up and unable to move hand or foot. Somewhat similar treatment of infants is still practised in France and other civilised countries. That such treatment would lead directly in course of time to the atrophy of the hair is a suggestion by no means improbable or far-fetched. It is supported by the comparison of the condition of the young in different animals. The horse, calf, or lamb, for instance, which are dropped in the open air and run about a few hours afterwards, are born fully clothed with hair, while mice and rabbits are born naked, and are suckled in a dark warm nest in which they are closely covered up by the nest and the mother. Women in the primitive state probably had to carry their children in frequent wanderings until they were long past the period of babyhood, and for this reason, if for no other, probably covered them with some kind of garment which made them into a more portable bundle. Such treatment may possibly have been the original cause of the greater hairlessness of children. That clothing does, as a matter of fact, tend to the loss of hair, seems to be proved by the development of baldness in civilised nations. This character, however irregular it may appear in its development, seems undoubtedly on the whole to be intimately associated with the wearing of hats or head-gear, and to be developed more quickly by heavy head coverings which prevent ventilation. Baldness is much more characteristic in civilised nations of men than of women, and those who lead sedentary lives in ill-ventilated rooms seem more prone to it. As woman's head-gear is usually light and open, and often more of the nature of ornament than covering, it would naturally not tend to produce baldness to the same degree.

The retention of hair on the head in man would therefore agree with the view that the loss of hair on the body was due to the wearing of clothes. But the length of the hair on the head, especially in women, is not a universal character in Primates. In some degree this increased length is perhaps due to what may be called the cultivation of the hair. In many races, as among women in our own society, the hair of the head is regularly dressed and tended, and such manipulation, involving as it does a frequent mechanical irritation of the hair follicles, has very probably caused a more vigorous proliferation of the epidermic cells which form the hair.

Another unisexual character in man is the lower pitch of the voice, which is the result of a rapid alteration of the larynx occurring at the period of puberty. That this change and the growth of the beard are secondary sexual characters of the typical kind is shown by the fact that they do not develop in castrated individuals. The change in the voice was probably originally due to the shouting of the male under the influence of sexual excitement in contests with other males.

Among the Primates the difference between the sexes is in no case more marked than in the Mandrill, which is a species of baboon (*Cynocephalus maimon*). In the adult male the brow ridges are very prominent, and the small and closely

approximated eyes are deeply sunk beneath them. The
canine teeth are of immense size and the maxillary bones are
developed into a pair of oval prominences rising on each side
of the elongated snout. These prominences are covered by
naked skin which is marked with longitudinal ridges and
furrows. The colour of this skin is an intense blue, the
furrows being of a darker tint, while the central line and end
of the nose are of a bright scarlet. The tail is extremely short
and turned upwards, and the buttocks as well as the upper
part of the insides of the thighs are destitute of hair and of
a crimson colour, which, depending not upon pigment but
upon injection of the superficial blood-vessels, varies in
intensity according to the condition of the animal, increasing
under excitement, fading during sickness, and disappearing
after death.[1]

It is only to fully adult males that this description applies.
The female is of much smaller size and more slender, and
though the general tone of the hairy part of the body is
the same, the prominences, furrows, and colouring of the face
are much less marked. In the females the end of the nose
becomes a little red during menstruation.[2] The young males
have black faces. At the age of three years (when the canine
teeth begin to develop) the blue of the cheeks begins to
appear, but it is not until they are about five years old,
when they cut their canines, that they acquire the characteristic red of the end of the nose.

All the authors who have described the Mandrill refer in
emphatic terms to the extraordinary ferocity and insatiable
lust of the adult male. Observations on the animal in its
wild state amid its native surroundings are very scanty. It
inhabits western tropical Africa, and the specimens brought
to Europe have been shipped on the coast of the Gulf of

[1] Flower and Lydekker, *Mammals Living and Extinct*, 1891.
[2] E. G. St. Hilaire et Fréd. Cuvier, *Hist. Nat. des Mammifères*, 1819-35.

Guinea. It is said to be so powerful and dangerous an animal that the natives are exceedingly afraid of it, and that in particular it is given to ravishing the native women. But it has been pointed out that these assertions are difficult to reconcile with the fact that so many specimens have been captured alive and sold to European shippers.

However, we have it on the authority of Cuvier and Geoffrey St. Hilaire, that the adult male in captivity in Europe exhibits the most violent and continual sexual excitement, often exhausting himself by excess, and actually shows sexual inclination towards women, distinguishing particular individuals among them by voice and gesture. On the other hand, towards his keepers and men in general he shows the greatest ferocity and rage, and is one of the most formidable and dangerous of wild animals. The young male and the female are comparatively quiet and docile. A remarkable and I think significant characteristic in the behaviour of the mandrill, is that when not enraged it obtrusively turns its remarkable buttocks towards the spectator. Cuvier's description gives a vivid idea of this gesture:—" La partie postérieure du corps n'est ni moins extraordinaire ni moins révoltante. Sous une courte queue sans cesse relevée est un anus entouré d'un gros bourrelet d'écarlate; de larges fesses nues, que l'animal semble montrer sans cesse avec autant de lasciveté que d'impudence, sont colorées d'un rose vif nuancé sur les côtés de lilas et de bleu. Les parties génitales enfin sont d'un rouge de feu d'autant plus tranché qu'elles sont absolument nues, et qu'elles viennent à la suite d'un abdomen revêtu de poils blancs."

It seems to me we have here a degree of correspondence between the habits of the animal, so far as we know them, and the character peculiar to the adult male, which has a profound significance. It is clear that the cheek prominences are connected with the great development of the canine teeth. It is an inevitable inference from what has been mentioned above, that the adult male mandrills in their native condition fight constantly and fiercely with one another. It is true that large canines exist in other animals without the remarkable cheek prominences of the mandrill. But it seems to me a probable suggestion that the mandrills in their fighting contend face against face and jaw against jaw. The mechanical irritation of the maxillary bone would in that case not be merely from the pressure of the canine tooth within, but from the scarifying action of the adversary's tooth without. In this way the superficial part of the maxilla might well be stimulated to increased growth, and the growth might take a ridged form in correspondence with the direction of the usual wounds. The same habitual actions might also produce the effect visible on the skin, denuding it over the prominences of hair, and setting up a permanently congested condition of the blood-vessels. This suggestion is founded on the fact that the colour of the skin of the cheeks is stated not to be due to pigment, but to the condition of the blood-vessels. Cuvier says that it is easy to see this with a lens, and that the colour appears to depend originally on the irritation which the growth of the canine tooth produces on the maxillary nerve. My suggestion is different from Cuvier's, but it is remarkable that so great an authority should have attributed the feature to a physiological action of a similar kind. Another expression employed by Cuvier in speaking of the face is, from my point of view, very significant; he uses the expression: "achève de faire croire que toute la face est meurtrie ou écorchée." It is certain, I think, that if a male mandrill fought in the manner which I have described, his face actually would be wounded and flayed. Supposing the same result, repeated generation after generation, to be at last inherited, we should have the condition which exists. The furrowed

naked prominences may thus be regarded as inherited swell-
ings and scars. If this were true we should at any rate
understand why the peculiarity only develops in the adult,
since the males evidently fight only when they are sexually
mature, and, as in other cases, fight for the possession of the
females. As for the possible objection that a similar result
has not been produced in other cases, I would reply that
the gregariousness of the mandrill, and the violence of his
sexual excitement, would account for the unusual frequency
and fierceness of his combats, and that these peculiarities are
due to the conditions of his life.

We have next to consider the peculiarities of the posterior
aspect of the animal. Here again the appearances are due
not to pigment but to the absence of hair and dilatation and
congestion of the superficial blood-vessels. These appearances
are similar to those which in the individual would be produced by frequent and energetic friction. Such friction
would be produced by the habit of squatting on the haunches
on the hard, bare rocks among which baboons live, and I
have no doubt that this habit among baboons and monkeys
in general is the cause of their naked ischial callosities.
But the callosities of the mandrill are exceptional in their
colour, and the bare skin thus brightly coloured is more extensive than usual. This exceptional condition corresponds, or is
associated with, the peculiar habit of presenting the buttocks
to persons approaching the animal, a habit which is noticed
in the earliest description of the mandrill by Gesner.

This gesture must have some meaning, and its probable
significance is sexual. It is possible that the libidinous
nature of the mandrill has developed some habitual artificial
irritation of the region of the generative organs. The animal
probably presents its buttocks from the desire of having them
rubbed, and possibly it is accustomed to have them rubbed
or scratched by the female. Some action of this kind would

tend in the individual to produce an inflamed condition of the skin and its blood-vessels, and if inherited would explain this peculiar feature of the animal. If this were the case we could understand more completely why the colour of the skin increases under excitement, fades during sickness, and disappears after death, for a physiological association would have been set up between the sexual excitement of the animal and the results produced by friction.

One other unisexual character in the mandrill is mentioned by Cuvier: it occurs in the female. Menstruation, which takes place regularly once a month, is accompanied by a swelling of the parts round the anus, forming a protuberance which is red and inflamed in appearance, and is as big as the head of a child. This may well be due to the accumulated effect of the violence and frequency of copulation.

More definite information on the indecent gesture of the mandrill, which is performed also by certain other species, is given in a communication published by Darwin in *Nature* in 1876, and printed as a supplemental note to the second edition of his *Descent of Man*, 19th thousand, 1885. Joh. von Fischer of Gotha observed that a young male mandrill in his possession, when he first saw his reflection in a mirror, after contemplating it for some time turned round and presented his red hinder end to it. He subsequently ascertained that not only the mandrill, but the drill, *C. leucophulus*, and three other kinds of baboon, *C. hamadryas, sphinx,* and *babouin*, as well as *Cynopithecus niger, Macacus rhesus,* and *Macacus nemestrinus,* turned this part of their bodies, which in all these species is more or less brightly coloured, to him when they were pleased, and to other persons as a sort of greeting. Von Fischer concludes that the animals acted as though their reflection in the mirror were a new acquaintance, that is to say, were another individual of their own species.

The mandrill and drill, which have their callosities especially ornamented, display it, even whilst quite young, more frequently and more ostentatiously than do the other kinds. Next in order comes *Cynocephalus hamadryas*, whilst the other species act more seldom in this manner. It deserves especial attention that Von Fischer never saw any specimen of a species in which the buttocks were not coloured make this gesture: for example, it was never observed in *Macacus cynomolgus*, *Cercocebus radiatus*, three species of *Cercopithecus*, and several American monkeys.

With respect to the origin of the habit (continues Darwin) Von Fischer remarks that his monkeys like to have their naked hinder ends patted or stroked, and that they then grunt with pleasure. The habit of the adults is connected to a certain extent with sexual feelings. Von Fischer watched a female *Cynopithecus niger* through a glass door, and saw her turn her posterior, which is strongly reddened, to the male, uttering a gurgling sound the while; the male evidently became sexually excited and likewise made similar sounds with his voice. It would appear from the description that the male was in a separate cage, or separated by a grating from the female.

Von Fischer suggested that the coloration served to render one sex conspicuous at a distance to the other, while Darwin thought that the bright colours served as a sexual ornament or attraction. It seems to me that while the appearance is doubtless associated in the mind of the monkeys in question with sexual desire, the origin of the condition is sufficiently explained by the habit of the monkeys of scratching the parts in one another. It is evident that the desire for the sensation produced by the scratching is due to the pleasure which the sensation gives, and that the sensation is connected with excitement of the sexual organs, but with regard to the condition of the parts of the body concerned, as compared with the usual condition in other animals, the important point is the physiological effect of the habitual friction and scratching on the skin and its blood-vessels. This is the point which was overlooked by Von Fischer and by Darwin. The effect on the individual has, after a great number of generations, been accumulated by heredity in the species.

Von Fischer refers to a fact well known to everyone who has much experience of dogs, that these animals also are very fond of having their back and loins rubbed, that they not uncommonly turn the hinder end of their bodies to persons in their company inviting this action, and that the result of the sensation is to excite their sexual feelings and sexual organs. The comparison shows how naturally the habit would have arisen and been carried to excess in the apes and baboons, in which the nervous system is so much more active and excitable.

The drill on which Fischer made observations was a young female, so that the redness of the buttocks and the gesture described occur in this species in both sexes. The gesture is especially exhibited during the rutting season.

Darwin states that in *Macacus rhesus* the naked skin on the buttocks is only red in the female, and that the face also is pale red in the female but not in the male. We have seen that this species is one of those mentioned by Von Fischer as performing the gesture above discussed, and we may surmise that in this case the habit is confined to the female, or at least more strongly developed in the female sex.

At the Zoological Gardens in London, on February 10, 1897, I had an opportunity of personally observing the performance of these gestures, and had some conversation on the subject with one of the keepers, an experienced and intelligent man. In one cage were two young Chacma baboons, less than half grown. This species is not mentioned by either Darwin or Fischer among those which have the buttocks coloured, or

which have the habit of presenting their buttocks when
approached. But the two specimens to which I refer knew
the keeper very well, and I noticed that when the male ran
up at his call, he turned his buttocks, which were not red
beyond the callosities, towards the man, and showed pleasure
when the latter scratched them with his finger. I noticed
that at the same time an incipient erection of the penis took
place, showing that the gesture is essentially sexual. I asked
if the female behaved in the same way, and the keeper called
her and showed me that she did.

I also saw a large female, *Macacus inuus,* the Gibraltar
species, in which the parts below the anus and about the
vagina were immensely swollen and protuberant. These
parts were naked and blue in colour. The keeper told me
that the animal was "in use," and that the swelling always
occurred during that condition.

There was in the collection a full-grown male *Cynocephalus
anubis,* in which the buttocks were red beyond the callosities,
but I did not see the gesture above considered practised by
him. He had a mane round the neck, thick but not long.

Darwin mentions that in two other species of *Cynocephalus*
the adult males have a great development of hair on the nape
of the neck, forming a mane. In the *C. porcarius* of the Cape
of Good Hope the mane is longer and the canine teeth
larger than those of the female, and in *C. hamadryas* the
mane is absent in the young male and in the female. Darwin
was informed by the keepers in the Zoological Gardens that
monkeys did not attack each other by the nape of the neck
except in the case of *C. porcarius.* Doubtless this is also true
of the *hamadryas.* Darwin of course interprets the facts as
evidence that the mane is a protection. The Lamarckian
interpretation is that the irritation of the attack has stimulated
the hair to increased growth. It may be objected that in
the case of the mandrill the absence of hair on the cheeks

was attributed to the same cause, but this is a misconception. The attack of the jaws directed to the back of the neck would result in the seizing of the hair in most cases by the teeth, and this pulling of the hair would stimulate the follicles, while on the cheeks the hair would be too short to be grasped, and the skin tightened over the bones would be scratched and torn. It is also possible that the hairs of the mane are erected by the skin muscles in male baboons, as they certainly are in the lion, and this would add to the irritation of the hair follicles, but it does not seem likely that this action is the sole cause of the development of the mane.

The voice is developed to an extraordinary degree in the South American monkeys of the genus *Mycetes*, and the vocal organs have a corresponding development. Both voice and larynx are considerably more developed in the males than in the females, but in accordance with the general rule when a character is present in both sexes, the peculiarities are developed not at maturity, but in the embryo before birth. The case, however, deserves mentioning, because it indicates in so convincing a manner the connection of the modification with the mechanical effects of the action to which it is subservient. The anatomy and evolution of the vocal organs in these howling monkeys have been discussed by the distinguished anatomist Dr. Hans Gadow,[1] on whose authority the following facts are stated. The thyroid cartilage and basihyal cartilage are hollowed out and expanded into large globular receptacles which are occupied by air sacs opening from the larynx. These cavities act as resonators, and to them the extraordinary volume of sound produced is due. It is difficult, if not impossible, to conceive how such structures could have been evolved, except on the view that the form of

[1] "Description of the Modifications of certain Organs which seem to be Illustrations of the Inheritance of Acquired Characters," *Zoologische Jahrbücher*, Bd. V.

the cartilages has directly adapted itself to the pressure produced by the compressed air in the larynx. But this is not all: in the majority of species of these monkeys the front part or the whole of the manubrium sterni, instead of being single and median as it usually is, is divided into two halves. The enlarged parts of the larynx do not lie between the two halves of the manubrium when the animal is at rest; but when the dilated thyroid and basihyal are expanded by the inflation of the larynx in the production of the prolonged howl, then the upper part of the trachea is forced against the inside of the manubrium and presses its two horns apart. To suppose that a mechanical influence apparently so obvious has no physiological meaning is contrary to reason and common sense. On the view that the mechanical effects of the actions of the body in course of generations become converted by heredity into the regular course of development, the evolution of the condition is intelligible; on any other view it is impossible to explain it. The selectionist doubtless supposes that the loudest voiced individuals leave most progeny, and that any variations of structure which increase the power of the voice are thus selected. But there is no reason for the suggestion that such variations as are necessary would ever occur except as a mechanical consequence of the exertion of the voice. The howl seems, like that of the domestic cat, to be sexual, but we have no evidence that it is competitive. The truth seems to be that sexual excitement is expressed in various ways, and that a special habit, once begun, tends to increase by inheritance till it is carried to a maximum, and becomes an instinct. The reason why the howling is practised by the young and by the females may well be that the monkeys imitate one another, as gregarious animals are apt to do.

In the Cheiroptera or bats sexual differences are not strongly developed, and we may therefore pass on to the

CARNIVORA.—Darwin remarks that male animals which are provided with efficient cutting or tearing teeth for the ordinary purposes of life are seldom furnished with weapons specially adapted for fighting with their rivals. Thus the male carnivora in fighting together use the teeth which they generally use for killing their prey. The most conspicuous male character in the carnivora is the mane of the Lion. Darwin states that he is the only polygamist among the terrestrial carnivora, and he alone presents well-marked sexual characters. But the importance of his polygamy seems to lie in his greater pugnacity, for, according to Sir Andrew Smith, lions engage in terrible battles. The mane is erected by the angry lion, and the same arguments apply to this character as to the manes of baboons. The aquatic carnivora or seals exhibit some interesting cases of special characters confined to the males, and in these the connection between the special modifications and special stimulation is very obvious. Among the true Phocidæ, the family of the common seals, there are two species known as the Sea-Elephant, also called the Elephant Seal, and the Bladder-nosed Seal. In both of these, the snout of the male is enlarged and can be erected or inflated. There is no such peculiarity about the nose of the female.

The Elephant Seal is an Antarctic species, and formerly was abundant at many places where it is now seldom or never seen. At present it is for the most part restricted to a few remote islands, such as Kerguelen's Land. In the eighteenth century, Anson, in the course of his voyage round the world (1740-44), found it abundant on the shores of Juan Fernandez. He described the males as having a large snout or trunk hanging down five or six inches below the end of the upper jaw. The description, with figures of the male and female, are contained in the narrative of the voyage by Richard Walter, and the copy of this figure of the male printed in Moseley's

Naturalist on the " Challenger " is by no means accurate, the
original figure representing the snout much more correctly.
Anson landed at Juan Fernandez at the beginning of June
and left at the end of September, so that he was there in the
southern winter, and he states that the elephant seals come
ashore at the beginning of winter. He states that the noise
they make is very loud, and sounds sometimes like the grunt-
ing of hogs, sometimes like the snorting of horses in full
vigour. He says that the males have furious battles with each
other, principally about their females, and that they are much
larger than the females, being 12 to 20 feet in length.

Perhaps the best account ever written of the habits of
these animals is that given in Péron's *Voyage de Découvertes
aux Terres Australes.* I refer to Freycinet's edition, published
in 1824, vol. iii., but the observations were made between
the years 1800 and 1806. Péron studied the animals on the
islands of the Bass Straits, where at that time they were very
numerous, but were being ruthlessly slaughtered for the sake
of their blubber. He states that the enlarged snout is flaccid
when the animal is in repose, but when he raises himself,
breathes strongly, or commences to fight, it elongates and
takes the form of a tube a foot in length. He says that
when this takes place the nature of the voice is much
modified. The cry of the females and young males resembles
the lowing of a vigorous bull, but that of the adult males
has much resemblance to the noise made by a man when
gargling.

Péron gives a graphic description of the behaviour of the
males when fighting. They fight only in duels, one male
against another ; each raises its head and shoulders erect on
its fore flippers, then they fall upon one another with their
whole weight, teeth against teeth, jaw against jaw. Sometimes they lose an eye in such fights, and the possession of
the females is the reward of the victor.

Lesson's account,[1] on which Darwin relied, follows Péron's in most respects, but states that the erection of the snout or trunk is due to congestion of blood, as in other erectile tissues, and that the trunk seems to disappear gradually after the rutting season. I have found no authority whatever for this statement, which seems to be unsupported by any evidence; perhaps it was merely suggested by analogous changes in other animals.

Moseley had opportunities of studying the sea-elephant

FIG. 1. — A male Sea-Elephant (*Macrorhinus proboscideus*), showing the snout in the uninflated condition. From a photograph of the living animal taken by R. Vallentin, Esq., in the Falkland Islands.

when the *Challenger* visited Kerguelen's Land and Heard Island. He describes one male, 12 feet long, which raised its head on its fore flippers and lifted up its tail from the ground in the attitude described by Anson. Moseley thought the animal was too young to have a fully-developed trunk, but he evidently had exaggerated ideas of the extent of this organ. He states that the erection of the trunk is due to inflation with air, combined with contraction of the muscles at the side of the nose.

[1] *Dictionnaire Classique d'Histoire Naturelle*, vol. xiii.

On February 6, 1899, my friend Mr. Rupert Vallentin
had the opportunity of seeing a living male elephant seal on
the beach of Stanley Harbour in the Falkland Islands, and
was able to take several photographs of it, showing the snout
in the collapsed and the inflated condition.   The latter was
produced by striking the animal on the snout with a stick,
which enraged him greatly.   This specimen measured 17 feet
8 inches from the tip of the snout to the end of the tail, 18
feet 11½ inches from the snout to the end of the hind flipper.

FIG. 2.—The same Sea-Elephant with snout inflated and mouth open.   From a photograph
of the living animal taken by R. Vallentin, Esq., in the Falkland Islands.

Two of the photographs, showing the trunk both flaccid and
inflated, are reproduced in Figs. 1 and 2.

The inflated trunk in this specimen was about a foot in
length from base to tip, and this is the measurement which
Péron gives.   Anson also states that the trunk only projects
5 or 6 inches from the end of the jaw.   Darwin and others
seem to have supposed that the snout was prolonged to a
length of 1 foot beyond the mouth, but this is a misunderstanding.   The greater part of the inflated snout is situated
above the jaw, not in front of it.

Péron visited the King's Island in Bass Straits in

December 1802, and as he states that the female sea-elephants bring forth their young there in July, and that the pairing or rutting season is in September, it is evident that his account of the habits of the animals is largely founded upon information obtained from the sealers, not from his own observations. He states, however, that while many of the animals migrate to the south after September, a considerable number remain during the summer, and there were plenty of them on the island when he was there. The *Challenger* was at Kerguelen's Land in January 1874, at Heard Island in February, and Mr. Vallentin's photographs of the living sea-elephant were obtained in February. Thus of all the authorities to whom I have referred Anson only actually saw the sea-elephants during the breeding season. It is evident, therefore, that the so called proboscis does not disappear after the breeding season, as stated by Lesson, for it was present in the male specimens seen by Moseley and Vallentin in January and February. It is even doubtful whether the proboscis is more developed in the breeding season than at other times of the year. The extreme development, according to Anson, is a length of 6 inches from the upper jaw, and in Mr. Vallentin's specimen the free portion in the inflated condition would not be much less than that length.

A careful anatomical examination of this organ is still a desideratum, and it is to be regretted that the naturalists who have hitherto made observations on the animal have not made a more particular study of the structure and function of the proboscis. Seals have the power of closing the external nostrils, a power which they exercise when under water, and judging from the figures, the inflation of the nasal cavities in the sea-elephant is due to the closure of the external openings when air is forced in from the throat. But it is difficult to understand how the inflated proboscis can affect the voice, unless the snorting or gargling sound is produced by the nose itself, and on this point the witnesses give us no information. It is clear, I think, that the male sea elephant does inflate his nasal cavities when angry and when fighting with rivals, and this inflation, with the muscular movements and contractions associated with it, constitutes the mechanical cause which, according to my views, has in course of time produced the hypertrophy. But it is by no means clear what is the object of the inflation. It may be merely the result of emotional excitement, and may be of no real use to the animal at all; the jealousy and rage of the creature must, as in other animals, find vent somehow, and as seals, when they come to the surface of the water, expire violently through the nose, snorting or distension of the nose may be to them the most natural way of expressing their feelings. On the other hand, it might be supposed that the enlarged and distended nasal region served to protect the animal's head from its adversaries' attacks. If this were the case we should expect to find the proboscis lacerated with the adversaries' teeth, and we are not told that this is the case: nothing at present known suggests that the animal inflates his trunk for the purpose of defence, except that, according to Moseley, the animal cannot be stunned by blows on the snout as other seals can. Moseley says that this is due to a bony crest on the skull and the strength of the bones about the nostrils.

In the Bladder-nosed Seal, *Cystophora cristata*, which lives on the ice-fields of the North Atlantic, the peculiarity of the mature male is also connected with the nose, but is of a different character. The nose, instead of being elongated, is dilated at the base on the dorsal side, so that its walls here have been modified into a bladder which can be inflated until it is as large as the head. The voice of these animals is also very loud and is uplifted during their combats, when they fight furiously on the ice. The only difference between this and the preceding case is in the shape of the distension produced, a difference easily accounted for on the supposition that the walls of the nostrils were more easily distended in an upward and outward direction than in the elephant seal.

Almost all that has been stated above concerning the proboscis of the elephant seal applies to the bladder of the bladder-nose. The bladder is only developed in the males towards maturity; the males inflate the head when enraged and when fighting, and they have a very loud roar. But whether the roar is connected with the inflation there is no evidence to show. There are, however, rather more definite statements about the value of the hood or bladder as a means of defence, for R. Brown[1] states that it protects the animal from any stunning blow on the nose, the most vulnerable place in a seal, and, according to Carroll,[2] it even protects the animal against shot. But this does not prove that the bladder protects the seal when fighting, for they do not fight against one another with clubs or guns, and it is not certain that the nasal region is particularly exposed to the adversary's teeth. Blows and wounds in combat, if usually received on the snout, might form in part the irritation to which the hypertrophy is due, and the snout might have been inflated by the animal in order to better resist the teeth of its adversary. If this were proved to be the case it would afford some support to the selection theory. At present, however, it is not certain that the hood or bladder serves as a defence in the fights of rival males, while, whether selection occurs or not, it is certain that the animal when enraged inflates its snout by forcibly distending it with air. Whatever gave rise to the habit of inflation, whether it was as a means of

---

[1] *Proc. Zool. Soc.*, 1868, p. 437.
[2] Allen, *North American Pinnipeds*, Washington, 1880, p. 741.

defence, or for producing a sound, or was merely an expression of the emotions, it is evident, I think, that the importance of the bladder depends upon the inflation. The habit of inflation would tend in the individual to distend the wall of the nasal cavities, and, therefore, in this case also the unisexual modification corresponds to a mechanical strain which affects only the mature males under the influence of sexual excitement, or at least under the influence of rage and ferocity originally associated with the sexual instinct.

The habits of the fur seal of Behring Sea, *Callorhinus ursinus*, are perhaps more accurately known than those of any other species, on account of the political and commercial importance attached to questions concerning them. The male is polygamous, and the difference in size between the sexes is extraordinarily great, the adult male being six times as large as the female. At a certain time of the year these seals land in large numbers at particular places on the Pribylov and other islands in order to breed. The males wait for the females as they land, and each keeps as large a number as possible in his harem, guarding and fighting for his wives with all his might. The young males are not allowed among the adults, but are compelled to herd by themselves. The extraordinary activity and exertion of the male in the breeding habits, and the comparatively passive and submissive part played by the females, is evidently the only cause of the great difference between them in size and strength, but there are no special habits in fighting and courtship, and accordingly no special organs or characters.

The tusks of the Walrus are enlarged canines continually growing at the roots. They are larger in the males than in the females, but not exclusively confined to the former. Occasionally they are absent in the female, and the males fight ferociously with these weapons.

It is mentioned by Darwin that those species of seal in which sexual differences are conspicuous are polygamous. But as we have seen, the significance of this fact is that the polygamous males fight more than the others. Polygamy means the exclusive possession of several females, and the exclusive possession of one female may, as in the case of the moose deer, necessitate habitual fighting. The male cat and the buck rabbit are not strictly monogamous, and they indulge in occasional fights, but they use as weapons only the teeth and claws which the female equally uses in ordinary life. Sexual intercourse with these animals is promiscuous, and therefore they do not fight so habitually as those who assume the exclusive possession of the females.

CETACEA.—The most conspicuous instance of unisexual characters in Cetacea is the single spiral tusk of the male narwhal. This tusk is sometimes from 9 to 10 feet in length, and is an enlarged, continually growing, canine. The canine of the opposite side is usually about 10 inches long, though occasionally both are equally developed. In the female both are rudimentary. It is believed that the males use these weapons in fighting together, but no information is given by Darwin concerning the period of life at which they develop, nor concerning the relations of the sexes in the species. Male sperm whales fight with their heads and jaws, and the head of the male is larger than that of the female.

UNGULATA.—Among the even-toed ruminating ungulates secondary sexual characters are more strongly developed than in any other group of Mammalia. The antlers of deer are, in fact, among the most interesting and remarkable of such characters. It is well known that these antlers are in reality branched outgrowths of the frontal bones of the skull, and their development in the common stag does not merely take place once in each individual, but is repeated every year.

The theory of sexual selection does not attempt to explain this annual recrescence of the antlers. That theory is based on the existence of individual differences or variations, but these differences do not generally or necessarily take the form of annually repeated outgrowths. We cannot be content, therefore, with the theory that the stags with the finest horns conquered their rivals and left most progeny; we must inquire why the antlers are shed and reproduced every year.

As the starting-point of this inquiry we take the well-known fact of the correspondence between the growth of the antler and the activity of the sexual organs. The sexual organs in the stag are only active during a certain portion of the year, the rutting season, which in the red deer, *Cervus elaphus*, lasts from September or October to the beginning of December. At this time the antlers are completely developed, and have shed their covering of vascular skin or "velvet." The stags during this season are in a constant state of sexual excitement, and each has to fight continually with rival stags for possession of the females. The fighting weapons are the antlers, which are crossed and interlocked and pushed against one another, until one of the combatants is exhausted. After December the fighting and pairing ceases, the stags turn their attention to feeding, and begin to herd peacefully together apart from the hinds. Soon after this the antlers are shed. According to the Rev. H. A. Macpherson this takes place in Britain usually in April, but a Highland stag has been known to drop his antlers as early as December, and in the Lake District of Cumberland some immature animals carry them until May.[1]

After the old antlers are shed, the new soon commence to grow out again from the stumps or pedicles. The growth is

[1] *The Red Deer*, Fur and Feather Series, Longmans and Co., 1896.

rapid, and takes place chiefly in July and August. When the antlers have reached their full size the "velvet" is shed, and this takes place between August 20 and September 15. The size of the antlers and the number of branches or points increases every year until the vigour of the stag begins to decline from old age.

It is clear, therefore, that there is a periodical mechanical irritation of the antlers corresponding to their periodical development. They are strained and rubbed in the fights of the stags, and these fights take place only at a certain period of the year lasting not more than three months. We know that irritation of a bone by blows will cause exostosis, and we may therefore consider it probable that the growth of the antlers was caused originally by the ancestral stags butting their heads together, and so irritating the frontal bones. When the fighting ceased the bony outgrowths so caused were shed, and when the rutting season came on again, the fights and irritation of the bones were repeated, and the exostosis or outgrowth of bone was reproduced.

This hypothesis harmonises well with the important fact of the increased development of the antler in successive years. For there is a tendency for any physiological modification to become either periodical or chronic; that is to say a process once set up by a certain irritation is more easily produced the second time than the first, and the more often it is produced the more energetic its action, and the more extensive its results. The hypothesis also harmonises with the known connection between the development of the antlers and the normal condition of the testes. If a stag is castrated the antlers are not fully developed again. The growth of the antlers is of course in existing stags an inherited process; it is independent of any mechanical stimulation in the individual, but is associated inseparably with the maturation and periodical activity of the testes.

We must, however, consider the possible course of the evolution more particularly, for when we examine the subject in detail we find many difficulties. The mechanical straining of the antlers in a living stag takes place after the velvet is shed, and when the antler is fully developed, so that it produces no growth of the antler, is on the contrary followed by the shedding of the appendage, while the growth of the new antler takes place without any mechanical irritation, before the rutting season, and therefore the fighting, has commenced. My hypothesis assumes that originally the fighting took place while the antler was covered with skin, and capable of growth, so that the growth followed the irritation, not preceded it. Further, the explanation offered above does not give sufficient reasons for the regular shedding of the antler by separation below the burr as a definite natural process, not an accidental removal.

We will consider, therefore, what is known concerning the historical evolution of the typical antler, and see if it enables us to remove these difficulties. Some of the extinct deer, and doubtless the primitive ancestors of all antlered deer, were entirely destitute of antlers, and there are certain existing deer which do not possess these appendages. The latter are *Hydrelaphus*, the Water-deer of China, and *Moschus*, the Musk-deer. The last is somewhat aberrant, but the former is a true deer, and probably has never developed antlers because it fights with its canine teeth, which in the male are long, and grow from persistent pulps.

We seem to get evidence of the actual origin of the antlers in the extinct genus *Dremotherium*, the bones of which have been obtained from the Miocene beds of France, Bavaria, etc. According to Mr. Lydekker[1] these are probably the actual ancestors of the modern deer of the Old World. The earlier forms are all without antlers, while those from the Miocene

[1] *Deer of All Lands*, Rowland Ward, 1898.

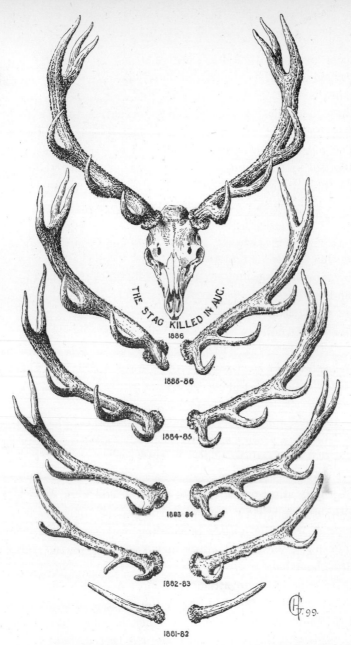

THE STAG KILLED IN AUG.
1886

1885-86

1884-85

1883-84

1882-83

1881-82

CH. 99.

FIG. 3.—The six pair of antlers produced in six successive years by a Red Stag. From the actual specimens obtained, excepting the first pair, from a single stag and exhibited in the British Museum of Natural History.

have antlers with a long peduncle and an incipient burr, beyond which they are divided into a long fork. It is believed that these antlers were never shed, and were covered with skin throughout life. This condition is not represented in existing deer, and is not exactly similar to that seen in the Giraffe. The nearest approach to it among living forms seems to be afforded by the Muntjacs, *Cervulus*, which inhabit India and the East Indies. The antlers in this genus are very small with two points, and are supported on a long pedicle, from which they are separated by a burr. The antlers of the Indian species, although so small, seem to be shed annually in May, and to be replaced by August. On the other hand, Sir Samuel Baker and other authorities state that the Indian sambar, *Cervus unicolor*, whose antlers are much larger, does not shed them every year, but carries them often three or four years, and then sheds them and reproduces them. Mr. Lydekker, however, states that the stags of this species at Woburn Abbey shed their antlers annually, but the time of shedding and the time of year at which the fawns are produced by the female are very variable.

It would appear from this that the annual shedding of the antlers was a process acquired some time after the evolution of the structures themselves. Mr. Lydekker refers to the fact that there were certain extinct ruminants more or less intimately allied to the giraffes whose heads were furnished with branching bony appendages apparently agreeing in all respects with the antlers of existing deer, except that they were never shed, and apparently remained in the velvet throughout life.

Now, in order to attempt to form a conception of the manner in which the shedding of the antlers arose, we must have some knowledge of the manner in which it actually takes place at the present time, and the best account of this matter known to me is that given by J. D. Caton in his work on the *Antelope and Deer of America*.[1] This author states that the blood-vessels of the antler are derived from three sources : (1) the arteries of the periosteum, which, as in the long bones of the skeleton, pass into the bone transversely to its surface ; (2) arteries from the periosteum of the pedicle, which turn in at the top of the pedicle, and thence pass up through the interior of the new antler ; (3) arteries which pass up through the interior of the pedicle into the growing antler. He states that, as ossification proceeds, the tips of the antlers first become solidified quite through, and the solidifying process extends downwards, so that the apertures which admitted the arteries from the periosteum become closed. This, however, does not destroy the periosteum or velvet, because the former is still provided with a venous as well as an arterial system, running in its own substance. Some authorities have maintained that the death of the velvet was due to the fact that the deposit of bone which forms the "burr" at the base of the antler constricts the arteries which enter the velvet, and so cuts off its supply of blood. But Caton asserts from his own observation that the velvet is rubbed off purposely by the animal against small trees, etc., and that it is at the time gorged with blood.

It seems probable that if an ungulate fought violently with horns covered with velvet, one of two results would follow : either the skin and periosteum would be torn, or the skin would be hardened by the friction. Possibly this is the true explanation of the different courses taken by the evolution of the horns in the Bovidæ and the Cervidæ. In the former a slowly developing horn, having a tough and not very vascular skin, was subjected to frequent but not very violent friction, till the skin became a horny covering. Horn is thickened epidermis, and the development of horn therefore implies that the true derma and periosteum were not lacerated. But

[1] Second edition, New York, 1881.

in the Cervidæ, on the other hand, when the rutting season
came and fighting commenced, or even before that time,

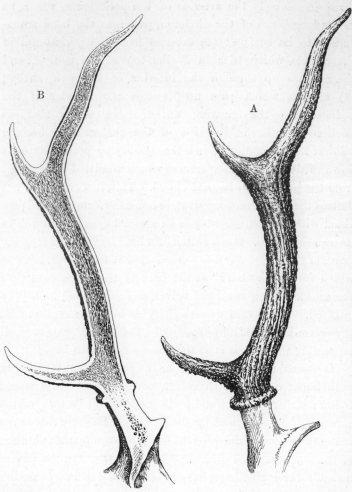

FIG. 4.—A, Antler of a Stag, probably a young Red Deer, to show the grooved surface,
the burr, and the relation to the skull. B, A similar antler cut through the middle
longitudinally to show the internal structure. From specimens in the British
Museum of Natural History.

when the animal rubbed its horns against trees in consequence of the irritation felt in them, the vascular skin and

periosteum were torn off in strips as they are at the present day. The formation of the burr was probably the result of this, for the injured blood-vessels at the base would continue to deposit bony matter after this process was stopped on the surface of the naked antler.

We have then reached the condition of the bony antler stripped of skin and periosteum: what takes place afterwards? According to J. D. Caton, after the periosteum has gone, there is still a considerable blood supply passing up internally from the pedicle, and internal ossification of the antler proceeds. The interior, however, does not become completely solidified : a thin solidified plate of bone is formed at the level of the burr and this ultimately cuts off the supply of blood, by closing the apertures through which the internal blood-vessels pass. At this stage the pedicles are carrying masses of dead bone. These are cast off, not irregularly or accidentally, but by a regular process. Caton states that the blood-vessels which pass in from the periosteum of the pedicle into the "articulation" of the antler perform the function of absorbing bony tissue until the connection between the antler and the pedicle is destroyed, and the former drops off and is detached by a slight blow. We do not know whether the shedding of the antler was from the first an annual process, or whether it occurred originally at longer intervals, and afterwards became annual. The case of the sambar, if it is true that it does not shed its horns every year, would support the latter conclusion. But it seems reasonable to suppose that the absorption process to which the shedding is due was the necessary physiological result of the loss of the periosteum and gradual death of the antler. The commencement of the process may be determined either by the cessation of vitality at the base of the antler, or by the lowering of vigour in the whole body which follows the rutting season, an exhaustion partly due to the preceding excitement and expenditure.

partly to the scarcity of food. The sambar at Woburn Abbey is stated to shed its antlers every year, and the experience of surgeons proves that absorption naturally follows on the death of a portion of bone.

We have next to consider whether the growth of the new antler after the old was shed was originally a spontaneous process of recrescence, like that of the arm of a star-fish after amputation, or whether it was dependent on renewed irritation. It is certain that if the growth did not occur spontaneously, the irritation would be renewed at the next rutting season, and the previous course of growth and shedding of the antler would be brought about again. If, on the other hand, the growth always took place as it does now, before the rutting season, and without any external irritation, it is difficult to see any reason for the increased development in successive years. It seems most reasonable to suppose that in the early stages of the evolution, after one pair of antlers had been shed, the growth of the succeeding pair was stimulated by irritations of the periosteum before the growth was completed.

This view seems also to be required to explain the branching of the antler, which when first developed is a single spike. Darwin remarks that although the antlers are efficient weapons, there can, he thinks, be no doubt that a single point would have been much more dangerous than a branched antler. He thinks that they do not appear perfectly well adapted as a means of defence against rival stags, as they are liable to become interlocked, and he thinks that they may serve in part as ornaments. But we have no evidence that the female deer has any choice but to accept the victorious stag, except that she occasionally pairs with an unoccupied stag while her original lord is engaged in combat. I think, therefore, the branching must have been originally caused by irritation of the periosteum before the velvet was shed.

From the above considerations it seems to me there are two possible views concerning the evolution of the antlers in the Cervidæ. The first is as follows. We may suppose that the young stags fought with their heads, and as a result of this, inflammation of the periosteum was caused. This inflammation caused a process of hypertrophic ossification or exostosis. We may suppose that as the inflammation ceased, and the ossification was completed, the stag felt an irritation in the previously inflamed skin, and rubbed it violently against trees, laying the new bone bare. The ossification went on longer and more rapidly at the base of the projection, where the laceration of the skin caused more inflammation, and so gave rise to the burr. Then, when this also had run its course, the exostosis was shed naturally in consequence of the absorption of the dead bone by the living blood vessels at the base. We may suppose all this to have happened within a year, the process being repeated *da capo* at the next rutting season. According to this hypothesis the loss of the velvet and consequent death and shedding of the antler is due not to fighting, but to a spontaneous effort on the part of the stag, and this is due to an irritation caused by the acute and inflammatory character of the process by which the exostosis was formed. In this respect the hypothesis agrees with that which occurs in the existing stag, but it does not agree with the fact that in the latter the antler develops before fighting commences, and that during its development the velvet appears to be so sensitive that any contact is painful. On this hypothesis, therefore, we must assume that when the process of hypertrophy became hereditary, it was so hastened as to follow soon after the shedding of the old antler, instead of following the irritation of the fighting period.

Objections to this hypothesis arise also from the possibility mentioned above, that the regular shedding of the antlers was a peculiarity not originally connected with them, but acquired at a later stage of their evolution. The short horns of the giraffe are covered with hairy skin, which, however, is nearly hairless and rather horny on the blunt extremities. They are present, too, in both sexes, though larger in the male. It is curious that the bones of these horns are at first united with the skull by suture, and are not, therefore, strictly speaking, outgrowths of the skull bones. In the extinct *Sivatherium*, which, though allied to the giraffes, had a neck and legs of ordinary proportions, there were two pairs of horns, the anterior short and conical like those of the giraffe, the hinder long and palmate, somewhat like those of the elk. As there is no burr, it is fairly certain that the latter were not shed, but it is not so certain whether they were covered with horn or soft skin. The latter seems more probable, because appendages covered with horn are not usually branched. It must be noted, however, that these giraffe-like forms are not more ancient, but more recent, than the extinct deer of the genus *Dremotherium*, which belong to the Miocene, while the former are found in the Pliocene. They indicate, however, that large and to some degree branched antlers might exist which were permanent and covered with skin.

Our second hypothesis, therefore, is that the original antlers of deer were in this condition. Then they may have grown and branched gradually in consequence of pressures and blows received in fighting. We may suppose that at a certain stage of evolution the fighting became more severe, so that the skin and periosteum were torn off the bone. This may have happened first in old stags in which the bone of the antler was harder. The loss of the periosteum would cause the death and shedding of the bone, and this process would not at first be annual. The renewal of the lost part might be due to renewed irritations at first, and became normal by heredity afterwards. Also by the operation of heredity the loss of the skin might become more and more early and regular until it took place as soon as fighting commenced, and then reached the present condition in which it takes place before the fighting, and the skin is voluntarily rubbed off by the stag. One advantage of this hypothesis is that it enables us to attribute the progressive size and branching of the antlers to an original progressive development of permanent antlers in the same individual in consequence of continued irritation.

On the whole, however, I am inclined to think that this hypothesis does not agree with the facts. In the earliest fossil forms already mentioned, *Dremotherium* or *Palæomeryx*, there is at least an incipient burr, and we have no evidence of the existence of any antler in ancestral deer more complicated than a simple fork, which was not periodically shed.

The truth, therefore, seems to lie somewhere between the two hypotheses I have outlined. The earliest stag probably had a simple undivided antler, the point of which at some stage of life was partly denuded of skin. A laceration of skin from the point downwards caused the formation of a nodule of bone at the base of the laceration, and this was the commencement of the burr. Such destruction of skin and the underlying periosteum, whether caused by fighting or by voluntary effort, ultimately caused the shedding of the dead bone ; but this may not have happened at first till late in life. When it had happened, the stag fought with the pedicle and irritated the point of it to greater hypertrophy than before. Thus arose the forked antler, at first a simple fork, afterwards a more complicated branching. In this way, the progress in the size and complexity of the antler went on equally with the increase in the regularity of the shedding. There is, however, a difficulty in the fact that the small forked antler of the existing muntjacs, although shed every year, does not increase in size or complexity. This may be due merely to a difference in the degree of irritation, especially considering that the muntjac in fighting uses its canine teeth, as well as its antlers.

I am well aware that the above suggestions are very speculative, and to many readers they may seem entirely without foundation. There are, however, certain established and accepted facts which, I believe, cannot be ignored in considering the physiology and evolution of antlers, namely, the facts concerning the development of exostoses as the result of mechanical irritation. Having but a limited knowledge of comparative pathology myself, I will refer to certain statements in an authoritative manual of veterinary surgery.[1] It is here stated that "in horses periostitis sometimes develops on the lower margin of the mandible, at the level of the first molar tooth. External stimulation, especially knocks against narrow cribs in feeding, generally cause this malady. The exostoses so formed are sometimes flat, but usually round, well-defined, and often stalked. They are painless, and firmly connected to the bone." These exostoses are not deciduous, and remain covered with skin.

In another chapter of the same work, the injuries due to pressure of the bit on the diastema, or toothless part of the lower jaw, are described. This sometimes causes a *periostitis ossificans*, which leads to the formation of exostoses, and on the skeletons of old saddle-horses these are *often* found. Sometimes it leads to *periostitis purulenta*, which affects the substance of the bone, and causes necrosis or death of portions of it. Dead pieces of bone, as big as a finger, are sometimes expelled through abscesses on the lower margin of the mandible. The latter process is not similar to the

---

[1] *Lehrbuch der speciellen Chirurgie für Thierärzte*, Dr. H. Möller, Stuttgart, 1891.

shedding of an antler, but it illustrates the fact that the shedding of dead bone is a normal physiological process.

Periostitis is very frequent in the legs of horses. In the fore-leg it is generally known as splint; in the hind-leg as spavin. These affections concern chiefly the carpal and metacarpal bones, or tarsal and metatarsal, as the case may be, and they are usually accompanied by the formation of exostoses. It is stated by Möller that the periostitis, whether in fore-leg or hind-leg, is usually caused by internal strains, not by external injury or irritation. I need not, therefore, discuss these cases, as they are not analogous to the formation of antlers. There are, however, plenty of cases where exostoses are caused on the metacarpal by friction with the hoof of the other leg. Möller states that the two kinds are easy to distinguish clinically, because the exostoses due to external irritation are round, and situated on the large metacarpal only, while the others are lengthened, and affect the splint bone of the inner side of the leg.

I am not able to give instances of abnormal exostoses being shed like the antlers of deer, but it is a well-known fact that destruction of the periosteum causes death of the bone it covers, and that dead bone may be extruded. I think, therefore, that if a superficial exostosis were denuded of skin—in the horse, for instance—absorption at the base would occur, and the exostosis would drop off.

I have referred above to the effects of castration on the growth of the antlers, and will here state more precisely what has been definitely ascertained concerning these effects. All the evidence of any real value seems to be mentioned in two accounts; a paper by Dr. Fowler,[1] and Caton's work already cited. Some of Caton's experiments were made on mature stags which had large branched antlers. He found that if the testes were removed from the stag after the

---

[1] *Proc. Zool. Soc.* 1894, p. 485.

antlers were mature, that is, after the velvet had been shed, or was ready to be shed, the antlers always dropped off within thirty days afterwards, however distant might be the time at which they would have been shed in the entire stag. In the following summer the antlers develop again, as in the entire stag, but with important differences. In the first place, if the castrated stag is young, having only a spike antler, the new antler will be a spike of nearly the same length, no more advanced stage will be reached, as in the entire stag, but the same stage is repeated. Secondly, the new antlers *never lose their velvet.* In the winter the abnormal antlers may be frozen and broken off nearly down to the burr, but not below the burr, or they may be carried through the winter, only a few points being broken. In the following summer irregular growths take place on the old antler, covered with its persistent velvet. These growths usually take the form of large irregular tubercles. As in winter, projections are continually broken off, and in summer more tubercles grow, a very irregular antler is the result, and on the whole more loss takes place than growth, so that the whole mass gets smaller. These experiments were made on the wapiti, the Canadian deer, which is very similar to the European red deer. The results agree very closely with those described by Dr. Fowler from experiments which have been made on fallow-deer. There is this addition, however, to be made from Dr. Fowler's paper; that when castration is performed at birth, little processes are developed two to four inches in length, covered with skin. It will be seen, therefore, that castration does not entirely prevent the development of antlers, but it does entirely prevent the normal peeling of the velvet and normal shedding of the antler developed after castration. This strongly supports the theory that the peeling of the velvet, and consequent shedding of the antler, were originally due to mechanical irritations associated with sexual activity, and are therefore associated in heredity with the same activity. When the testes are removed, the hereditary tendency in this direction ceases to manifest itself.

The case of the Moose Deer shows in a most interesting manner that it is more or less permanent possession of the female, and the habits associated with this, which give rise to sexual dimorphism, and that polygamy, or the possession of several females, is by no means necessary. The Moose, *Alces palmata*, differs from all other species of the Cervidæ in being monogamous, and yet the male has very large antlers. According to J. D. Caton, " when he finds himself accepted by an agreeable partner, they retire to a deep secluded thicket in low marshy ground, where they spend their honeymoon of three or four weeks. If, however, his quiet privacy is disturbed by a rival, his fierceness and rage are at once kindled into a fury, and he goes to meet the foe." The moose fights like other stags, but fights for the possession of one mate, not of several.

A statement concerning a modification in the antlers of deer is quoted by Darwin, which, if true, would be very strong evidence in favour of spontaneous variation and selection, and difficult to reconcile with the views maintained by me. A writer in the *American Naturalist*, who had hunted *Cervus virginianus* in the Adirondack Hills for twenty-one years, stated that he had frequently killed bucks or stags in which the antler consisted of a single unbranched spike projecting forward from the brow and terminating in a very sharp point. The spike-horn was alleged to be superior to the normal antler, as a weapon, and in consequence the spike-horn bucks were said to be gaining upon the common bucks in numbers, so that in time all the stags would be spike-horned. This is a curious instance of the influence of an accepted doctrine on an imaginative and superficial observer. J. D. Caton, who made a special study of the natural history of deer in Canada, states that this question was of the greatest scientific importance, and that he took pains to investigate it to his satisfaction, with the result that he was entirely convinced that there was no truth in the belief above mentioned. *The spike-horn bucks seen and killed in the Adirondacks were all yearling bucks with their first antlers.* In all species of *Cervus* the horns which first grow are simple, pointed, unbranched spikes, and to prove the existence of spike-horned bucks as a variety, it would be necessary to show that when they cast their horns they developed simple spikes every year throughout life. No attempt was made to produce evidence of this, and Caton describes cases which came under his own observation in which spike-horned bucks of large size, which might have been supposed to be full grown, developed branched horns in the following year. The spike-horns belonging to stags supposed to be adult were stated to be longer than the normal simple horns of yearling stags, but Caton points out that in the first place accurate measurements were not made, and in the second, that the length of normal simple antlers varies considerably in different individuals.

In the family Cervidæ the Reindeer—*Rangifer*—forms a single exception in the fact that both sexes bear antlers, although those of the female are considerably smaller and less branched than those of the male. Darwin lays much stress on the fact that in the Reindeer the horns in both males and females first appear at a period of life considerably earlier than in the males of the other species in the family. In seven species in which the males alone bear antlers, he ascertained from trustworthy observers that they first appear at periods varying from nine months after birth in the roebuck, to ten, twelve, or even more months in other and larger species; while in the Reindeer, according to Professor Nilsson, they appear in both sexes within four or five weeks after birth. As the fawns are generally conceived in autumn, and brought forth in spring, this means that antlers are

FIG. 5.—Head of a male American Reindeer, with the antlers in the "velvet." From a stuffed specimen in the British Museum of Natural History.

developed in the first summer in the Reindeer, and not until the second summer in the stags of other species. Another peculiarity in the Reindeer is, that whereas the male sheds his antlers immediately after the rutting season, at the end of November, the female retains hers until April or May, when she produces her young.

Now, if we suppose that some modification in the process of heredity has caused the antlers to be developed in the young males and females in the Reindeer, this does not diminish in the least the force of the argument that the usual limitation of these structures to mature males is due to the habit of fighting. But it is interesting to enquire whether there is any peculiarity in the habits of the Reindeer to which the change in the development of the antlers might be attributed. My search for evidence of this kind has not been very successful, but there are peculiarities in the habits of reindeer in which they differ from other species. The most obvious suggestion which presents itself is that perhaps the young males and females also fight, although their pugnacity must arise from some other cause than the sexual excitement which enrages stags.

That the female reindeer uses her antlers as weapons is indicated by the statement that in order to milk those of the domesticated breed the Laplanders fasten them by a lasso thrown over the antlers, and that even then some of the deer are very refractory and often throw down the women, and butt at them with their antlers, for which, however, it is stated that the women care little (*Standard Natural History*). In the same work it is stated that in the rutting season each old stag is polygamous and has a large harem, and that when two stags fight, the victor adds the harem of his opponent to his own herd. But after the fawns are born the mother and fawn are said to be accompanied separately by a single male, while large herds of young males and females are led by *an old female*. Admiral von Wrangel, in his account of his experiences in Siberia, states that he saw large herds of wild reindeer migrating, and that each body

was led by a deer of unusual size, which his guides assured
him was always a female. The stags and hinds of red-deer,
on the other hand, out of the pairing season, generally do not
mix but form small herds, each containing animals of one
sex. A herd of stags is said during this part of the year to

Fig. 6.—Head of a female Norwegian Reindeer, with mature antlers. From a stuffed
specimen in the British Museum of Natural History.

live in perfect harmony, always under the recognised leader-
ship of one of their number, while a herd of hinds is more
republican.[1]

Another view of the development of antlers in female reindeer may be taken, namely, that it is an instance of the

[1] Lydekker, *Deer of All Lands*, 1898, p. 72.

general tendency of all unisexual characters ultimately to become common to both sexes. It is possible that unisexual characters originally developed by special stimulations related to reproduction, tend sooner or later to be inherited in common by all individuals of the species, that considered in relation to periods of evolution their sexual limitation is only temporary. This view would be in harmony with many cases besides that of the reindeer. The latter species would therefore have acquired horns at an earlier period than other deer, and have thus got to a later stage in their evolution.

This view is in direct opposition to that of Mr. Gordon Cameron, and to some extent in agreement with that of Mr. Lydekker.[1] The former author considers that the possession of defensive weapons, whether cranial or dental, by both sexes, was a primitive character, and concludes that therefore *Rangifer* represents the oldest line of antlered deer, from which the dimorphic forms have diverged. Mr. Lydekker, on the other hand, points out that in the Bovidæ it is mostly in the specialised and modern forms that the females, if horned at all, bear large horns, that in the gazelles and their allies, which are an ancient group dating back to the Miocene, generally the males only are horned, and that in the extinct Cervine genus *Dremotherium* of the Miocene, some specimens, probably the females, are hornless. In my own opinion the conclusion to be drawn is that whatever the geological age of the species or genus, the possession of horns, or other secondary sexual character generally confined to the males, by both sexes, is a recently acquired character. Palæontology tells us that the earliest deer possessed no antlers at all, and as species in these were already differentiated, it is not certain that all antlered deer are descended from one original antlered species. It is thus possible that antlers were acquired separately in distinct lines of descent, in consequence of the same

[1] *Deer of All Lands*, 1898, p. 35.

habit of fighting with the head. Thus the ancesters of the reindeer may have had antlers before those of typical deer, and the species may therefore be now in a more advanced stage of evolution, the stage in which the female has inherited the antlers, or rather in which the hereditary tendency latent in the female has manifested itself in the actual development of the antlers. Thus, according to my view, the three stages in the evolution of antlers, and of horns too, are (1) the excrescences entirely absent, (2) present in the male only, (3) present in both sexes.

The evidence concerning the effects of castration on the reindeer is a little uncertain. It is discussed by Caton. The Laplanders castrate their male reindeer at the age of three years, and one whom Caton questioned supposed that the antlers were cast off and renewed after castration as usual. Owen states that this was the case with two castrated males at the Zoological Gardens in London. Caton points out, however, that the Laps do not remove the testes, but crush and bruise them, and thinks that the castration is imperfect, and therefore the effect on the antlers is comparatively slight. He has overlooked the importance of the fact that the female reindeer has antlers. Castration of the male in this species might be expected to reduce the male only to equality with the female, and this probably explains why the effects of castration are less marked than in other species. A character which has been inherited by the female, can no longer be entirely dependent on the functional activity of the male organs of generation. For this reason more exact observations on the effects of castration in male reindeer would be of great importance.

Another peculiarity of stags is their voice. The roar or bellow of the rutting stag is very deep and loud, and is used chiefly as a challenge to rival stags, but there is no evidence that it has any importance as a call to the female. Here I can cite the authority of Darwin himself in favour of my argument, as the following quotation will show :—" As the case stands the loud voice of the stag during the breeding season does not seem to be of any special service to him, either during his courtship or battles or in any other way. But may we not believe that the frequent use of the voice, under the strong excitement of love, jealousy, and rage, continued during many generations, may at last have produced an inherited effect on the vocal organs of the stag as well as of other male animals ? This appears to me in our present state of knowledge the most probable view." The vocal organs of the stag are specially developed, like the antlers, in the rutting season, and reduced in the intermediate time of year. The necks swell and their voices become hoarse, and as the season advances the discordant bellowing of the love-sick brutes becomes more and more persistent, especially on cold clear nights (Macpherson). Here then we have a structural modification associated with the periodical exertion of a certain organ, and having no relation to any form of selection or competition.

The Musk-deer, *Moschus moschiferus,* and its allies have no antlers, but in the males the upper canine teeth are developed into long curved tusks pointing downwards. These tusks doubtless in their late development and function correspond to the antlers of the Cervidæ or true deer, but are permanent, not shed annually. As in other deer, the breeding of these animals is confined to a special rutting season, and at other seasons they are solitary in their habits. The enlargement of a tooth is as natural a consequence of excessive use as is that of an antler, the pressure stimulating the papilla or pulp from which the tooth is developed. The evolution of the musk gland situated in the skin of the abdomen, and also confined to the males, is more difficult to explain.

Darwin has discussed at considerable length the horns of

sheath-horned ruminants, pointing out that in these all degrees exist between the complete absence of horns in the females and their equal development in both sexes. Here as in the case of deer we can scarcely doubt that when the horns are present only in the mature males, their presence is associated with fighting habits also confined to the males, but it is more difficult to decide whether the development in

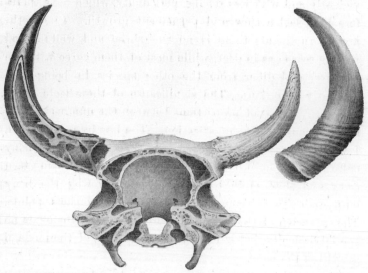

FIG. 7.—The horns and part of the skull of an Ox, to show the relations of bone, skin, and horn-sheath. The horn of the left side in section. The space between the bony core and horn sheath is occupied during life by vascular periosteum and skin, and non-vascular living epidermis. From a specimen in the British Museum of Natural History

the females is dependent on the practice of similar habits, or is merely due to some change in the course of heredity which is not directly dependent on special habits in the female. Before, however, discussing such questions in detail it is necessary to consider the difference between these horns and the antlers of deer, and to state what reason there is for attributing the former also to mechanical irritation of the frontal bone, or more correctly of its periosteum.

The peculiarities of horns, then, as distinguished from

antlers are the following:—Firstly, they are permanent, not
annually shed and reproduced; secondly, they are encased in
cornified skin; thirdly, the bone itself is hollow, not merely
spongy in the interior like the antler; fourthly, they are
simple and not branched. It seems to me that all these
peculiarities are chiefly, if not entirely, due to the fact that
horns have been developed by impacts and blows applied less
violently and with less regular periodicity, which have therefore produced a slow and permanent growth. In sheath-
horned ruminants there is no such brief and well-marked
rutting season as in deer, while most of them agree with the
Reindeer and differ from the other species in being permanently gregarious. The significance of these facts is far
greater than that of proportions between the numbers of the
sexes or any process of selection. The less intense friction,
I would suggest, is the reason why the skin over the bony
outgrowth has been hardened into horn instead of being torn
away and shed as in the antler, and also why the bony
outgrowth itself has not branched out at various points.
The extension of the frontal sinuses into the horns offers no
special difficulty, but is merely a consequence of the mode of
growth of the bone.

The antelopes form in some respects a transition from
deer to cattle in their habits and form of body. *Antilope
saiga*, which lives in eastern Europe and Asia, is stated by
Darwin, on the authority of Pallas, to be the most inordinate
polygamist in the world, a single male being found with about
a hundred females and kids. It is in accordance with this
that the females should be without horns, for all the fighting
is done by the male. The graceful spiral horns of the kudu
of South Africa are also confined to the males. In the eland,
Ant. oreas, on the other hand, and in several other species
the horns are developed in both sexes.

In *Antilocapra americana* the horns are rudimentary in

the females, and the species is unique among the Cavicornia or sheath-horned ungulates in shedding, not the bony core, but the horny covering every year. The horns are also unique in being forked instead of simply pointed. The regular periodical shedding of the horns was regarded as so

Fig. 8.—Head of the Prong-Buck, *Antilocapra americana*. From a stuffed specimen in the British Museum of Natural History.

extraordinary a phenomenon, that for a long time naturalists refused to believe it when sportsmen asserted that it occurred. Yet from the Lamarckian point of view it is possible to understand and explain it, for the simple reason that the shedding of the entire horn occurs occasionally in domesticated cattle in consequence of definite external irritation.

J. D. Caton has described at length, and I believe

accurately, the process of shedding and regeneration of the horn-sheath in *Antilocapra*. The growth of the new horn begins before the old is shed, and is simply the normal process of horn-formation intensified, so as to be acute at a certain season instead of chronic as in ordinary cases. The horn is produced, like normal horn, by proliferation of the cells of the epidermis and the hardening of the outer layers of cells. There are, however, important peculiarities in the mode of development. The growth proceeds from above downwards. When the old sheath has been just cast off there is a new horn extending several inches from the top of the core. The top of this for nearly half an inch is already hardened into perfect horn. Below this it is softer, and a little way down it has lost the horny texture, then it passes by gradual transition into thick massive skin of a high temperature and with much blood. Still lower down the core is covered with thinner, ordinary skin bearing coarse hairs.

FIG. 9.—Horn-sheath of *Antilocapra* as it appears when shed. From a specimen in the British Museum of Natural History.

As the development of the horn proceeds the outer part of the epidermis is converted into horn from above downwards, and when the lower part is mature the hairs are embedded in the horn. From Caton's description it appears that the progress of the horn downwards is caused by the conversion of the epidermis between the hairs into horn, not by the displacement of the skin by the horn coming down from above. This suggests that the horn was originally produced by the hardening of hairy skin, the hairs, having deep roots, being involved in the process and embedded in the horn. But I cannot agree with Mr. Lydekker (*Royal Natural History*) that the horn of the prong-buck is in reality nothing more than a mass of agglomerated hairs. This seems to me quite a mistaken view.[1]

Fig. 10.—Head of *Antilocapra* showing the horn-sheaths in process of regeneration. From *Proc. Zool. Soc.* 1880.

The shedding of the horn-sheath follows the rutting season, and Caton quotes from Audubon and Bachman an account of the ferocity of the adult males at this season :— "The rutting season of this species commences in September;

[1] That the view I have adopted above is correct is proved by the careful and detailed investigation of Nitsche (*Studien über Hirsche*, Leipzig, 1898, pp. 72-78) :—"The horn-sheath of *Antilocapra* consists of hairs, and horn-substance which subsequently encloses the earlier formed hairs."

the bucks run for about six weeks, and during this period fight with great courage and even a degree of ferocity. . . . Both parties run at each other with their heads lowered and their eyes flashing angrily, and while they strike with their horns they wheel and bound with prodigious activity and rapidity, giving and receiving severe wounds, sometimes, like fencers, getting within each other's points and each hooking his antagonist with the recurved branches of his horns, which bend considerably inward and downward." Caton states that in old bucks the horn is shed in October, and the new growth is not completed till July or August, so that the fighting is limited to the rutting season.

Comparison of these facts with the very brief paragraph in Möller's *Chirurgie für Thierärzte* concerning the shedding of horns in the ox, is sufficient to show the close similarity of the processes in the two cases. Möller merely states that loosening of one or both horns in cattle occurs under the same circumstances as fracture of the horn core, that is to say, from violent pushing or striking with the horn, from mechanical pressure and impact. The old horn-sheath may be merely loosened or entirely separated. The horn may be completely regenerated, but the new horn is never perfect in size and shape. The latter fact may to some appear inconsistent with my conclusions, but I think it is obvious at any rate that if irritation and renewal were frequent the growth of the epidermis might be stimulated so as to produce a new horn rather larger than its predecessor or as large.

It must be observed that the prong-buck differs from ordinary antelopes in the limitation and corresponding intensity of its sexual activity, and this would be the natural result of the succession of seasons. The prong-buck is confined to the temperate region of the western part of North America. Scarcity of food and cold would lower its sexual activity in winter, and the activity would revive again, as in deer, after the plentiful food of summer.

Antelopes generally belong to the warmer temperate regions if not specially to the tropical, and the ancestor of the prong-buck probably entered America from Asia. The species, however, is not necessarily derived from a form which had fully-developed permanent sheaths like other antelopes. If this were the case it is doubtful whether the horn when the old sheath was cast would be covered with hairy skin at its lower portion. It is thus more probable that the shedding of the horn-sheath began at a stage when the conversion of the epidermis into horn had only recently taken place and the roots of the hairs had not degenerated. In this case when the sheath was separated the deeper parts of the hairs would, of course, be left alive in the uncornified part of the epidermis. I presume that when the horn-sheath of an ox or cow is shed from injury there are no hairs in the living epidermis left beneath. It is even possible that the shedding of the horn-sheath in the prong-buck commenced at a stage when only the apex of the horn was cornified, and that the extent of the cornified region extended gradually downwards after the periodical shedding had become established. The cornification might extend a little lower down after each shedding, and in each generation. In this case the reproduction of the new horn-sheath after shedding would follow the course by which it had been evolved.

The existence of the second or anterior point of the horn-sheath is to be attributed to more intense irritation at this point. The bony core is as simple as in other antelopes, so that the periosteum is not affected.

Strong support to the above arguments is afforded by the statement of Caton, that the older the animal the earlier the horn matures and the sooner it is cast, though, of course, it is never shed till after the rutting season. "On old bucks the horn is shed in October, while on the early kids it is shed in January, and still later in later kids, or else it is carried over till next year."

Darwin states on the authority of Canfield that horns are present in a small proportion of the females, only in one out of four or five. Caton, however, states that the horn is present in the female, but much smaller. He had not seen any in this sex more than an inch long, but others have seen them three inches in length. Darwin states that in all the wild species of goats and sheep the horns are larger in the male than in the female, and are sometimes quite absent in the latter, while in cattle or the Bovinæ, likewise, they are usually more developed in the male.

In camels and guanacoes the males have large canines, which are smaller in the females.

In horses the stallion does not possess any very conspicuous unisexual characters. He has canine teeth which are rudimentary in the female, but he is said to fight chiefly with his incisors. The mane of the stallion is thicker and fuller than that of the mare, and Darwin was informed that in fighting they invariably endeavour to seize one another by the neck. Here, therefore, as in the case of the lion, we have perhaps a mechanical reason for the evolution of the mane. Darwin (*Variation of Animals and Plants under Domestication*, vol. i. p. 50, 1868) states that in various countries horn-like projections have been observed on the frontal bones of the horse as an individual variation; and Mr. Alfred Russel Wallace has referred to this statement as evidence against my argument that such outgrowths of the frontal bones first arose in consequence of animals butting with their heads against each other, not as a spontaneous variation. I have, therefore, taken the trouble to examine the evidence concerning horned horses, with the following results:—

Darwin's authority was the French translation of the *Quadrupèdes de Paraguay* by Azara (vol. ii. p. 313, 1801). That author says that he had heard as a certain fact that at Santa Fé de la Vera Cruz there was born a horse on which there grew behind the ears two horns, like those of bulls, which acquired a length of over 4 inches, and which were straight and pointed. Another similar horse was brought from Chili to the house of the Alcade of Buenos Ayres where many saw it. " Il étoit doux et cependant il s'animait quelquefois, et il se présentait comme le taureau pour frapper de ses cornes." Some one took the horse in order to breed from it, but the results had not been ascertained. A note of the translator states that Hazard, in his translation of the *Traité des Haras* by Hartmann, says that he had been told that in Spain there are special races of horses which have for the most part one or two protuberances on the parietal bones (*sic*) where the horns of cattle grow.

The above is all the evidence, and it is obvious that it is not very satisfactory. There is no statement by an actual observer; all the assertions are made on the strength of verbal and vague reports by others. No description of such horns on the skulls of horses has been given, so far as I have been able to discover, by a competent observer. At the same time it is worth noting that the horse mentioned by Azara is stated to have presented his horns when irritated, like a bull. Therefore, if such a horned horse really existed, it is at least possible that the action of striking with the forehead preceded the development of the horns, and actually was the cause of the development in the individual. Without more precise and definite evidence, however, it would scarcely be profitable to devote further consideration to the matter.

Passing next to the even-toed ungulates which do not ruminate, we find numerous cases of sexual dimorphism in

the Suidæ or swine family. In the common wild boar the
lower canines are developed into long curved tusks, which
are employed in fighting with other boars, and Darwin
quotes Sir W. Elliot as authority for the belief that in the
breeding season in India the boar consorts with several
females, an indication of exclusive possession of the latter.
On the shoulder there is an area of gristly skin, which
receives the blow of the opponent's tusk. Here once more
we find the direct effect of mechanical impact.

In the Babirusa boar of Celebes the upper canines are
enlarged into enormous tusks, so much curved that their
points cannot be presented, while the lower are shorter, less
curved, and very formidable. The upward curvature of such
tusks in the upper jaw is to be attributed in the first
instance to the pressure of the lower tusk, which, as it
elongates in evolution, necessarily turns up the point of the
upper canine. Afterwards the continual use of the upturned
tusk will cause its continued enlargement. Darwin gives a
description of the African wart-hog, *Phacochœrus œthiopicus*,
and no one can help being struck with the correspondence
between the character and position of the skin pads beneath
the eyes, and the stroke which the tusk of an opponent must
give. The stroke of the tusk would necessarily harden the
skin, and the peculiarity which is now specific and hereditary
is evidently only an intensification of the effect which would
be produced in the individual. The tusks and the "wart"
are both present in the female as well as in the male, but on
a reduced scale in the former, and this is possibly due to
similar pugnacious habits in the female. A similar but more
prominent wart is present in the African river-hog, *Pota-
mochœrus penicillatus*. Darwin mentions that after a fight
between a river-hog and a wart-hog, these thickened parts
of the skin were covered with blood, and were scored and
abraded in an extraordinary manner. Is it possible, in

the face of such facts, to attribute the evolution of these structures to anything but mechanical stimulation ?

In India and Malacca the male elephants alone are provided with well-developed tusks, while the female of the African elephant has tusks almost, but not quite, as large as those of the male. There is no doubt that the elephant fights with his tusks. In India the habits of the elephant appear to resemble somewhat those of the red stag; the male is often solitary, but associates in the breeding season with several females, and fights with other males for their possession.

In Marsupials no well-marked unisexual characters occur, but the male is usually larger and stronger than the female.

In *Ornithorhynchus* and *Echidna* there is an interesting peculiarity in the male, namely, a spur on the hind-leg which is hollow, and through which passes the secretion of a gland. This spur fits into a groove on the leg of the female.

CHAPTER II

DIFFERENCES between male and female are more conspicuous in birds than in any other class of animals, chiefly in consequence of the great development and brilliant coloration which parts of the plumage exhibit. The sexual dimorphism reaches its maximum in three families: the Trochilidæ or humming-birds, the Paradiseidæ or birds of Paradise, and the Phasianidæ or game-birds.

In the mammals, as we have seen, unisexual male characters when present belong usually to the first of the kinds which I have distinguished in the Introduction; they are either weapons or modifications produced as the result of blows and impacts habitually inflicted in the fights of rival males. In birds characters of the second kind are more common, that is characters or appendages which are employed in courtship to please or excite the female. Characters of the third kind, those which are due to the effect of different modes of life in the two sexes, not related to warfare or courtship, also occur, but are less common.

With regard to the plumage, the chief point which I wish to emphasise is the invariable association between excessive development and erection or display of the feathers. Darwin has collected and set forth the facts bearing upon the gestures

and attitudes of display in so forcible and picturesque a
manner that they have become familiar to all who take an
interest in natural history.   But he regarded them as the
most important evidence of the exercise of choice and
selection on the part of the females.   Their chief significance
appears to me to be quite different.   The feather is erected
by muscular action ; the quill of the feather is a hard, rigid
body, implanted in a socket in the living skin ; and the
growth of the feather is due to the growth of the living cells
which form the papilla at the base of the feather.   The
habitual erection of feathers is, therefore, a constant irritation
of the papilla, and there can be no doubt that the effect of
such irritation must be, and is, to cause the feather to grow
larger.   If it be urged that the feather ceases its growth
after a certain time, I would reply that the irritation either
acts before growth has ceased, or else produces its effect on
the succeeding feather when the first is shed.   With regard
to the coloration and markings of special plumage I have
little to say.   I regard them as due partly to the same
excessive growth as that which increases the size of the
feather, partly to the universal regularity and symmetrical
repetition of marks, due to the rhythmical nature of growth
processes, and partly perhaps to the action of the light from
particular surroundings.

Darwin has referred to the polygamy of certain birds as
associated with the presence of marked unisexual peculiarities
in the males, and, as in the case of other animals, considered
that the reason of this was that polygamy involved severer
competition, because it implied the triumph of a few of the
best developed males, and therefore the failure of a large
number of the inferior among them.   In mammals it has
been pointed out that it is not polygamy in itself which is of
importance, but the pugnacious habits of polygamous males.
In birds the same truth is evident, but the peculiarities of

the males consist more in characters whose function is to act upon the senses of the female, than those used in fighting. There are reasons for this in the main structural characteristics of the two classes. The viviparous mode of reproduction in mammals has led to a periodical congestion of the female generative organs, and to physiological processes in them which act powerfully on the nervous system, so that copulation in most cases takes place only when the female organs are in a particular state, and at that season the female has almost as much desire as the male. The mammal also has from his structure more power of grasping the female than the male bird. In birds the consent of the female is both more necessary and more difficult to obtain, and therefore the male has acquired the habit of appealing to the eyes of the female by gestures of courtship, etc. The degrees in the development of special organs of courtship, however, will be found to correspond to the proportion of his time and energies which the male habitually devotes to courtship. This will be found to be a principle of general application, holding good both for polygamous and monogamous species, while, as Darwin admitted, sexual dimorphism is not exclusively associated with polygamy. The actions connected with nest-building and incubation are sometimes performed exclusively by the female, as in Phasianidæ; sometimes by both sexes equally, as in pigeons; sometimes by the male alone, as in *Turnix;* and the degree to which the male or female is specialised for courtship exactly corresponds to these differences.

To some minds, however, it may appear difficult to understand why a male bird should commence the habit of erecting and displaying particular feathers in the beginning, when he had no special plumage to display, and when, therefore, the erecting or spreading of his feathers would have no effect upon the feelings of the hen. This difficulty arises entirely from the hitherto accepted ideas concerning the process of courtship in birds, ideas which prevent the matter being seen in its true light. The hen-bird is supposed to choose one male from a number because he has the most beautiful plumage, and the male is supposed to spread out his special feathers because he knows they are beautiful. This is anthropomorphism; there is no reason to suppose that æsthetic ideas exist in either male or female bird. The male, when in the beginning he is quite similar to the female, erects and moves some part of his plumage under the influence of sexual excitement. When he fights he erects his neck feathers partly to ward off the blows of his enemy's beak. When he courts he erects or vibrates other feathers. Nearly all the feathers of a bird can be voluntarily moved or erected. The particular feathers which the male moves when sexually excited depends on the peculiarities of the species previously evolved, and its habits in ordinary life. Thus a flying bird will fly about when courting, like the humming-bird, a ground bird will strut like the peacock. The male, when he has no voice like that of a singing bird, moves about and agitates his feathers, partly because his excitement finds vent that way, partly to show the female what he desires. Thus for each species particular gestures and erection of particular feathers become habitual, and if the male bird, from his polygamous habits and entire freedom from the cares of incubation or nursing, devotes himself with increasing energy to the practice of these special gestures and movements, the result will in course of time be visible in the corresponding excessive growth and development of the feathers and organs stimulated.

The classification of birds is a very difficult and complicated subject, and considerable progress and improvement has been made in it in recent years, so that modern systems differ very greatly from those formerly employed. They also differ to a great extent from one another. My present subject, however, has nothing to do with difficult or disputed points of classification, and I have nothing to gain by strictly following the order of affinity in considering various cases, unless the affinity is so close that it shows itself in similar habits and similar degrees of dimorphism. This is generally the case within the same family. For the definitions and limits of the families I have followed the system employed by Mr. A. H. Evans in the "Birds" of the *Cambridge Natural History*, a system which, with very slight modifications, is that laid down by Dr. Gadow.[1]

Phasianidæ.—The cock of our domestic poultry offers an excellent example of the unisexual peculiarities occurring in this family,

The ancestral species, *Gallus bankiva*, exhibits the original habits and peculiarities from which those of domestic poultry are derived. The neck feathers are longer and more brightly coloured in the cock than in the hen; the tail feathers, both the rectrices and the tail coverts, are elongated; the comb and wattles are larger than in the hen, and there is a spur on the inside of each leg. The cock lives permanently with several females, and takes no part in incubation or the care of the young. He fights frequently with other cocks, and makes gestures of courtship to the hens. In fighting, the neck hackles are erected, which accounts for their elongation, and the spur is the result of striking with the legs against the legs or head of the opponent. The tail feathers, on the other hand, are chiefly moved in courtship. The comb and wattles are special vascular developments of the skin on the crest of the head and about the cheeks. I see no reason why these should not have been originally due to pecking by the beaks of other birds. This influence would have come into play chiefly in the fights between cocks, and the comb and wattles are developed also in hens by inheritance, but to a lower degree.

[1] Bronn's *Thier-Reich, Aves, Syst. Theil*, 1893.

The peacock, *Pavo cristatus*, erects his beautiful tail, which is of such extraordinary size, in the manner known to every one. It is not the rectrices or steering feathers, but the tail coverts which are so much enlarged and so beautifully ocellated. The head crest, which consists of a row of slender feathers, is present in both sexes of peafowl, and the presence of a spur on each leg in the male is evidence that they fight. It is very probable that the crest has been produced, like the comb of the common cock, by the strokes of the beak, which here being less violent have plucked at the feathers instead of injuring the skin, and so causing an outgrowth from it. Until the second year male and female peafowl have the same plumage. In the third year the long dorsal plumes of the male begin to appear, and it is then that these birds begin to whirl about the tail and to court the attention of the females. The peahen does not begin to lay till the third year.

The display of plumage by male pheasants, especially of the Argus pheasant, has been described at length by Darwin. In the Argus pheasant the principal adornment consists of the secondary and primary wing feathers, each of the former being ornamented with a row of delicately shaded ocelli. These ornaments are confined to the male, and only visible when the male displays before the female. The two central tail feathers are much elongated, and all these feathers are erected in courtship, the wing feathers forming a circular fan and meeting in front of the head.

The gold and Amherst pheasants have beautifully coloured frills on the neck, and these are specially erected and displayed to the female in courtship. As Darwin says, they likewise turn their beautiful tails and tail coverts sideways to the female, and these feathers are very much longer in the adult male than in the female.

In *Polyplectron* both the tail feathers and the wing feathers are ornamented with ocelli, and both are erected in courtship. This genus is remarkable for the possession of two spurs on each leg in the male, and in the latter there is also a crest of feathers on the head.

Darwin himself mentions that the females of the several species of *Polyplectron* exhibit in a dim condition, and chiefly on the tail, the splendid ocelli of their mates. He cites this fact in support of his view that the characters of female birds are largely due to the greater or less transference to them of the characters acquired by the males through sexual selection. But the fact admits of another interpretation. The female most probably represents the original condition of the male, and in this case the increased development of the wing and tail feathers in the male in consequence of their erection and movement during sexual excitement, would explain the elaboration and increased brilliance of the ocelli as a concomitant of their greater size and more vigorous growth.

Darwin remarks that the eared and Cheer pheasants do not display, as though conscious that they have little beauty to show. In another place he states that both sexes of the former species, *Crossoptilon auritum*, possess the fine caudal plumes, the large ear-tufts, and the crimson velvet about the head, and all these characters appear very early in life. It is therefore evident that, whatever may be the explanation of these characters, they are not secondary sexual characters, and the fact that the males do not display is perfectly in accord with my arguments. On the other hand, the adult male possesses spurs, which he doubtless uses in fighting when mature, and these do not begin to appear before the age of six months.

Mr. Ogilvie Grant[1] states, on the authority of Prjevalsky, that in autumn and winter the birds of this species in their

[1] "Game Birds," Lloyd's *Natural History*, London, 1896.

native haunts in Asia congregate in small flocks, but very early in spring separate into pairs, when the males begin to crow. The fact that they are monogamous explains why they do not display and have not developed sexual dimorphism.

In *Numida*, the guinea-fowls, placed in the same family, there is no difference between the sexes. The cocks do not fight and are monogamous.

In the sub-family Tetraoninæ there are species in which sexual dimorphism is strongly developed, and others in which there is little or no difference between male and female. Darwin has pointed out that this contrast corresponds to the polygamy of some species and the monogamy of others, but it is the differentiation of habit associated with polygamy which really affords the explanation of the matter.

The capercailzie and the black-cock (*Tetrao urogallus* and *T. tetrix*) are both polygamists, and have regular places where they meet together to fight and display their plumage before the females. Their principal weapons are their beaks. The capercailzie differs from the female in size; in the black-cock the colour is black, while that of the hen is gray, and the outer feathers of the cock's tail are elongated and curved outwards.

Darwin has described the unisexual peculiarities of the male *Tetrao cupido*, or prairie cock of North America, and has figured the bird in the attitude assumed during courtship. There is a bare orange-coloured sac on each side of the neck, which is inflated when the male utters his loud note, and which is obviously to be compared with the sacs in the throat of the howling monkey, producing a similar effect, and due to similar causes. There are two ear-tufts of feathers, considerably elongated, and these are erected so as to meet over the head.

Tetrao urophasianus of North America affords similar illustrations of the precise correspondence between structure and mechanical action. His bare yellow œsophagus is inflated, his neck feathers erected, and his long pointed tail spread out like a fan when he courts.

We must conclude from these cases that stretching of the skin of the neck by inflation is unfavourable to the growth of feathers, so that the inflated parts of the skin become bare. One reason of this is very probably the expulsion of the blood from the skin caused by the distension.

The male partridge, *Perdix cinerea, Perdix rubra, etc.*, does not differ much from the female. The cocks are said to fight at the pairing season, but they are monogamous, and consequently neither their fighting nor courting are constant occupations. The cock partridge is a respectable father of a family. He does not sit on the eggs, but he remains with one mate, and when the brood is hatched continues with his family.

The grouse, *Lagopus scoticus* and *albus*, are also monogamous, and sexually monomorphic.

The Turkey, *Meleagris*, is placed by recent authorities [1] in the family Phasianidæ, by Claus in 1882 it was joined with the Curassow and *Penelope* in a distinct family Penelopidæ. Whatever its position and affinities, its sexual dimorphism is interesting. The head and neck in all the species are naked and wattled in both sexes, with only a few hair-like feathers. On the forehead is a long fleshy process, which in the ordinary condition is pendulous, and hangs over the base of the beak on one side, but during excitement is erected. In the female this process is present, but much smaller than in the males, and the latter alone possess a large spur. Ogilvie Grant distinguishes three wild species, of which *M. gallopavo*, the Mexican Turkey, is the original form of our domestic breeds. In this species the males have an additional peculiarity, namely, a tassel-like bunch of long, coarse, black, hair-like feathers on the middle of the breast.

[1] "Game Birds," Lloyd's *Natural History*, London, 1897.

In all probability the naked head and neck of the turkey, with the blue and red wattled skin and long fleshy process, are to be regarded as exhibiting the inherited scars of a long line of pugnacious ancestors. Darwin mentions that young turkey cocks in fighting always seize hold of each other's wattles, and he presumes that the old birds fight in the same manner. It is known that in the wild state the males are polygamous, and that the female attends exclusively to the duties of incubation. Darwin considered that the fleshy caruncle served as an ornament, supporting this opinion by the fact that it is erected in courtship. But this fact is better explained by the view that it owes its evolution to congestion and hypertrophy caused by blows and tensions received in fighting during the influence of sexual excitement. On this view the turgescence or erection is due to the hereditary association or correlation between the state of sexual excitement and the congestion of the organ.

The female turkey has to a certain extent inherited the modifications of the head and neck acquired by the males. It does not appear that the females themselves fight, and they have not inherited the spurs.

I have not found any mention in the literature of special habits in the Mexican turkey which correspond to the tassel of hair-like feathers on the breast of the males in that species, but it is quite possible that there is some peculiarity of habit corresponding to the character.

In the Curassows of South America, genus *Crax*, sexual dimorphism occurs in some species but not in others. When present it is not carried to an extreme degree. In both sexes there is a median crest of semi-erect and curled feathers on the head, which may possibly be related to courtship. In some species, *e.g. Crax carunculata*, there is, in the male only, a large swollen knob at the base of the upper mandible, and a wattle on each side of the base of the lower mandible, all

these excrescences being of a scarlet colour. The account of
the habits of this species quoted by Ogilvie Grant suggests
that its habits are polygamous and pugnacious, while other
species are said to live in pairs, or to be gregarious. The
crest is erected during excitement.

In some of the genera of Cracidæ, namely, *Crax*, *Pauxis*,
Mitua, and *Ortalis*, the trachea or windpipe has an extraordinary development in the males, which is absent in the
females.[1] This modification consists in such a great lengthening of the trachea that it forms a loop, which is accommodated
beneath the skin of the breast, in some cases extending back
as far as the end of the breast-bone. The trachea is bent upon
itself, and returns to the front of the breast-bone to enter the
thorax in the usual way.

Although the evidence is not very clear, I think it will be
found that this lengthening of the trachea is associated with
internal pressure of air, but whether this straining of the
trachea is related to the voice proper or not I cannot say. I
have pointed out the difficulty of the question in reference to
the pouch of the emeu.

The genera *Turnix* and *Pedionymus* were placed by Dr.
Gadow in the sub-order Turnices, next to the sub-order Galli,
in the order Galliformes. They are regarded by Ogilvie
Grant as forming the order Hemipodii, which is intermediate
between the Gallinæ and the Rallinæ or Rails. In all the
species of these genera the female is considerably larger, and
usually has more handsome plumage than the male. They
are small quail-like birds, with very short tails, and the hind-
toe absent, or in *Pedionymus* rudimentary. There are
twenty-one species of *Turnix* distributed from the south of
Spain to Australia. The Indian species, *Turnix taigoor*, lives
in India, Northern Ceylon, Burma, Malay Peninsula, China,
and the Liu-Kiu Islands. The total length of the male is

[1] Forbes, "On the Convoluted Trachea," etc., *P.Z.S.*, 1882.

5·6 inches, of the female 6·7 inches. The chief difference between the sexes in marking is that in the male the chin and throat are white, in the female black. The upper parts of the body are rufous or brown in both sexes, but in the female this is mottled with black.

Mr. A. G. Hume, as quoted by Ogilvie Grant, says of this species that the females only call, the females only fight. In this species no male will ever come to a cage baited with a male, whereas every female within hearing rushes to a cage in which a female is confined, and if allowed to meet during the breeding season any two females will fight until one or other is dead, or nearly so. The males, and the males only, sit upon the eggs, the females meanwhile calling and fighting without any care for their obedient mates. The males, and the males only, tend the young brood. Darwin mentions that the females and not the males of this species are kept by the natives of India for fighting, like game-cocks.

It is not difficult to form an idea of the way in which such exceptional habits could have arisen. In the ancestors of these birds probably a male and female paired for breeding, as in several other species of Gallinacei. For some reason or other the females may have become more numerous than the males, in which case unmated females would naturally endeavour to allure any male they came across from his fidelity to his mate and nest. His mate would then give battle to the intruder, and if such battles became frequent the females would in time gradually abandon the cares of incubation and give themselves up entirely to courtship and warfare, while the males took upon themselves the task of incubation. An excess of females has in this case led to a condition which is the opposite of that more commonly existing among the Gallinacei. When the male was the less devoted of the pair to family cares the unmated female who approached him was welcomed and added to his scraglio, while the first mate took no notice of her. In this way the polygamy of the jungle fowl and pheasant tribe doubtless arose, the males after a time having entirely abandoned the care of their progeny. It is impossible to say what determined the greater domesticity or pugnacity in male or female; it is sufficient to attribute it to the principle which Herbert Spencer calls the instability of the homogeneous. Among the various forms of Gallinacei there are some in which males and females are equally peaceful and attentive to their families, some in which the males are more so than the females, and some in which the females are more so than the males. To my mind the important point is that difference of size and structure correspond to difference of habit, and only manifests itself in the individual when the breeding habits come into play. In the species of Turnix the *young* females are similar to the adult males. I think it is evident from these facts that the slight peculiarities of plumage in the adult female *Turnix* must be due to the conditions of life, although the physiological explanation is yet to be found. It is possible, as I have suggested in the case of fishes, that the continual sexual excitement produces a nervous influence on the secretion of pigment in the skin and feathers. In the Spanish Bustard Quail, *Turnix sylvatica*, and some other species the difference in the colour and markings between the sexes is very slight, while in several Australian species there is no difference except in size.

It would be interesting to know what kind of wounds the females inflict on one another in their combats, and on what parts they are commonly inflicted. No modifications like those which I have attributed in other species to wounds or blows exist in *Turnix*, although the females are so pugnacious. Probably one reason of this is that the pugnacity of the females has but recently arisen in the evolution of the genus, but it may be that the wounds inflicted are not very severe.

The Columbidæ present a striking contrast to the Phasi-anidæ, in the general absence of sexual dimorphism. They are monogamous birds of gregarious and gentle habits. The male birds do not fight very fiercely, and the gestures of courtship are not very elaborate. It is true that the male pigeon, as seen in the domesticated state, expresses his desires and his authority to the hen by loud cooings, by swelling his crop, and scraping the ground with his wings. But on the other hand he has but one mate, and she lays but two eggs, and the male pigeon, very soon after he is mated, is incubat-ing the eggs, and afterwards feeding the helpless young from his own crop with quite as much assiduity as the hen. The hen also coos in response to the male, and thus there is little differentiation in the habits and actions of the two sexes.

There could not be a greater contrast than that between the habits of the cock pigeon and the jungle cock or cock pheasant, nor better evidence for the conclusion that uni-sexual characters are the definite result of particular habits, movements and mechanical stimulations.

Darwin remarks that in the English Carrier and Pouter pigeons the full development of the wattle and the crop occurs rather late in life, and that conformably with his "rule of inheritance" these characters are transmitted in full perfection to the males alone. As it may appear that these cases show how unisexual male characters may be produced by artificial selection without such special stimula-tions as those to which I attribute their origin in wild species, it is worth while to examine them in some detail.

Now I do not deny for a moment the importance of selection. I take it to be a truism that whatever peculiarity or modification we may consider, such peculiarity will usually be increased and developed, by breeding from the individuals that possess it in the highest degree, and also that by breeding one stock for one character and another for another, without crossing the stocks, two distinct breeds or varieties may be produced. I also admit that variations in domesticated animals occur spontaneously, *i.e.* apparently without relation to special conditions of life. The question here, however, is whether variations occur spontaneously under domestication which are in all respects similar to the secondary sexual characters so common in nature.

The chief peculiarities of the Carrier breed are the beak-wattle and the eye-wattle, the former a large wrinkled excrescence of bare skin and tissue around the base of the beak, the latter a flat circular expansion of similar skin, not much projecting, around the eye. Now these peculiarities are not confined to the male bird. I rely for the evidence I am about to use on the *Book of Pigeons* by Robert Fulton, edited by Lewis Wright, and published by Cassell and Co. The hen at four years of age has in some individuals *almost* as large a beak-wattle as the cock at the age of three years when the latter is fully developed. Still there is a certain inferiority of development of the beak-wattle in the hen as a general rule. In the eye-wattle there seems to be scarcely any difference between the sexes.

The beak-wattle begins to "break out" at the age of nine or ten months. This does not mean that it is entirely absent before that time, but that it begins to show the bulbous protuberances at that period. Now of course the wattles are not entirely new structures in the Carrier. In the wild original the skin at the base of the beak over the nostrils is naked, scaly and protuberant, and there is some naked skin around the eye. The wattles of the perfect fancy Carrier are only produced by the hypertrophy or excessive growth of these parts of skin.

In the book to which I have referred it is stated that the Carrier variety is more quarrelsome and spiteful than all others; that its sight is much obstructed, so that the weaker specimens are often attacked before they know their danger, and finally that the eye-wattle when pecked or injured in such quarrels is peculiarly liable to become inflamed and develop canker. What then is more probable than that the breed originally arose through fanciers breeding specially from individuals in which enlargement and excessive growth of the skin at the base of the beak and around the eye had been caused by the blows of the beak inflicted in fighting? This would explain why the excrescences are not present at hatching, but develop gradually during three or four years, and why they are more developed in the cocks, since the latter are, to begin with, more pugnacious. This would account for the origin of the excrescences, though it need not be denied that the proliferation of tissue once started has increased during subsequent generations under the condition of selective breeding.

But this is not all. The same book describes in detail how fanciers frequently, we may say, in considering the period of the breed's evolution, habitually, "doctor" or trim the wattles artificially with knife or scissors. In reference to an excess of eye-wattle in proportion to beak-wattle, the following remarks are made in the work cited: "To remedy this, some cut off a portion of the eye-wattle, and even of the beak-wattle, while others cut the beak-wattle at the root, and then by continually working it towards the beak, as the wound heals, cause it to tilt more forward and retain the desired position: but such doctoring gives more trouble than it is worth or than most fanciers care to take. A little simple cutting off, though it will never make a bad bird appear good, will often so improve a really good one, and make it appear so nearly perfect, that very few can resist the temptation." In the chapter on Carriers in the book in question there are many other remarks on surgical treatment, too lengthy to be all quoted in full. The beaks will not remain close-fitting after the age of three years, the portion of the upper mandible which overhangs the lower is therefore to be cut off level and carefully pared. The beak is also manipulated in the nest-pan, in order to straighten and lengthen it, the beak being gently straightened by the fingers on successive days. Some fanciers never allow the eye-wattle to appear thick and ragged, but remove all the offending portions. The eye-wattle often from excessive growth forms a spout, that is, a fold under the eye, which is stated to irritate the eye and cause a discharge, for which it also forms a channel. It is recommended that the spout should be cut off. The spout itself often owes its immediate origin to another bird pecking at the wattle, and thereby causing injury and inflammation. The following remarks deserve to be quoted in full:—" We certainly have seen a very few large-eyed Carriers which never had a spout; but they are *very* few indeed, and many which are thought such have simply been operated on early in life, as we have already advised. We do so openly, as we do not wish to lose the sight of nearly all our best birds, or think it wrong to perform an operation which enables the subject to live in comfort afterwards instead of misery: we openly and avowedly recommend and practise it, and enter into the matter here that the proper mode of procedure may be known to all." After all this it is difficult to decide whether surgery or selection has had most to do with the evolution of the chief " points " of the Carrier.

Another interesting remark in the same work is that the progeny of young birds do not attain a proper development of wattle, however " good " the parents may ultimately become. Two parents over three years old produce more wattle in the young.

To turn next to the consideration of the Pouter, taking the book above mentioned again as our chief authority. The excessively developed crop is by no means confined to the male. Mr. George Ure, who was a pre-eminent breeder and judge of Pouters, writes as follows: "Hens have the crop, but in a less degree. Their style of showing is also a little different from the cocks'. There are hens now and then to be seen with crops as large as cocks', and they will strut about as if they wanted to be taken for one." The enlarged crop, and the extreme development of the habit of inflating it, are then most marked in the male, but present in a less degree in the female. Have these peculiarities been developed by selection alone? In other words, have the variations been spontaneous? The evidence of the fanciers themselves is directly to the contrary. One fancier writes: "I wish to impress on all fanciers who intend to show their Pouters, the necessity of training them well. After they have got fairly through the first moult, commence training such birds as you intend to be shown. They must be so penned that they cannot see any other bird; they must be taught to keep their block in the pen, and frequently talked to and handled, to make them familiar, so that they will 'show' when anyone approaches the pen." If this were all it would perhaps be enough. The cock-pigeon in the original condition is in the habit of strutting and inflating his crop under the influence of sexual excitement, and a bird systematically trained would naturally perform similar actions under the influence of the pleasurable excitement of its owner's voice and presence. In the same way, as was mentioned above, the Mandrill and other baboons make a sexual gesture when they feel pleasure at the sight of a familiar keeper. But this is not all. The author of the *Book on Pigeons* goes much further. According to his advice two pens should be placed together with a sliding partition between them, and a *hen* in one and a cock in the other. The owner should visit them as often as possible, and use always the same call, at the same time removing the partition so that the two birds can see each other, " the instant this is done they will generally put themselves into the best and most striking attitudes. By doing this on each occasion they will soon learn, every time the owner goes near or speaks to them, to expect to see their mates, and will begin to fill their crops and strut about with delight, unless in the case of a very few sulky birds. If you have one familiar hen it is also a good plan to train her to stand on your hand, and thus show her in front of a pen containing cock birds. This will set them all into fine show, which should of course be accompanied by the call, and is an excellent way of training Pouters." After this it is of little use to dispute whether selection alone could produce the chief peculiarity of the Pouter. The important fact is that the peculiarity has not been produced by spontaneous variation and selection, but by the excessive stimulation of a certain action associated with pleasurable and essentially sexual excitement. It is scarcely possible to deny that the action of " showing " in the Pouter has influenced not merely the size of the crop, but also the general shape and carriage of the bird, which are considered equally important by the fancier.

In contrast with these characters we may consider the feathering of the legs, which occurs in the Pouter and in several other fancy breeds of pigeons. No training or other special conditions can be discerned which might have produced this character, which is common to both sexes. This is a spontaneous variation of the typical kind. But it is the expression of a general tendency, a variation in a definite direction. It is an example of the general principle that serially homologous parts tend to resemble or imitate one another, just as offspring resemble their parents. The feathering of the legs is an "imitation" of the wings. It occurs in the domesticated birds more than in the wild, because the former are protected from the struggle for existence, and therefore their development tends to follow mere laws of growth, like that of plants, and is not controlled, as in wild birds, by the working of the body as a mechanism to effect certain ends under certain conditions. It must not be forgotten, moreover, that feathered legs occur in many species of Gallinacei in the wild state, and in several breeds of domesticated poultry as well as in pigeons. Such a variation is similar to that of doubling in flowers, and is by no means of the same kind as the modifications due to function or stimulation.

Dididæ.—The extinct birds forming the family Dididæ were allied to the pigeons, and are placed with them in the same group or sub-order Columbæ. One of these extinct species was originally described as the Solitaire of the island Rodriguez, by François Leguat, who resided in the island from 1691 to 1693. The history of this bird and of our knowledge of it may be read in the excellent article under the name Solitaire in the *Dictionary of Birds* by Newton and Gadow. Its great interest in relation to our subject consists in the fact that the males were larger than the females, were very pugnacious, and possessed a rounded protuberance on the bone of the wing, which was used in fighting. This protuberance was, according to Leguat's description, "as big as a musket-ball," and the examination of the hundreds of fossil bones which have been obtained shows that this was no exaggeration. The bird was larger than a swan, the males standing about 2 feet 9 inches high, and in some cases reaching a weight of 45 lbs., while the females were distinctly smaller.

The protuberance mentioned is situated on the anterior edge of the metacarpal bone, near its proximal extremity.

Messrs. Newton[1] describe it as being situated "immediately beyond the proximal end and the pollex, which last would appear to be thrust away by it to some extent." The

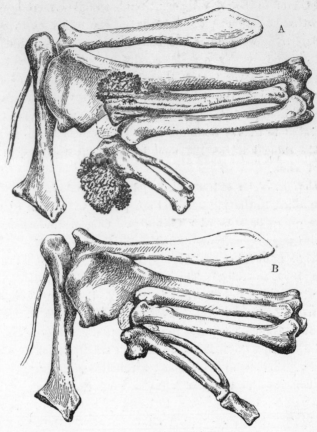

FIG. 11.—Bones of the wing of the extinct Solitaire of Rodriguez, *Pezophaps solitarius.* A, male; B, female.   From mounted skeletons in the British Museum of Natural History.

pollex, however, has not been found, and it seems to me rather that the tubercle occupies the very position of the pollex in normal birds.   Possibly the pollex had disappeared, or was really included in the formation of the bony tubercle.

[1] *Phil. Trans.* 1869.

It seems to me unlikely that the pollex should have existed between this tubercle and the excrescence on the radius, as it would have done according to Messrs. Newton's description. These authors state that the tubercle sometimes projects downwards rather than laterally, and is always more or less pedunculate. As far as I can judge from the skeleton mounted in the Natural History Museum (British), this means that the tubercle projects from the anterior or outer edge of the bone, and a little downwards or inwards; certainly in this skeleton the tubercle is larger towards the inner side when the wing is folded, and it shows an incipient division into two parts. The metacarpal is shorter and thicker than in ordinary birds.

The radius is much thicker and stouter than in ordinary birds, and bears at its distal end on the anterior edge a rugged excrescence or exostosis, similar in appearance to the tubercle on the metacarpal, and evidently associated with the latter in function and development, but not so prominent and not pedunculate.

In the female the radial exostosis is absent, and the metacarpal either absent or much smaller than in the male.

There can be little doubt that these exostoses were used in fighting by the males, and that, therefore, the facts are in harmony with the view that their unisexual development is explained by unisexual irritation of the bones affected. But the subject is worth examining in more detail. Everyone has seen domestic pigeons occasionally buffeting each other with their wings, but their fights are not very violent, nor of long duration. They naturally, however, suggest the supposition that the male Solitaires fought in a similar way, but it seems to me that if this had been the case the exostoses would have been on the outer or dorsal surface of the wrist and not on its anterior edge. The actual position of the principal tubercle indicates that, if it was used offensively, the blow was delivered not outwards but forwards and somewhat downwards.

Our knowledge of the birds' habits is almost entirely derived from Leguat's description. He says that they were monogamous, and moreover paired for life, like modern pigeons. The male and female incubated alternately, and incubation lasted seven weeks. If a female came near the nest, the female possessor drove it away, while if the intruder were a male, he was attacked by the male. This is all far from being in harmony with pronounced sexual dimorphism, but other actions are mentioned which are probably more relevant to the question in hand. To quote the original words : " Ils ne volent pas, leur ailes sont trop petits pour soutenir le poids de leurs corps. Ils ne s'en servent que pour se battre, et pour faire le moulinet quand ils veulent s'appeler l'un l'autre. Ils font avec vitesse vingt ou trente pirouettes tout de suite du même côté pendant l'espace de quatre ou cinq minutes : le mouvement de leurs ailes fait alors un bruit qui approche fort de celui d'un crécerelle, et on l'entend de plus de deux cents pas." Thus, besides fighting with their wings, the birds, probably the males only, had a habit of twirling round in one direction four or five minutes at a time, during which process the wings made a noise like a rattle. The anonymous manuscript, *Relation de l'Ile Rodrigue*, says that the noise is made with the wings when the birds are angry, and that the noise is like rumbling thunder :—"le bruit approche fort de celui du tonnerre qu'on a un peu de peine à entendre." Neither of these descriptions attempts to explain exactly how the noise, which evidently impressed the writers as very remarkable, was produced. Judging from the shape of the skeleton, I have come to the conclusion that the noise was produced by the striking of the wings together in front of the breast. In this case the wings would strike one another exactly where the exostoses are situated, and thus several things otherwise obscure would be explained. The rapid beating of the bony knobs against one another, the knobs being covered with horny skin or cartilage or some such covering, would produce exactly the kind of noise indicated by the above descriptions, a rattling or rumbling noise, similar perhaps to that of a kettle-drum, or of the "bones" of a negro orchestra. Secondly, the wings would naturally meet, not only at a particular spot on the metacarpal, but along a greater length of the edge in the wrist region, and thus we can understand the exostosis on the distal end of the radius, and the greater size of that bone. Thirdly, the wings would meet edge to edge at the carpal region, with a slight inward direction, and that is the precise position of the exostoses. It is obvious enough how thoroughly this hypothesis agrees with the principle by which I explain the evolution of such structures. It is the case of the stag's antler over again. The bones are violently hammered, and the irritation causes a kind of hypertrophy, which may in a sense be considered pathological, but which in the course of generations becomes normal, because constant and hereditary. Some may be inclined to maintain that even if my suggestions are correct, the exostoses were not hereditary, but were entirely due to irritation in the individual. That in my opinion is very improbable.

The birds, doubtless, used their exostoses as weapons in fighting, and perhaps struck with the wing in the same way as when beating the wings together. In the bones examined evidence of reunited fractures of the radius and ulna have frequently been seen, and these are considered to show the "effect of the cestus-like armature of the wing" in fighting. Probably this is true, though the bones may have been sometimes broken in the beating of the wings together, for the descriptions indicate that the whirling and

flapping were performed under the influence of a sexual
frenzy in which the bird would be regardless of pain or
injury.

Trochilidæ. — The Humming-birds, Trochilidæ, with the
Cypselidæ or Swifts, are now regarded by many ornithologists
as allied to the Pici or Woodpeckers, not as formerly classified,
to the Passeres like the Hirundinidæ or Swallows.   It is un-
necessary for the purpose of the present work to consider
the structual features on which this change of classification is
based.   We have to consider only the sexual dimorphism
which is developed to such a high degree in the Trochilidæ.
In these birds the beauty for which they are renowned is
chiefly possessed by the males, and consists in various special
adornments of plumage, such as feathers of extraordinary
length or shape, and tufts of feathers of the most intensely
brilliant metallic colours.

Belt, in his *Naturalist in Nicaragua*, gives evidence of the
special display of plumage by male humming-birds while on
the wing before the females, and says that two males of
Florisuga mellivora, after such a display of the expanded
white tail, engaged in a fight.   The important point for my
argument is that in the case of the humming-birds, as in so
many others, the special enlarged tufts of feathers are not
mere passive ornaments, but are definitely and specially
erected, and the irritation thus caused accounts for their
increased growth.

Although many interesting points about humming-birds
are mentioned and discussed by Darwin, it is curious that
he does not mention the habits of the sexes in incubation
and care of the young.   In one place he states that they are,
in the opinion of Mr. Salvin, polygamous.   Other naturalists
whose works I have consulted are similarly silent concerning
the incubation.   It was, therefore, with much interest that I
read a statement concerning this question in an article in a

popular magazine.[1] Although the magazine in question had just incurred some ridicule and discredit from the proof that the sensational contributions of De Rougemont were not as veracious as the author declared them to be, there can be no reason for doubting the accuracy of the observations in the article to which I refer. The authoress simply described how she watched a female humming-bird and her nest while the bird hatched and brought up her two young ones. The observations were made in the island of Dominica, the species of the humming-bird is not mentioned. It is expressly stated that the males take no part in building the nest, sitting on the eggs, or obtaining food for the young, but " fly away to the mountains and spend their time in sucking nectar from the wild-flowers and dancing about in the sweet sunshine." Fighting, sporting, and love-making are therefore doubtless the chief occupations of male humming-birds, and thus, as in the case of the Pheasant or Pea-fowl, the dimorphism in plumage corresponds to dimorphism in habits. The male has specially developed feathers, because in his habitual gestures the growth of those feathers is stimulated, while in the female no such stimulation takes place.

Darwin mentions, on the authority of Mr. Gould, that in one species of humming-bird, *Aëthurus polytmus*, in which the male is distinguished both by vivid colours and two immensely elongated tail feathers, these characters begin to appear in the young bird from the first. He explains this and other similar cases on the hypothesis that the males have transmitted their peculiarities to their male offspring at an earlier age than that at which they were first acquired. With this explanation I fully agree, if it be true that the habits of the male bird to which the peculiarities correspond are limited to a later period of life. But it is possible that the habits also

[1] "Among the Humming-birds with a Camera," by Elizabeth Grinnell, *Wide World Magazine*, March 1898.

are practised earlier. We know that in domestic poultry young cocks begin to fight long before they are sexually mature. Humming-birds very possibly reach maturity at a very early age, and possibly begin to practise their special movements as soon as they can fly. In this case the development of their special plumage would likewise be hastened. In another species it is mentioned by Darwin that both male and female are brilliantly but very differently coloured, and the young begin to show the difference from the first. This case I cannot pretend to explain satisfactorily. As I have remarked in reference to other cases, we know less of the influences that affect colour than of those which affect size of organs, although there are indications that greater sexual activity is one of the conditions influencing the development of pigment. I have no doubt, however, that in all cases where inheritance of certain characters is limited to one sex, it is because those characters are due to conditions of life which affect that sex, and not the other.

I have already referred to Mr. Belt's interesting description of the very definite erection and display of special plumage in male humming-birds, namely, *Florisuga mellivora*. The description is quoted in Darwin's *Descent of Man and Sexual Selection*. Two males were displaying their ornaments before a female sitting on a branch. One after the other shot up high into the air and slowly descended with expanded tail. The tail was white, and when expanded covered more space than the rest of the bird; it was " evidently the grand feature of the performance."

The special modifications of the male in the Night-jars, *Caprimulgidæ*, consist in the elongation of particular feathers, different feathers being enlarged in different species. The important facts about these characters are scattered separately in Darwin's work, but when brought together they suggest an interpretation different to that which he maintained.

In an African species, *Macrodipteryx vexillarius*, the male
during the pairing season has the ninth of its primary
feathers developed into a streamer of great length, namely,
26 inches, although the length of the bird's body is only
10 inches.   In an allied species, named *M. macrodipterus*, the
same feathers are elongated, and in addition their shafts are

Fig. 12. *Macrodipteryx macrodipterus*, an African Night-jar, after a sketch from life by
Mr. Jos. Gedge.   From Newton and Gadow, *Dictionary of Birds*.

naked except at the ends, so that the two feathers are racquet-
shaped.   Mr. Joseph Gedge, who accompanied Sir Samuel
Baker's expedition to the Soudan, saw one of these birds
sitting on the ground with its two long primaries erected
perpendicularly over its back, and made a sketch of the bird
sitting in this attitude among grass and reeds.   This sketch
is reproduced in Newton's *Dictionary of Birds*, and might
suggest to some minds that the feathers mimicked the reeds!

But if concealment was the object to be attained, probably the absence of the erected feathers would be more effective.

I have not found a detailed description of the function of these feathers in courtship, but Audubon describes how the males of certain species of the family, presumably American, fly about with great rapidity and very sudden turns, making in the movements a singular noise by the vibration of their feathers. They perform these evolutions in order to attract the attention of the female, and when she has paired with one the others are driven away. It does not follow that the single elongated feather in the wing of *Macrodipteryx* is used to produce a sound during flight, but it is developed only in the males and only in the breeding season, for which reasons I conclude that it owes its development to some special stimulation which a knowledge of the habits of the bird would soon disclose. In the fork-tailed goatsucker of the Brazils, *Macropsalis*, the outer tail feather on each side is elongated, and these feathers diverge and converge during flight. The elongation of these feathers is peculiar to the male, but whether they are present only in the breeding season I do not know. The curious habitual movement of the outer tail feathers during flight perhaps explains their hypertrophy, and the movement seems to be associated with sexual excitement, since it is confined to the males.

Trogonidæ.—The birds of this family, generally of brilliant and beautiful plumage, inhabit tropical forests in Asia, Africa, and America, but they are most numerous and most magnificent in Central and Tropical America. In the Asiatic species the sexes are, if not exactly alike, usually similar, and not very brilliant in colouring. In some of the American species the males are resplendent, while the females are rather dull-coloured like the Asiatic forms. In other American species, again, the males are very brilliant, and possess enlarged and specialised feathers, while the females are adorned but to a lower degree. I cannot attempt to show how these degrees of dimorphism correspond to the differentiation of habits in the male and female, but shall content myself by referring to the celebrated species called the Quezal, which is the culminating example of the condition last mentioned. The Quezal, *Pharomacrus mocinno*, lives in the forests of Guatemala. The body is no larger than that of a turtle dove. The special adornments of the male are a rounded crest on the head, enlarged scapulars or shoulder feathers, and much elongated tail coverts, corresponding to those of the peacock. These hypertrophied feathers and the upper part of the body generally are of a beautiful iridescent green colour, while the under parts are of a gorgeous crimson. The female is also green above, but her crest is less developed, and her tail coverts are not elongated beyond the true tail.

Mr. O. Salvin (*Ibis*, 1861, pp. 66 and 138) gives reasons for believing that the male Quezal takes no part in incubation, and describes the behaviour of the living male bird under his own observation for a few minutes in its natural condition. The bird sat on a bough with its tail hanging down, and this was occasionally jerked open and closed again, which caused the long tail coverts to vibrate gracefully. Here at any rate is the agitation of the specialised feathers, which I contend to be universal, but we may be very confident that a great deal more agitation and erection of all the special feathers takes place when the male bird is in active courtship, although he is commonly found in company with a single female.

Paradiseidæ.—The Paradiseidæ are included among the Passerine birds, Dr. Gadow's Order Passeriformes, and are considered to be undoubtedly allied to the Corvidæ, to our common Rook and Jackdaw, notwithstanding the sombre plumage of the latter.

In the Birds of Paradise, the males are distinguished from

F<small>IG</small>. 13.—The Quezal, *Pharomacrus mocinno*, male and female. From Newton and Gadow, *Dictionary of Birds*.

the females by gorgeous colours, and by the great development of special plumes, which are invariably erected in a special manner in sexual excitement. Mr. Wallace has observed that a dozen or more full plumaged males congregate in a tree to hold what the natives call a dancing party. They fly about, raise their wings, erect their beautiful plumes and make them vibrate till the whole tree seems to be filled with waving plumes.

In the Great Bird of Paradise, *P. apoda*, which is found chiefly in the Aru Islands, the chief ornament is the great bunch of long and delicate plumes on each flank. These plumes are of an intense golden orange colour, changing at the tips into pale brown, and are sometimes two feet in length. When erected and made to vibrate, they form a sort of golden fountain almost concealing the body of the bird. In the female all the ornamental plumes are wanting, and the colour is a uniform coffee brown.

Some of the Birds of Paradise, according to Darwin, cast their special plumes directly after the breeding season, others retain them throughout the year, after the first year, or always. In the first case they illustrate the principle, that the characters due to special stimulations only appear in the individual at the season of the year when the special stimulations are brought into action.

In the Huia of New Zealand the beak of the male is short, strong, and nearly straight, while that of the female is much longer, more slender, and curved. In the Museum of the College of Surgeons there are stuffed specimens of a pair of these birds, labelled *Heterolocha acutirostris*. The species is generally considered to belong to the family Sturnidæ, or Starlings. It is stated by Dr. Buller, author of *Birds of New Zealand*, 1872, that the male uses his strong beak in chiselling insect larvæ out of decayed wood, while the female probes the softer parts for the same purpose with her longer

and more pliant instrument. It appears, therefore, that the
male and female co-operate in obtaining their food, and it is
not improbable that the male makes openings into cavities
which the female explores. In this case the dimorphism is
not related to courtship and reproduction in the usual way,
but is adapted to a special division of labour between male
and female in constant companionship. In each sex the
special mode of employing the bill is evidently the cause of
its special shape and structure; the mechanical effects on the

FIG. 14.—The Huia of New Zealand. A, male; B, female. From Newton and Gadow,
Dictionary of Birds.

bills would obviously be, in the individuals, in the direction
of the modifications actually existing in the species, and it is
reasonable to conclude that the individual effects have been
accumulated in the evolution.

Cotingidæ.—The Cotingidæ are a family of Passerine birds
belonging to South America, which are sexually dimorphic. In
some species of *Pipra* the secondary wing feathers of the male
are much modified, while in the female they are normal. The
modification consists in the great thickening of the shaft and
the narrowness and distorted shape of the vane. The males
make an extraordinary noise by means of these feathers in

flight, and the sound appears to be employed in courtship.
Darwin mentions several other cases in which peculiarly
modified feathers are used to produce special sounds, such
modifications being confined to the males, and the sounds
being used in courtship. In the snipes, *Scolopax*, the outer
tail feathers are modified, the shaft being stiff and curved
like a sabre. Both sexes are furnished with these feathers,
but they are generally larger and produce more sound in the
male. The male bird during the pairing season flies to a
great height, and then descends in a curved line with great
velocity with the tail spread out. The sound is only produced
during this rapid descent. In one of the Indian bustards,
Sypheotides auritus, the primary wing feathers are narrowed
at the tips in the males only, and are probably used to
produce a humming sound in courtship. In *Chamœpetes
unicolor*, belonging to the Turkey family, the first primary wing
feather is arched towards the tip, and narrower than in the
female : it is probably used to produce a sound in courtship.

In all the above cases it is most probable that the
modification of the feather has been directly brought about
by the use made of it. I do not mean by this to maintain
that the mutilation of a feather can be inherited, such inheritance seems inconceivable. But particular pressures and
strains due to the resistance of the air when certain feathers
are moved in a particular way must necessarily cause special
pressures and strains on the papilla at the base of the feather,
and these mechanical irritations would modify the growth of
the feather or of its successor. The feather is not a living
tissue, but the papilla and skin to which it is attached are
certainly alive, and must be greatly affected by any movements of the feather, whether these are produced by the
muscles of the skin itself or by the pressure of the air. In
this way it is possible to understand why specially modified
feathers occur in one sex only which performs special motions

in flight, whereas we have no evidence that the modifications arose spontaneously without the physiological influence of the special mechanical irritations.

Rupicola crocea, described by Darwin as one of the most beautiful birds in the world, also belongs to the Cotingidæ. The male is of a splendid orange colour, with some of the feathers truncated and plumose. The female is brownish-green, shaded with red. Probably in this case the pigments are the same in both sexes, as in other species in which the male and female are of different colours. The male *Rupicola* has a large median crest, which is much less developed in the female. Sir R. Schomburgk has described the systematic display of the male birds before the females, many males assembling to compete with one another, without fighting. The male is stated to spread its wings, throw up its head, open its tail, and hop about; erection of the crest is not mentioned, but I suspect it is one of the chief actions in the performance.

In the sub-family Gymnoderinæ, which also belongs to the Cotingidæ, there are some remarkable unisexual characters in the males. One of the species is the Bell-bird, *Chasmorhynchus niveus*, which inhabits the forests of Guiana. The female and young male are dusky green, the adult male pure white. The male possesses a fleshy appendage nearly three inches long at the base of the upper mandible, and this is entirely absent in the female. The male utters also a particularly loud clear note, which gave it its popular name. The chief authority for the habits of this bird was, for a long time, Waterton's *Wanderings in South America*, published in 1825, in which work it is stated that the appendage has a communication with the palate, and is erected by inflation with air. It is stated by Evans,[1] I do not know on what authority, that the appendage is erected when the bird utters

[1] *Cambridge Natural History, Birds*, 1899.

its note. I was inclined for a time to suppose that the
appendage was connected with the production of the voice,
being erected by distension with air, and acting as a resonator.
Another species, however, the *C. nudicollis* of Brazil, whose

Fig. 15.—The Bell-bird of Costa Rica, *Chasmorhynchus tricarunculatus*, male on the right,
   female on the left.   From specimens in the Brit. Mus. Nat. Hist., and published
   figures.

voice has been heard at the Zoological Gardens, utters a
similar loud bell-like note, and is entirely destitute of the
appendage on the bill.

There is another species found in Costa Rica, *C. tricarun-*
culatus, which instead of one has three elongated appendages,

one median at the base of the upper mandible, and one at each angle of the gape. Mr. Osbert Salvin [1] has stated that he was unable to ascertain from dried specimens whether there was any communication by which air could be passed into these caruncles, but his own impression was that no inflation takes place, and that the bird has no voluntary control over the excrescences; that they elongate or contract only like the fleshy caruncle of the Common Turkey. It must be remembered, however, that Waterton distinctly mentions the erection of the appendage in *C. niveus*.

Evidently further investigation is here required, but it seems most probable that the appendages are erectile and solid, having nothing to do with the voice. In other words, they are probably composed of erectile tissue, and erected by influx of blood. If this be the case they are probably erected during sexual excitement. Salvin mentions that they only appear with the adult plumage, and develop rapidly. In my opinion their evolution is probably due to some mechanical irritation connected with the habits of sexual maturity; perhaps the males fight with their beaks, as in the case of the Turkey. This suggestion is supported by the condition found in a fourth species, *C. variegatus*, occurring in Trinidad and neighbouring parts of South America. In this species there are no caruncles on the upper side of the beak or head, but the skin of the throat is bare of feathers and provided with numerous slender caruncles, which seem, from Salvin's paper, to be about $1\frac{1}{4}$ inch long in the adult, and to be absent in the immature male. In *C. nudicollis*, also mentioned above, although there are no actual caruncles, the skin of the throat and around the eyes is destitute of feathers, bearing only scattered black bristles; this bare skin is of a green colour in the breeding-season.

It is unfortunate that we have no evidence from actual

---

[1] "Note on the Costa-Rican Bell-Bird," *Ibis*, 1865.

observation that these birds peck at each other when fighting, or that their habits in one way or another involve a special mechanical irritation of the skin about the bill. But I feel strongly convinced that the modification of the skin in that region, which occurs in the males of all the species, corresponds to, and is due to, some such irritation; and further, that it will some day be proved that the special excrescence or modification in each species has been developed in the particular point or area to which the irritation is habitually applied. The most probable conjecture is that the males fight a great deal, and that in combat they seize their adversaries by the skin at the base of the beak, the attack being directed to the chin or the forehead according to the species. If this were true it would be an excellent illustration of the superiority of the Lamarckian explanation to that of sexual selection, for the caruncles would serve rather as an advantage to the adversary who seized them with his beak, than to the bird that possessed them.

In all the species of *Chasmorhynchus* the male differs from the female in structure, colour, and voice. *C. nudicollis* and *C. niveus* have pure white plumage, *C. tricarunculatus* has a chestnut body with white head and neck, *C. variegatus* has a white body with brown head and black wings. The females of all four species are closely similar, and Mr. P. L. Sclater [1] has discussed the divergence of the four species on the selection hypothesis. With regard to the colour, I have only to remark that if we attribute it to sexual selection we have to suppose that the hens have in one case preferred one colour, in another another, and that the divergence of the males is due to a variety of taste in females originally of one species.

The Umbrella-bird, *Cephalopterus ornatus*, belongs to the same family, and lives likewise in South America. This

---

[1] *Intellectual Observer*, 1867.

bird owes its name to its large top-knot, formed of bare quills, ending in dark blue plumes. It likewise has a long cylindrical fleshy appendage, not on the bill but on the throat, covered with a pad of glossy steel-blue feathers. The bird utters a deep, loud, prolonged note. The head-crest, and throat-caruncle are rudimentary in the female.

Darwin considered that the caruncle here was partly ornamental and partly a resonator to the voice, and states that it is dilated when the bird utters its note. Bates, in his *Naturalist on the Amazons*, states that the appendage is " connected with an unusual development of the trachea and vocal organs, to which the bird doubtless owes its deep, loud, long-sustained, fluty note." He also observed it in the act of " performing." " It drew itself up on its perch, spread widely the umbrella-formed crest, dilated and waved its glossy breast-lappet, and then in giving vent to its loud, piping note bowed its head slowly forward."

Mr. Fraser, however,[1] was unable to inflate the lappet in another species by blowing into the mouth or nostrils, and there is nothing in Bates's words denoting that the appendage contains a cavity communicating with that of the trachea. It seems more probable that, as in *Chasmorhynchus*, the appendage is only erected by distension of the blood-vessels.

The performance described by Bates is apparently of the nature of a challenge to other males, as well as a call to the female. The erection of the crest and distension of the breast-lappet, constitute mechanical stimulations such as I am endeavouring to indicate in every case, but probably more external stimulations than these come into play. As suggested in the case of *Chasmorhynchus*, the males may fight with one another, each seizing the other by the breast-lappet.

[1] *Proc. Zool. Soc.*, 1859, p. 143.

This suggestion is supported by a comparison between the different species of the genus. Three species are known. If my views are correct, mechanical irritation of the skin of birds,

FIG. 16.—*Cephalopterus glabricollis*, the Umbrella-bird of Central America, male on the left, female on the right. From specimens in the British Museum of Natural History, and published figures.

when excessive, leads to the disappearance of the feathers. Now in *C. ornatus*, although the caruncle itself is feathered, there is a bare space on the neck at its base, which is covered

by it. In *C. penduliger*,[1] the caruncle is very long and cylindrical, having a length of 10 inches, the bird being only
17½ inches in total length, and there is no bare patch. In
C. glabricollis,[2] on the other hand, around the base of the
caruncle there is a large area of skin which is entirely naked,
and of a reddish-orange colour, while the caruncle itself is
small and slender, and bears only a few feathers towards its
extremity.

As in the case of *Chasmorhynchus*, the species of *Cephalopterus* are geographically separated, *C. ornatus* being found
to the east of the Andes, *C. penduliger* to the west, *C. glabricollis* in Central America.

The Lyre-bird of Australia, *Menura*, belongs to the Order
Passeriformes, of which it forms a family by itself, although in
habits it rather resembles the Phasianidæ. The male has a loud
and peculiar voice in addition to its beautiful, greatly developed
tail. The tail of the female is much elongated, but is simply
brown in colour, and composed of similar straight feathers,
whereas that of the male is of various rich colours, and consists of three kinds of feathers, of which the most conspicuous
are one on each side gracefully curved in shape. The relation
between the special development of the tail in the male, and
its erection and movement in courtship, is as well established
in the Lyre-bird as in many other cases. According to
Gould's description, one of the habits of the male is to form
small round hillocks, which are constantly visited during the
day, and upon which the male is continually tramping, at the
same time erecting and spreading out its tail in the most
graceful manner, and uttering its various cries, sometimes
pouring forth its natural notes, at others imitating those of
other birds. Mr. Gould never saw more than two specimens
of *M. superba* together, and these only in a single instance,
when he saw two males chasing one another round and round,

---

[1] *Proc. Zool. Soc.*, 1859, p. 143.   [2] *Ibid.*, 1850, p. 92.

as though in play.   Mr. Leycester, whose evidence is quoted
by Gould, says that each male of *M. Alberti* seems to have
its own walk or boundary, and never to infringe on the
other's ground.   He says that while singing they spread
their tails over their heads like a peacock, and droop their
wings to the ground, and at the same time scratch and peck
up the earth.

There is thus no reason to doubt the erection of the tail and
the gestures of the male, which resemble those of a barn-door
cock in courtship; but the particular relation of these actions
to the behaviour of the female or the rivalry of other males
has not been described.   Darwin states that *M. Alberti* makes
shallow holes, in which it is believed that both sexes assemble,
but in Gould's *Handbook* we find it stated that only a single
bird is found in one of these holes, in which it seems to be
feeding.   It would almost seem from these observations
that the male performs his duties all by himself, without any
stimulus from the immediate presence of the female or rival
males.   But the bird is exceedingly shy and difficult to
observe.   It may be conjectured that when the male is showing off the female is in sight of him, and it is possible that
one male visits three or four females which are building
nests in different inaccessible places.   At one period or
another also there must be rivalry between the males.   One
traveller, quoted by Mr. Wood in 1870, is said to have once
observed about 150 male lyre-birds all fighting together
with indescribable fury, but this is the only evidence
known to me of the birds assembling together.   It is
generally concluded from the evidence available that the
bird is monogamous.

The remarkable tail of the Lyre-bird is not fully developed
until the third or fourth year of age, and at the end of the
breeding season, in October, the feathers are shed, not to be renewed, at any rate in the same form, till the following summer.

This is, therefore, one of the numerous cases in which the special development of plumage is limited not merely to one sex, but to the season of the year during which the male practises certain violent movements and gestures under the influence of sexual excitement.

The published observations prove that the habits of male and female in relation to breeding are as different as their plumage. The female alone performs the duty of incubation and probably builds her nest without aid from the male. The nest is roofed over and has an aperture only at one end. It has been considered strange that so large a bird with so long a tail should sit in a roofed, enclosed nest, but it has been observed by Mr. Ramsay that she enters the nest head first and then turns round, bending the tail over her back or to the side. We may infer therefore that the length of tail in the female is due to partial inheritance from the male, and not to any special stimulation involved in her own habits.[1]

Ploceidæ.—Among the Ploceidæ or Weavers the Widow-bird of South and West Africa is remarkable for the extremely long tail-feathers of the male. These are present only in the breeding season, and in winter plumage the male is scarcely different from the female. Darwin mentions a statement that the female rejected the male when he was deprived of his long tail feathers, and considers the observation as evidence of the occurrence of selection. But it would rather tend to show that in the female the sexual instinct was associated with the perception of the special male adornment, an association which probably exists in all such cases. The growth of these feathers, taking place every year at the approach of the breeding season, like the growth of the antlers of stags, must, I believe, be due to some special stimulation of the feather-papillæ produced by movements associated with the instincts

---

[1] See Gould, *Handbook to the Birds of Australia*, 1865, vol. i. Ramsay, *Proc. Zool. Soc.*, 1868.   T. W. Wood, *The Student*, April, 1870.

of courtship. The mere process of selection affords no explanation whatever of a special process of growth, occurring regularly at every breeding season, and dormant during the rest of the year. Mr. Bowker, as quoted in the *Royal Natural History*, says, that the male *Vidua paradisea* enjoys himself in a high wind, spreading out his tail like a fan, but it is stated also that the Kaffir children often succeed in running the bird down, because the nuptial feathers impede his flight. The actual erection and display of the feathers in courtship does not seem to have been observed.

Many of the other families of Passeres consist of singing birds, and in these the power of song is generally confined to the males, and is associated with an absence of other secondary sexual characters. In these cases the energy of the male under the influence of sexual excitement has been exerted in his voice, and this is the reason why the voice has developed in the male and not in the female.

In the Falconiformes or Birds of Prey sexual dimorphism is slight, and this is in harmony with the fact that these birds are monogamous, and both sexes take part in obtaining food for their young. There is a slight difference between the male and female Condor. The male has a small dull-coloured comb of somewhat flat shape. I have not found any mention of special habits related to this peculiarity; perhaps the males fight with one another, and in fighting strike at the top of the adversary's head.

In most of the members of the order the female is the larger. This is well seen in the Sparrow-hawk. It does not seem likely that this is due to the same conditions as in *Turnix* and *Rhynchœa*, for generally hawks and falcons pair together for the season, if not for life, and it has not been stated that the female takes the initiative in courtship or fights with rivals. The fact is probably due to greater activity on the part of the female in capturing prey for her young, who remain long in the nest. The superior size and strength here, in fact, are, I think, related to hunting rather than to fighting.

Otididæ.—In the Bustard family, Otididæ, sexual differences of some importance occur. In the Great Bustard, *Otis tarda*, the male is considerably larger than the female; he has curious whisker-like plumes on the cheeks, which are absent in the female, and has a great air-pouch opening from beneath the tongue, which is also absent in the female. The female differs slightly in colour. Considering the very marked and elaborate " display " or erection of the feathers which is performed by the male in courtship, it might be suggested, that if the views I am maintaining are correct, the peculiarities of the male ought to be more developed than they are. But the erectile feathers are probably larger in the male than in the female, though they are of the same colour, namely, most of them white. In the attitude of display the throat pouch is inflated so as to distend the neck and throat to a prodigious extent. The tail is turned forwards flat on the back, and the white under tail-coverts are erected to form a frill behind. White secondary wing feathers are erected on each side of the back, and the head is buried in the feathers of the neck, so that the whiskers are caused to stand erect on each side.[1] In these movements we have stimulation applied to the special feathers on the cheeks corresponding to their special development, and also a mechanical explanation of the throat-pouch. In other species, there is, in the male, a special shield of feathers over the crop, composed of the elongated feathers of the throat and neck, an erectile crest on the crown of the head, and a large ruff of soft plumes on the sides of the neck (genus *Houbara*). These adornments are much less developed in the female, and doubtless all correspond to special movements in the sexual gestures.

[1] R. Bowdler Sharpe, *Birds of Great Britain*, vol. iii., 1896.

An interesting paper on the throat-pouch of the Bustard appeared in *Natural Science*, November 1898, by Mr. W. Pycraft of the Natural History Museum, London. He gives a full account of the literature of the subject, pointing out that in certain male specimens dissected by experienced anatomists the pouch was not found. The specimen dissected by himself had the pouch fully developed. This specimen died in May, at the height of sexual activity. It is very probable that the absence of the pouch in other specimens was due to the fact that the pouch disappears almost, or quite completely, after the breeding season. If this be the case it is, as in many other cases, a very strong argument in favour of the view which attributes the origin of the pouch directly to the pressure of the air in the mouth when the bird shows off.

It is a curious fact that in *Otis australis*, which shows off in much the same way as the Great Bustard, A. H. Garrod found there was no gular pouch at all. When this bird courts the female the neck swells, and the feathers of the lower part bulge out and descend gradually downwards in the form of a bag, often nearly reaching to the ground. Dr. Murie having found the sub-lingual pouch in *Otis kori*, and witnessed the "show" of the species mentioned above, concluded that the inflation in the latter was due to the same cause. A. H. Garrod, however, found that in *O. australis* the distension was produced by the inflation of the gullet with air, as in the Pouter pigeon.

The wings in the family are strong and short, and while ill-adapted for sustained flight are much used in fighting. In accordance with this fact they are often provided with spurs, which, when single, is the nail or claw of the thumb or first digit. *Palamedea cornuta* has two spurs on each wing and an erect horny filament on the head, but the spurs are stated by Darwin to be no larger in the male than in the female. They are, however, used to give blows, and from my point of view that is the principal fact.

Charadriidæ. — In the male of the common Peewit, *Vanellus cristatus*, the tubercle on the wrist of the wing becomes more prominent during the breeding season, and the males fight with their wings, that is to say the tubercle is the result of the blow on the wings.

In *Lobivanellus* a similar tubercle becomes developed during the breeding season into a short, horny spur. In *L. lobatus* of Australia both sexes have spurs, but they are much larger in the males than in the females.

In *Hoplopterus armatus* the spurs do not increase in size during the breeding season, but the males fight with them.

These weapons resemble in position and function the exostoses of the Solitaire, and support the conclusion that the mechanical irritation is the cause of the growth, more especially when we see that the structures wax and wane in the individual with the periodical increase and decrease in the stimulation.

In the Herons there is often a summer or breeding plumage, but it is usually alike in both sexes, and both sexes take part in incubation.

Scolopacidæ.—Among the Scolopacidæ or Snipes, *Machetes pugnax*, the Ruff affords one of the most convincing instances of the connection between erection and movement of plumes and their excessive growth. The males and females migrate in separate flocks, and remain separate throughout the winter. In the spring, in their northern breeding places, the males fight together and acquire their breeding plumage, which is chiefly distinguished by the ruff of long neck-feathers. These are erected in combat. It is curious that the colours of the plumage of the males should be so remarkably various, scarcely two individuals being alike, but in the development and erection of the ruff they are all similar. The females and young are all alike, and the males take no part in incubation. The male retains his ruff for barely two months, and there is little difference in the winter plumage between the two sexes. The males are considerably larger than the females, and fight very much like game-cocks, seizing each other by their beaks and striking with their wings. Here we have another instance of a character only developed in the individual male at the time of the year when it performs certain gestures in fighting, gestures which directly affect the development of the character in question.

Phalaropus is another genus of the same family. In the two species, *P. fulicarius* and *P. hyperboreus*, the females are larger, and in their summer plumage more gaily attired, than the males, and according to Professor Steenstrup the male of *P. fulicarius* alone incubates. The females do not appear to fight, and their greater size must be attributed to their greater activity, for the sex which incubates is necessarily the more sedentary. The habits of the red-necked Phalarope, *P. hyperboreus*, are described in detail by Mr. Nelson, and his description is quoted by Bowdler Sharpe. The birds breed in Alaska and other circumpolar regions. The female pursues the male, who resists her advances with apparent indifference for some time. She swims along by his side, and at intervals rises on wing above him, and, poised a foot or two over him, makes a half dozen quick, sharp, wing-strokes, producing a series of sharp whistling noises in rapid succession. When paired the male sits on the eggs, while the female swims about close by. Both sexes have a distinct winter and breeding plumage, the Grey Phalarope, *P. fulicarius*, being grey in winter and sandy buff in the breeding season. The more intense colouring of the female is probably merely due to its greater sexual excitement, as it is difficult to perceive anything in the external influences, such as light or food, which could affect the sexes differently.

In the Charadriidæ, or intermediate between rails and snipes, are three species of the genus *Rhynchœa* in which the females are not only larger, but much more richly coloured than the males.[1] In *Rhynchœa australis* the trachea is simple in the male, while in the female it makes four distinct convolutions before entering the lungs. The male undertakes the duties of incubation. The female doubtless uses her voice in calling to the male, and the pressure of the air has caused the convolutions of the trachea.

Psittacidæ. — Sexual differences in colour occur in certain parrots. One of the most striking cases is that of *Eclectus polychloros*, of which the males and females were originally described as distinct species. Well-mounted specimens of these birds are to be seen in the Hunterian Museum of the College of Surgeons in London. The male is green, the female brilliant red and blue. Mr. Beddard[2] states that there is no difference in the pigments present in the two sexes in this species. In birds many colours, especially those known as metallic or iridescent colours, are due to minute structural markings on the feathers. They are produced by the phenomenon known in optics as the interference of the reflected rays of light. The case of *Eclectus* thus appears to be analogous to that of the Dragonet and other fishes, where also the same elements of coloration are present, but quantitative differences in these in the two sexes produce markedly different colours. I am unable at present to attribute the difference in colour between the sexes in *Eclectus* to any difference in the habits or conditions. of life, but it is not improbable that proper investigation

[1] Jerdon's *Birds of India*, vol. iii.   Gould's *Handbook to the Birds of Australia*.
[2] *Animal Coloration*, p. 4.   London : Swan, Sonnenschein and Co., 1892.

would result in proving that there are special conditions influencing the development and structure of the feathers in the two sexes, giving rise in the one case to green, in the other to blue and red. There is no evidence, so far as I know, that sexual selection has anything to do with the matter.

Anseres.—The wild drake, *Anas boschas*, pairs with a single female, and nevertheless has marked unisexual characters in his plumage. The green speculum on the wings is common to both sexes, though duller and somewhat smaller in the female, and is developed early in life, whilst the curled tail feathers and other ornaments are confined to the male, and are developed later. As in other cases, the drake loses his special plumage after the breeding season. He remains without it for three months, during which period he resembles the female.[1]

In *Anas acuta*, the Pintail Duck, the male loses his special plumage for only about six weeks or two months.

I do not know whether any special movements of the tail feathers are performed by the wild drake in courtship, but I think it is probable that some special stimulation of the papillæ of these feathers may take place, and may be the cause of their peculiar shape. The fact of the difference between the feathers, chiefly in colour, after the moult and those of the breeding plumage in the drake, suggests strongly that the action of the nervous system under the influence of sexual excitement has something to do with the brilliant colours of the breeding plumage. The special plumage of the male, as in so many others cases, is only developed at maturity, and the close correspondence of special brilliant coloration with sexual excitement is certainly, in my opinion, not without significance. This is one of the cases in which the conditions of life other than sexual excitement

---

[1] Macgillivray, *Hist. British Birds*, vol. v.

do not seem to be different in the two sexes, except, indeed, that the duties of incubation are performed only by the female. Another interesting unisexual peculiarity in drakes is the modification of the lower end of the trachea, some six or eight of the lowest cartilaginous rings being fused together and dilated to form a bulb, the walls of which are partially ossified. In the ordinary drakes of the genus *Anas* there is a simple enlargement or ampulla, protruding usually to the left side. In the Fulatulinæ, which includes *Somateria*, the Eider Duck, the enlargement is more complicated, having "fenestræ" or apertures in the bony walls which are covered by membrane; the bulb thus forms a "tympanum" or drum.

Darwin remarks that the meaning of these differences in the trachea of the two sexes of Anatidæ is not understood, for the male is not always the more vociferous. But Macgillivray, as quoted in the *Royal Natural History*,[1] says that although both sexes quack when alarmed, and the female the louder, the male also utters a rather low and soft cry between a croak and a murmur, and the female a louder and clearer jabber.

Yarrell[2] considers that the internal edge of the constriction between the osseous bulb and the trachea acts like the reed or tongue of a wind instrument, and writes: "A compound tone of voice is thus produced (in the male), by which wild-fowl shooters can distinguish males from females in the darkest night whenever the birds utter their note."

There is thus no doubt of the sexual difference in voice in the Common Mallard, and as it is known that the courtship of the drake is an elaborate process, it is probable that his peculiar voice is a kind of love-gurgle produced by the osseous bulb or drum. Thus there must be special strains

---

[1] Vol. iv. p. 344.   [2] *British Birds*, vol. iii., 1856, p. 276.

and pressures applied to the trachea in the production of the sound by means of muscles and air-pressure, and to these special strains the modification corresponds.

It is significant that in Anseres there are two pairs of extrinsic tracheal muscles, passing from the lower part of the trachea to clavicle or sternum, while in all other birds there is only one pair.[1] Another important fact is that in the male of *Œdemia fusca*, the Velvet Scoter, the modification of the syrinx occurring in most ducks is absent, but there is a spherical osseous enlargement above the lower end of the trachea, and from this bulb a muscle passes to the clavicle or merrythought.[2]

In the swans, Cygnidæ, there is a remarkable contrast in the condition of the trachea in different species, but in no species is the peculiarity unisexual. In the species of one group the trachea has a number of convolutions which are actually contained in a cavity excavated in the keel of the sternum. This group contains *Cygnus ferus*, the Whooper, and *C. Bewicki* of North Europe, *C. buccinator* and *C. americanus* of North America. Other species have a simple trachea. It is known that the four species mentioned above utter a loud trumpeting or whistling cry, while *C. olor*, the Common Swan, *C. nigricollis*, the Black-necked Swan, and *C. coscaroba* in which the trachea is straight, are all mute, or utter only a slight grunt. It seems most probable that the lengthening of the trachea is due to air-pressure, and there can be no doubt, I think, that the sternum has been hollowed out in course of generations by the pressure of the trachea, perhaps the most wonderful illustration of the physiological effect of mechanical causes. But the difficulty is to understand how the voice, if it is produced in the syrinx, can be connected with the compression of air in the trachea. Possibly

[1] Newton and Gadow, *Dict. Birds*, p. 938.
[2] *British Birds*, vol. iii. p. 318.

the escape of the air is obstructed at the glottis, and in this case the pressure within the trachea would be intelligible.

Pelecanidæ.—The differences between the sexes in the pelicans are generally slight or absent; but in one American species there is an interesting peculiarity in the male. This is the White Pelican, *P. erythrorhynchus,* of North America, in which a longitudinal vertical plate of horn is developed in the upper mandible in the breeding season. This excrescence is about an inch high and two or three inches long, and situated near the middle of the length of the bill. The most interesting fact about it is that it is bodily shed at the end of the breeding season, about the month of May.[1] Mr. Ridgway ascertained this fact from observation of the birds at Pyramid Lake in Nevada where they breed, but unfortunately he does not give any evidence as to the use made of the excrescence before it drops off. Audubon[2] expressed his belief that the bird uses the apparatus as a means of attack and defence when engaged with its rivals in the love season; and the same opinion is given in *Birds of North America* by Baird, Cassin, and Lawrence. Probably the opinion is correct, and this is another instance of epidermic hypertrophy taking place at the breeding season in response to irritations which are only applied at that season. We may assume that the excrescence now develops partly by heredity, though this has not been proved by direct experiment.

Ratitæ.—Darwin says of the African Ostrich that the male is somewhat larger than the female and has finer plumes, with more strongly contrasted colours; that nevertheless he performs alone the duties of incubation. This statement is made on the authority of Mr. P. L. Sclater; and on the authority of Captain Musters (*At Home with the*

---

[1] *Ibis*, 1869, p. 350.
[2] *Ornithological Biography*, vol. iv.

Patagonians) he states that the same is true of the American *Rhea Darwinii*, the male being larger, stronger, and swifter than the female, and yet taking sole charge of the eggs and young. If these conclusions were correct they would not afford any insuperable difficulty, for the males might be the more eager and the more pugnacious, and yet alone perform the function of incubation. This is the case also in the sticklebacks and other fishes, of which the males both take the initiative in courtship and build and guard the nest.

But in birds the general rule is that the sex which is most active in courtship and most pugnacious takes less part in incubation or none at all. Moreover, it has been generally stated that several hen ostriches lay in one nest.

In the *Zoologist* for March 1897 there is a detailed article, by Conrad Schreiner, on the habits of the ostrich of South Africa as observed on large ostrich farms. He states that the ostrich is monogamous, and that the cock does not alone perform the task of incubation. A cock and hen pair and make a nest by hollowing out the sand; the hen lays eggs and sits in the day-time, while the cock sits from evening to morning. Under these circumstances most chicks are reared. He goes on to say, however, that this system is comparatively seldom carried out, because the cocks from fighting become reduced, and there are always unattached hens which lay in the nest of a pair of mated birds. He says these hens court the cocks. When unattached hens thus disturb a couple they lay their eggs in the nest, often drop eggs around it, and in consequence of the disturbance few or no chicks are reared.

It may be objected that observations made on ostriches in a state of confinement and semi-domestication are not complete evidence concerning the habits in the wild state. But the conditions of ostrich-farming are not likely to modify the habits of the birds much, and the above evidence indicates

11

that the cocks, although they share in the duties of incubation, are pugnacious, and probably before eggs are laid
make the advances in courtship. Their habits are not,
therefore, inconsistent with their larger size and finer
plumage, and are in perfect harmony, according to the views
maintained by me, with the fact that they are less superior
to the females than the males of such polygamous species as
the pheasants.

In the Common Cassowary, *Casuarius galeatus*, the female
is larger, and the appendages and naked skin about her head
are more brightly coloured. The female, according to Mr.
T. W. Wood, is very pugnacious in the breeding season, and
then her wattles become enlarged and more brilliantly
coloured. This fact is evidence for the view that the
appendages and bright colour of the skin are the result
of the irritation produced by the blows of the beaks of the
birds when fighting, and are not necessarily related either
to a particular sex or to selection. The habit of fighting
with the beak also explains the presence of the bony crest
on the skull, although it is present in both sexes. It is
absent, however, in the young birds.

In the Emeus, *Dromæus*, similar differences of habit
correspond to a similar reversal of the usual differences in
the sexes. The male alone incubates the eggs and takes
care of the young ; he has even to defend them against the
attacks of their mother. She is considerably larger than
the male, and possesses a slight top-knot, but is otherwise
indistinguishable in plumage.[1]

During the breeding season, at least, the hen utters a
peculiar loud, booming sound, while the voice of the male,
according to Mr. Bennett, is much less powerful — " a
suppressed hiss when angry, or a croak." The peculiar
voice of the female seems to owe its character partly to a

[1] A. W. Bennett, *Land and Water*, May, 1868.

large air pouch in the front of the neck which communicates with the trachea by a narrow upright slit. The pouch was found by Dr. Murie [1] and other anatomists to be present in both sexes. But Mr. Bartlett observed that the lower part of the neck was much more inflated in the female than in the male when the call or voice was uttered. According to Dr. Murie the female forcibly dilates the sac by closing the glottis and forcing air through the tracheal slit; and he thought the sound was produced by the rush of air past the opening of the pouch, as when air is blown over the open bung-hole of a cask.

On the whole, it seems possible that the sound may be in this case of secondary importance, and that the primary fact is the inflation of the neck. We know that so many animals, and birds in particular, puff and swell themselves out under the influence of sexual excitement, e.g. the bustard. If sound were the object, why should it not be produced in the usual way in the syrinx, or lower larynx, which is situated not at the glottis but below the opening of the air pouch? Whether the bird is making an effort to produce a sound or merely to swell its throat, it is certain that it does close its glottis and then violently force air into its trachea. The trachea is therefore subjected to the pressure of compressed air, and thus there exists a mechanical cause corresponding to the existence of a dilatation of the wall of the tube at a particular point. The mechanical cause appears, like the structural modification, to exist in both sexes, but to a greater degree in the female. As is usually the case with organs associated with sexual activity, the pouch is much less developed in young and immature individuals.

It may be objected that it is difficult to understand why tracheal rings should be burst by internal pressure in such a

[1] *Proc. Zool. Soc.* 1867.

way as to form a longitudinal slit. Why should not the trachea be dilated generally, or form a bulbous enlargement ? For we suppose the pressure of air to have been originally applied in the mature bird with well-developed tracheal rings.

The answer to this objection could probably be obtained by sufficient investigation. The tracheal rings must have been weaker or less supported by surrounding parts in the place where the opening exists. When a rubber bicycle tyre is inflated strongly it frequently happens that a dilatation is formed at a particular limited spot, while the rest of the tube preserves its form.

On the other hand, it is impossible to conceive of the evolution of the Emeu's pouch by the selection of individual variations apart from the process of inflation.

Note.—In reference to the Oscines or Singing Birds, among the Passeres, it should be mentioned that Dr. A. G. Butler has discovered and described minute differences in wing and bill between male and female in several species. These differences he believes to be related to differences of function in flight and nest-building: they therefore can probably be explained by the principles maintained by me.

CHAPTER III

REPTILES

THE sexual differences of reptiles, as far as they are described by Darwin, support in a very remarkable and convincing manner the arguments I am maintaining. In reptiles as in birds the fertilisation of the ova is internal, in other words the sexes unite in breeding, although the males and females do not generally associate together for such long periods, and, except in rare cases and to a slight degree, no care is bestowed on eggs or young. In the Lacertilia, however, the males fight with one another for the possession of the females, and in this Order we find the most strongly developed unisexual characters. In many instances these characters are in the form of outgrowths of the head, which serve as weapons, and which, in their function and in their origin, are somewhat similar to the horns of the Ungulata among mammals.

In the genus *Ceratophora* the male bears on the end of his snout a simple conical projection, which is flexible, covered with scales, and apparently capable of erection. This appendage seems to be an outgrowth of the skin, and not to contain any outgrowth of the bone of the jaw. It is rudimentary in the female. In another species a terminal scale

forms a minute horn on the summit of the flexible appendage,
and in a third the whole appendage is converted into a horn.
In Darwin's opinion these appendages serve as ornaments.
But there can be little doubt that the males fight together
with their snouts, and the irritation of the skin of the tip of
the snout so produced would result in an outgrowth of the
kind described ; if this effect were in some degree hereditary
the character would be explained. On the other hand, we
have no reason whatever to suppose that such a character, or
the successive steps in its evolution, could have arisen apart
from the stimulation I have mentioned.

Unisexual characters are most developed in the chamœloons.
In *Chamœleon bifurcis* and *C. Willsii* of Madagascar the bones
of the face in front of the eyes are prolonged into two great
solid projections covered with skin and scales like the rest
of the head, and only rudiments of such projections occur
in the female. In *C. Owenii* of the west coast of Africa,
instead of two massive projections there are three slender
tapering horns, also bony and covered with smooth skin :
of these the female has not a trace. According to Darwin
it is not known that these horns are used in fighting, but
the animals are known to be quarrelsome, and it is probable
that the appendages are thus used. Here again, therefore,
we find that the existence of outgrowths corresponds to the
impacts produced by definite actions, both being confined
to the male sex. It is not stated that the appendages
are absent in the young males, but that is probably the
truth.

We find the same exact correspondence in *Anolis crista-
tellus*. The male is larger than the female, and has a crest
along the back and tail *which can be erected at pleasure*. Of
this crest the female does not possess a trace. The males
also have a pouch or frill beneath the throat, but this is
rudimentary in the female. By direct observation it is

known that the males of this species are extremely pugnacious and fight whenever they meet. As weapons they use their

FIG. 17.—*Chamœleon Willsii*, a Chamæleon found in Madagascar. A, male ; *a*, head from above ; B, female ; *b*, head from above.

teeth, a fact which corresponds to the absence of horns. The movement of the scales of the back under excitement corresponds to the development of the crest. The pouch is distended and expanded during fighting. We have no evidence that either the pouch or the crest are of any use in fighting, or are subject to selection by the female, but on the other hand we are justified in supposing that the movement of the skin and scales preceded the evolution of the crest and the pouch. Here also we find that special developments correspond to special movements, special stimulations, a correspondence which has no significance on the theory of selection.

The distensible throat-pouch is in some species of lizard equally, or nearly equally developed in both sexes, in others is larger in the males than in the females, in others again is confined entirely to the males. This character thus resembles a large number of other secondary sexual characters in these respects.

AMPHIBIA

URODELA.—It seems very remarkable, considering the mode of fertilisation in these animals, that sexual dimorphism should be developed in them at all, while as a matter of fact it is in many species developed to a high degree. There is no union between the sexes. The male deposits small masses of semen, or spermatophores, on the ground, in front of the female ; the latter grasps them with the lips of her generative opening, and they are then, as it were, swallowed by the oviducts.[1] The case of fishes, however, shows that internal fertilisation and copulation are by no means necessary conditions of the existence of secondary sexual characters. We have to consider whether the differentiation of males and females in external characters is related in these Amphibia

[1] See Gasco, *Ann. Mus. Storia Naturale di Genova*, vol. xvi. 1880-81, pp. 1-54.

to different modes of ordinary life, or to special habits connected with sexual activity.

The latter alternative is the true one. Notwithstanding
the curious mode of fertilisation, the generative act of the
male is not simply automatic, but is associated with sexual
excitement, and an eager pursuit and courtship of the female.
The mere presence and society of the female seems here to
afford the stimulation to the male organs which in mammals
and birds is supplied by the contact of her generative organs,
and the desire for the female produces the same sexual excitement and leads to actions of the same kind as in those
classes.

According to Darwin prehensile claws are developed on
the fore-legs of the males in some species during the breeding season, which if correct indicates that the female is
seized and held by the male. In this case the mechanical
stimulation is obvious, and the special growth is limited to
the season of the year at which the stimulation is applied.

In *Molge palmata*, the Webbed Newt, which is a British
species, the hind feet are webbed in the males during the
breeding season, when the animals live in the water. In
the rest of the year, when they live on land, the web almost
entirely disappears. Doubtless, as Darwin says, the structure
aids the male in his eager search and pursuit of the female,
but its origin is to be attributed to the effect of the resistance of the water and the stretching of the toes in swimming.
If it was a variation not due to the mechanical strains
involved in swimming, why should it diminish after the
breeding season, when the animal leaves the water?

The well-developed membranous crest on back and tail in
our two common species of newt, *Molge vulgaris* and *M.
cristata*, seems much more difficult to explain. Like the
web of the hind feet in the *palmata* it diminishes very much
after the breeding season, and is almost entirely absent in

the female. Darwin remarks that it is not provided with muscles, and therefore cannot be used in locomotion, but it must be admitted that it may be of great importance in locomotion in offering resistance to the water when the body and tail are swayed from side to side by the body muscles. The movement of the body in swimming mechanically tends to flatten the body in a vertical direction. If a round body covered with a flexible membrane is moved from side to side in water the membrane will be stretched in the vertical median plane of the body by the resistance of the water. In

Fig. 18.—*Molge cristata*, the Crested Newt, a British species. A, male ; B, female. From specimens in the British Museum of Natural History.

this way the skin of the newt would be mechanically stretched in the middle line, and growth following the mechanical tension would produce the crest. The membranous fin in the larva of a fish, or in the tadpole of the newt, doubtless arises in a similar way, and the crest of the male adult newt may be regarded to some extent as the retained membranous median fin of the tadpole. But not entirely so, because the crest disappears after the breeding season. It is therefore extremely probable that the crest of the male in these species of newt is due to the active movements of the male in courting the female in the breeding season.

In order to test the mechanical effect of the resistance of the water on the surface of a cylindrical body moved from side to side, as the body of a fish or newt is moved, I made the following experiment:—I took a cylindrical penholder and coated it with a thin layer of sealing-wax, making the layer as uniform as possible, so that the surface was still cylindrical. I then moved the penholder to and fro in hot water, holding one end of it in my hand. The heat of the water softened the wax, and after continuing the movement for some minutes a ridge of wax was formed in a position exactly corresponding to the vertical fins of a tadpole's tail, or of a fish, that is to say in a plane perpendicular to that in which the motion took place. Continuing the motion some minutes longer, I found that a thin lamina of sealing-wax was formed along the penholder above and below in the vertical plane, the motion being horizontal. This lamina was more than half an inch high. The cylinder of wood with its uniform coating of wax was thus converted in about five minutes into a structure corresponding, as exactly as the difference of materials would allow, to the structure of the tail of a newt or fish, leaving fin-rays of course out of consideration. The similarity between the laminæ of wax produced, and the fin membrane of a newt, tadpole, or fish is very remarkable. The wax does not pass off gradually from the penholder with a thick base and narrow edges. The origin of the lamina is quite sharply defined, just as is the origin of the membranous fin of a fish or newt, and the base of the lamina forms a very distinct angle with the surface of the penholder.

This is an experiment which anyone can repeat for himself with very little time or trouble, by means of materials usually at hand on any writing-table. Simple as the experiment is, it seems to me to be of far-reaching importance. Unless it can be disproved that growth of the skin takes place generally in the direction of mechanical tension, the experiment strongly supports the conclusion that in the majority of cases no other explanation of the evolution of dermal webs in animals is required than the tension produced by the resistance of the surrounding medium, whether air or water, but especially water. Thus we learn why aquatic birds and aquatic mammals have webbed feet. Probably the dermal membranes of flying mammals and reptiles owe their origin to a similar cause. The membranous vertical fins of larval fishes, of tadpoles, and of newts are thus explained directly as growths resulting from the tension caused by the resistance of the water, when the posterior part of the body is moved from side to side.

There are, however, various details to be considered in applying the above principle to the explanation of the dorsal crest in male newts. One question is, why is there not a corresponding ventral crest on the body, as there is to some extent on the tail ? Another is, why do some species possess the crest on the body and others not ? I believe that all such questions could be answered by a sufficiently minute study of the movements of the males in courtship in the different species. These movements have been described carefully by various observers in certain species. One of the best of such descriptions is that of Dr. Rusconi,[1] published at Milan in 1821. In reference to a species which he names *Salamandra platycauda*, and which is almost identical with our own *Molge cristata*, he writes that the female, when tired of fleeing, rests motionless on the ground, that the male then places himself with his side against her snout, bends his body, supports himself on his fore-feet alone, and, shaking his tail, commences to thrash the water. After having agitated his tail and body thus for half a minute, he strikes the side of the female with

[1] *Amours des salamandres aquatiques.*

deliberate blows of his tail. Rusconi was not aware of the method of depositing spermatophores which followed this courtship. He also describes the male of another species, apparently *Molge palmata*, as agitating his tail with great rapidity in front of the female. Gasco's observations were made at Genoa on *Molge alpestris*, which has a somewhat narrow dorsal crest. He believes the vibration of the tail by the male in front of the female is intended merely to stimulate and excite his own sexual organs, and states that the male never touches with his tail any part of the female. Zeller describes the male as beating his own flanks with his tail, and as performing, supported on his fore legs, a rapid undulating movement of the body. It is this latter movement which has caused, in my opinion, the development of the dorsal crest on the body. A similar excrescence is wanting on the belly, partly because the motion is more active in the dorsal region, partly because the pressure of the belly on the ground would prevent the formation of a vertical membrane. Zeller states that these actions of the male are continued usually for hours or even days with only brief interruptions, and thus we see that the mechanical forces at work have ample time to produce their effect. It would probably be found, if the precise movements of the different species were studied, that the degree of development of the dorsal crest on the body corresponded to the amount of lateral vibration in this part of the body.

An excellent summary of what is known concerning the courtship and fecundation of the Urodela is given by Dr. Boulenger.[1] He points out that the male is "ornamented" with more brilliant colours, and with dorsal and caudal crests, or other temporary appendages, only in those species in which no amplexus takes place, that is to say, in which the male does not clasp or embrace the female. This might be con-

[1] *Zool. Jahrb. systematik*, Band vi., 1892, p. 447.

sidered by some to support the selection theory. But it must be noted that in the descriptions of the habits of courtship there is nothing to show that the males perform their antics in rivalry with other males, their object is to excite the female sufficiently to induce her to take up the spermatophores they deposit, and according to Gasco, the movements themselves serve chiefly to excite the generative organs of the males themselves. Thus, if there is a selection, a superiority of some males over others, which I am not concerned to deny, it is not the selection of the most beautiful or the most ornamented by the females. Success is to the most eager and virile male, and the particular movements which express his virility have determined his unisexual characters, as the physiological effect of mechanical forces. The dorsal crest where it exists is thus the *result* of the habits of courtship, but there is nothing to show that it in any way contributes to the success of the courtship; it is the consequence of the behaviour of the sexes towards each other, not a means by which their union is effected.

On the other hand, amplexus occurs in other species of Urodela. In *Molge* (*Pleurodeles*) *waltlii* of the south of Europe, the male places himself beneath the female and clasps her fore limbs with his own. His tail performs rapid undulations, and the membrane of it is broadened in the breeding season, but in addition to this the epidermis of his fore limbs is thickened by the pressure and friction of the amplexus, as in the frog.

In *Molge aspera* the peculiarity of the male consists in a somewhat greater size of the hind limbs, and a shorter, thicker, and more muscular tail. There are no ornamental colours or crests. Even the tail is without a fin-membrane. This species lives in lakes at considerable altitudes in the Pyrenees. The peculiarities of the male as usual correspond to its mode of courtship. It seizes and holds the female by twisting its tail round her. The male in this amplexus is below the female, and his tail is passed over her loins from the left side to the right. The sexual difference is thus a functionally produced hypertrophy of the tail and hind limbs. The tail of the male has grown shorter because it is the proximal part which is most used.

In many species the males are more vividly coloured than the females, and there is probably no other reason for this than the greater sexual excitement of the males, which, as I have suggested in many other cases, causes through nervous stimulation more active production of pigment in the skin.

The above remarks all refer to the family Salamandridæ. I have not seen descriptions of any sexual differences in the other families of the Urodela.

ANURA.—In frogs and toads generally, prominences become developed on the front legs of the males during the breeding season. There can be little doubt that these are hereditary, but there can be equally little doubt that they are the direct result of the pressure to which the parts affected are subjected in the process of copulation. There is no penis or intromittent organ in the frogs and toads, but in the case of the Common Frog, the male seeks the female in spring, and clasps her body tightly with his fore limbs, remaining in this position for days or even weeks till the ova of the female are discharged, when they are fertilised by the simultaneous emission on the part of the male. The cushion or tubercle in the Common Frog is situated on the palmar surface of the innermost of the four fingers, and this is the surface which is pressed by muscular action against the body of the female.

Another male peculiarity in frogs is the possession of vocal sacs. These are not present in the Common Frog of England, *Rana temporaria*, but are well developed in the Edible Frog of the continent, *Rana esculenta*. The vocal sacs are large pouches formed from the skin of the mouth, into which they open. The males croak chiefly in the breeding season, the vocal sacs serve as resonators to the voice, and their formation is evidently due to the distension of the mouth with air in the effort of croaking. The croak may be of use to the male in attracting the female, and the loudest croakers may or may not be, on the whole, most successful in obtaining mates. But the fact that under the influence of sexual excitement the males croak, is the reason why the sacs have been formed in the males and not in the females. In one species, *Rhinoderma Darwinii*, belonging to the narrow-mouthed family, or Engystomatidæ, the male puts his vocal sacs to a strange use. The sacs are much enlarged and internally confluent, so that they form an extensive chamber on the lower side of the body. The chamber is entered by the two apertures at the sides of the tongue, and the eggs laid by the female are taken by the male into his mouth, and passed into this chamber, where the tadpoles are developed. It is difficult to understand how such a peculiar habit arose. But whether the eggs first got into the vocal sacs accidentally when the male was devouring them, or whether he took them into his mouth with the intention of protecting them, the only reasonable explanation of the enlargement of the vocal sacs is that it was due to the distension caused by the eggs and tadpoles.

In two other cases the female has a peculiar structure whose function is the protection of the eggs during development. In *Nototrema* the pouched tree-frog of tropical America (Fam. Hylidæ), the skin of the back is invaginated to form a pouch opening backwards. The eggs are pushed into this cavity by the male by means of his hind feet. Here again the pouch may be attributed to mechanical distension, although it is difficult to imagine how on a female, originally with no pouch, the male should have set about forming one.

Considering the attitude of the pair in copulation it may be suggested that the first step was due to some of the eggs having become pressed between the bodies of the pair at the posterior end, and thus made a fold in the dorsal skin of the female.

Similar accidents, perhaps necessarily occurring pretty frequently from the habits of the breeding pair, may well have led to the different condition of the dorsal skin in the Surinam toad, *Pipa Americana.* The skin of the female in the breeding season becomes soft and swollen, and the eggs are embedded one by one by the male in this soft skin, which soon closes over, so that each egg is contained in a separate cell.

CHAPTER IV

FISHES

In considering the sexual dimorphism of birds or mammals we are dealing with a number of species in all of which (omitting in mammals the Monotremata, which are peculiar) the method of reproduction is the same. In mammals the male is provided with a penis entirely separate from the rectum, and by means of this organ the semen is introduced into the female uterus. The fertilised ova develop within the uterus, and the young are born alive. In birds the penis is less specialised, but fertilisation is likewise internal. The fertilised ova, however, do not develop within the body of the mother, they are provided with yolk, albumen and shell, and then extruded. The great diversity that exists in both these classes with regard to the specialisation of unisexual characters shows that the degree of this specialisation does not correspond to peculiarities in the method of reproduction or fertilisation.

When we consider the various kinds of fishes we find great diversity in the methods of reproduction, and at the same time less diversity in the specialisation of unisexual characters than in the case of birds. In fishes sexual dimorphism is not necessarily associated with any one method of reproduction. The chief aim of this work is to point out that the degree of sexual dimorphism corresponds

with the degree of difference between the habits and mode of
life of the male and female, and such differences may arise
in many different ways. They may arise from courtship or
combat, or from circumstances unconnected with either of
these habits.

Some fishes are viviparous, and in these, of course, fertilisation is internal. An example of this is furnished by
Acanthias vulgaris, the Spiny Dog-fish, among the Elasmobranchs. Some Teleosteans are also viviparous, for example
the Cyprinoodonts, and the Viviparous Blenny. In all the
Elasmobranchs fertilisation is internal, those which are not
viviparous laying large eggs similar in size and structure to
those of birds. Among Teleosteans, however, fertilisation is
usually external, with the exception of the few species which
are viviparous. Yet external fertilisation is not incompatible
with sexual dimorphism. Where, as in the case of the
Herring, the males and females swim promiscuously in shoals
discharging their reproductive elements, sexual dimorphism
does not exist. But in many other cases the males exhibit
special habits and actions related to special modes of effecting
external fertilisation, or protecting the eggs. In such cases
the eggs are more commonly rather large, heavy or adhesive,
as in the Lump-sucker and the Gobies. Among the numerous
marine species whose eggs are small and "pelagic," *i.e.*
buoyant in sea-water, special habits connected with the
fertilisation or protection of the eggs are not generally
developed, and sexual dimorphism is not common. But in
one such species, the Dragonet, *Callionymus lyra*, the sexual
peculiarities of the male are very marked, and they correspond
to very peculiar habits of sexual co-operation in the shedding
and fertilisation of the ova. Other cases of sexual dimorphism associated with the production of pelagic ova are known,
but the habits to which they correspond have not in all been
yet observed.

ELASMOBRANCHS.—Darwin states that the "claspers" of Elasmobranchs serve to retain the female. It is known from one observation in the aquarium that they are really intromittent organs, inserted in copulation into the cloaca and oviducts of the female, but whether their function in this position is rather to hold the female, or to convey the semen into the female organs, is open to question. The claspers are great enlargements and modifications of the hinder parts of the pelvic fins, and such modification is entirely wanting in the females. They are only fully developed in mature males. Owing to the complicated muscular and skeletal apparatus they contain, it seems evident that they exercise a powerful dilating action on the oviducts and cloaca, and although the necessity of such muscular power is difficult to understand, the fact of its exertion agrees well with the view that the claspers owe their evolution to the functional activity of the muscles concerned in the act of copulation.

In the Rays the males have special spines which are absent in the females. They are situated on the dorsal side, some at the outer margin of the head, but more on the pectoral fins, a little distance from the extremities of these. They are rather long, simply bent or hooked, and very sharp. They are set in somewhat irregular longitudinal rows, and can be erected or depressed at the will of the fish. When depressed, they lie close to the skin, and may easily escape observation. These spines are stated by Darwin to be only developed during the breeding season, but I do not know on what authority.

In *Raia clavata* the teeth of the adult male are sharp-pointed and directed backwards, while those of the female are broad and flat, forming a pavement. In the young male the teeth are flat, like those of the female. Darwin suggests that the sharp teeth of the males may be used for fighting or for holding the female. It is more probable that the former is the true function.

In another British species, *Raia microcellata*, the teeth are in the same condition as in *R. clavata*, flat in the females and young males, pointed in adult males.

In *R. maculata* the teeth are pointed in both sexes, and also in *R. radiata* and *R. circularis*.

In the long-snouted species, or Skates, the teeth are pointed in both sexes, although more so in the male in the case of *Raia batis*, the Common or Blue Skate.

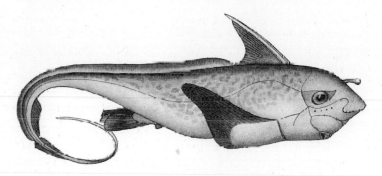

FIG. 19—*Chimæra monstrosa*, male. After Day.

It is difficult to explain these facts on Lamarckian principles, especially because we know so little of the habits of the living fish. We cannot maintain that the teeth are naturally flat, and only pointed in the males as a consequence of their use in fighting. It is a more plausible suggestion that in the females and young males of certain species they have become flattened, because the fish have acquired the habit of feeding on hard-shelled animals, namely molluscs and crustacea. The pointed teeth of the males, on this theory, might be due to their use in fighting. But then the question arises, how the effect of the use of the teeth in fighting could counteract the use of the teeth in feeding, unless we get over the difficulty by supposing that the adult males change their diet.

CHIMÆROIDS.—In *Chimœra* the sexual peculiarities of the males are highly specialised. The hinder part of the ventral fin forms a complicated intromittent organ of large size, and in addition to this there is in front of the same fin a flat projection provided with two curved spines, which is evidently used for holding the female. On the head there is further a remarkable knobbed and curved spine projecting forwards, and covered at its extremity with sharp denticles. There can be no doubt that this also is used for holding the female, although the exact mode in which it is used has not been observed.

The intromittent appendages of Elasmobranchs, and the various sexual appendages of male Chimæroids above described, differ from most of the cases previously discussed among the higher vertebrates in their antiquity and their uniformity throughout the orders. At the same time, there is no insuperable obstacle to regarding them as probably evolved in accordance with Lamarckian principles. The use of part of the pelvic fins as intromittent organs may well have been, at the very distant period when these fishes acquired their characters, the origin of the so-called claspers or pterygopodia. It has been suggested that the frontal clasper of the male Chimæroid is a modification of an anterior fin-spine; but as it is covered with skin and separate denticles, it is quite possible that it was formed independently by the use of the skin in this region. In this case we cannot reason with such a good basis as in that of the antlers of stags, because the habits of the living *Chimœra* are so little known.

TELEOSTEI—SUB-ORDER PHYSOSTOMI—*Siluridœ*.—Darwin refers to the sexual differences in *Plecostomus barbatus*, which lives in the fresh waters of South America, as described by

Dr. Günther.[1] In the male the mouth and interopercular bones are fringed with spines, of which the female shows hardly a trace. I cannot discuss this case, because I know nothing of the habits of the fish, or the function of the spines. In another species of the same genus soft tentacles are present on the front part of the head of the male, absent in the female.

Salmonidæ.—Male salmon fight constantly and violently with one another, and the turning up and enlargement of the tip of the lower jaw appears to be the result of the blows inflicted against the bodies of rivals. This growth of the lower jaw, like the antlers of stags, is present only during the breeding season. Darwin quotes Mr. Lloyd's testimony that the temporary hook-like structure serves to strengthen and protect the jaws when one male charges another with wonderful violence. We have here a mechanical violence and irritation which, as in the case of the antlers of stags, is evidently capable of producing to some extent in the individual the modification of structure, whose evolution we have to explain.

Cyprinodontidæ.—In many of the species of this family very distinct sexual differences occur. Darwin mentions only two species, namely *Mollienisia petenensis,* in the male of which the dorsal fin is enlarged and marked with ocelli, and *Xiphophorus Hellerii,* in the male of which the inferior margin of the caudal fin is developed into a long filament. S. Garman has recently published a memoir[2] on the Cyprinodonts, in which the characters of all the species are described, but the habits of the fish in life are not discussed in detail. In many of the genera the front portion of the anal fin is elongated and modified to form an intromittent organ for the milt, so that fertilisation is internal, and the young are born alive. In *Mollienisia* the anal fin of the

---

[1] *Proc. Zool. Soc.* 1868, p. 232.

[2] *Mem. Mus. Comp. Zool. Harv.*, vol. xix. No. 1.

male is thus modified, but is not tubular. Nothing is stated as to the use of the enlarged dorsal in the male. In young males the dorsal fin is not longer than that of the female. Similar remarks apply to *Xiphophorus,* in which also the modified portion of the anal is not tubular. In each case, the peculiarity of the dorsal or caudal in the male *may* be of special use in producing the proper movements of the body for the purpose of copulation.

The non-tubular modification of the anal fin in males occurs also in the sub-family Gambusiinæ, as well as in many other genera placed with *Mollienisia* and *Xiphophorus* in the sub-family Pœciliinæ. Observations on the copulation of *Gambusia* are mentioned by Ryder in his paper on the development of this form; the male is stated to have his head turned towards the tail of the female, and as the intromittent organ slopes backwards, this position would seem necessary; it may be suspected that the ventral edges of the pair are turned towards each other, otherwise it is difficult to understand how the projection of the fin is inserted into the female opening. In *Gambusia* and its allies, however, the males have no very important peculiarities in addition to the intromittent organ. In nearly all cases they are much smaller and less numerous than the females.

In *Jenynsia* and *Anableps* a tube continued from the urinogenital ducts runs down the front of the elongated portion of the anal fin, and thus forms a more specialised intromittent organ. In both cases copulation evidently takes place sideways, as there is a difference between the two sides of the copulatory organs which enables specimens to be distinguished as rights and lefts. Both rights and lefts occur, however, in each sex; the males are not all rights, and females all lefts, or *vice versa.*

In *Anableps* the structure of the anal, after its modification, which is not developed until some time after birth, is such as to allow a very limited motion downward, but much greater freedom of movement sideways. In the posterior half of the organ a bend is made either to the right or the left. Of 17 males, the bend was to the right on 11, to the left on 6. There is also a small fleshy tubercle at the side of the seventh or the sixth anal ray, at the middle of its length. When this prominence is on the left side, the organ bends to the right; when it is on the right, the bend is to the left. The urinogenital tube lies on the concave side of the bend. In the female a large scale covers the opening of the ovary and ureters. This scale may be called a shutter, or foricula. It is attached at one side and free at the other, the opening being to the right in some specimens, to the left in others. Thirty-four females were lefts, twenty-one rights: thus the proportion is the opposite of that found in the males, in accordance with the requirement that right males should copulate with left females, and *vice versa*.

In all these adaptations everything is in harmony with the theory that their evolution is due to gradual hypertrophy and modification due to the use made of the parts. The selection theory assumes that the necessary slight modifications have occurred, but we have no reason for believing that such necessary variations ever came into existence until the irritations caused by the habitual act of copulation produced them.

Cyprinidæ.—In many of the Cyprinidæ or Carp family, wart-like tubercles are developed in the male during the breeding season, chiefly on the head, but sometimes all over the body and fins. These disappear when the annual spawning has been accomplished. That these dermal excrescences are dependent upon mechanical irritations there can be no reasonable doubt, and there can also be no doubt that they are now hereditary. Fatio[1] and several other

---

[1] *Faune des vertébrés de la Suisse*, vol. iv. 1882.

authors have described the violent rushes and leaps of male
Cyprinoids when spawning is about to take place. Fatio
writes of the common freshwater bream, *Abramis brama*, as
follows:—" Les jeux de l'amour de ce Cyprin sont excessive-
ment tapageurs, et l'on entend souvent de très loin le vacarme
que font à la surface les bandes de Brèmes dans leur délire
amoureux. Ce sont des courses effrénées, des contorsions
variées, de puissants coups de queue lancés en tous sens, et
des baisements à fleur d'eau. Plusieurs mâles poursuivent
généralement une seule femelle." It is not evident from
this that the males intentionally push each other with their
heads, but in such manœuvres they must be continually
striking their heads against each other, or against the females,
or against the weeds, and Lunel,[1] in the case of *Alburnus
lucidus* and other species, speaks of the rubbing of the fish
against each other. On the other hand, the tubercles are
not described as present in the Tench, and this fish performs
its spawning quietly. In most species of the family the
males are distinguished by an enlargement, or swelling, of
the anterior rays of the pectorals, especially in the spawning
season; in the Tench by a thickening of the second ray of
the pelvic fin. These modifications also are doubtless due to
special exertions of the organs.

Murænidæ.—In the Murænidæ the chief sexual difference
is the small size of the male in comparison with the female.
Whether this is true throughout the family I do not know;
I am only able to give particulars concerning the two British
species, the Conger and the Freshwater Eel. No male congers
have been described which were more than 2 feet 6 inches in
length, and the weight of the largest would scarcely exceed
1 lb. Females, on the other hand, frequently exceed 5 feet
in length, and one has been recorded which measured 8 feet
3 inches in length, and weighed 128 lbs. Specimens weigh-

---

[1] *Poissons du bassin du Leman*, Geneve, 1874.

ing 50 lbs. and upwards are not uncommon. This refers to specimens captured in the sea. Ripe males have frequently been obtained by keeping specimens alive in aquaria, but the females always die before they are quite ripe. The weight of such nearly ripe females after death is much less than the weight of large specimens newly captured, and this is not surprising when we consider that the female in the aquarium takes no food when her ovaries begin to ripen, and continues to fast for about six months before she dies. The weights of gravid females, examined at the Plymouth Laboratory, varied from 16 lbs. to 33 lbs.; the lengths from 4 feet 6 inches to 5 feet 4 inches.

The ripe male in the aquarium was observed to differ from the young female in three slight peculiarities: (1) the snout was blunter and flatter; (2) the eyes appeared larger in proportion to the head; (3) the ventral surface was somewhat pigmented.[1]

It is difficult to offer any explanation of the small size of the male conger. The testes are not small in proportion to the body as in the male sole, on the contrary when ripe they distend the body cavity, as in the case of the male herring. It is easy to argue that the large size of the female is necessary to supply nourishment to the immense number of ova which she produces, but that does not show what conditions of life and growth have given rise to the difference of size between the sexes. It is possible, though not yet proved, that the difference is not so much rate of growth, as time of growth, the male becoming mature at an early age. The male salmon is known to become mature sometimes when only a few inches long; but then he grows afterwards, while the conger, whether male or female, ceases to grow when the generative organs begin to mature, and dies

[1] Cunningham, "Reproduction and Development of the Conger," *Journ. Mar. Biol. Assoc.*, vol. ii. 1892.

after the generative products have been once discharged. The increased size of the eyes in the mature male may be due to the greater use made of the organs, the ripe male perhaps ceasing to conceal himself and swimming about actively in search of the female.

A similar difference in size occurs in the Eel. The largest male eel described did not exceed 19 inches in length, while females, when adult, are from 27 to 39 inches long. Eels only become sexually mature in the sea, and like the conger die after breeding once. According to Grassi and Calandruccio, the discoverers of the *Leptocephalus* larva of the eel, the eyes are larger in mature eels, both male and female, than in the immature specimens which inhabit fresh water.

SUB-ORDER ANACANTHINI.—*Pleuronectidæ.*—In this family the males are invariably smaller than the females. This fact can be demonstrated in two ways : (*a*) by ascertaining the average size of a large number of males and a large number of females caught on grounds frequented by the adults of both sexes ; (*b*) by ascertaining the size of the smallest mature and largest immature specimens of both sexes, and the proportion of mature and immature specimens at intermediate sizes. Thus in the northern part of the North Sea the smallest mature female plaice were 13 in. long, the smallest mature males, 9 in. The largest immature females were 18 in. long, the largest immature males 16 in. According to Dr. Fulton the ratio of the average length of female plaice to that of males was 114 to 100, of turbot 118 to 100.

This difference of size is the opposite to that which occurs frequently in mammals and birds, and cannot be attributed to a general inferiority of size in the male sex. On the other hand, it is difficult to discover a reason for the larger size of female fishes, although the larger size of male mammals and birds can be attributed to their combats, etc. There is no reason to suppose that sexual selection takes

place, that either the smallest male or the largest female has
the best chance of finding a mate and leaving progeny.
Darwin gave the evidence he collected in support of the
conclusion that the males were more numerous than the
females, but in the flat fishes Fulton's researches have shown
that the females are much more numerous than the males,
and there is no reason to suppose that the males prefer or
select the largest females. It may be suggested that the
largest females leave most eggs, and that, therefore, there is a
tendency to increase in the size of the females, but this would
not explain why the females should be larger than the males,
for the males would inherit the large size of their mothers.

The difference in the size of body in the sexes may very
possibly be connected with the difference in the size of the
generative organs; the milts in the Pleuronectidæ are generally
small in comparison with the size of the body, while the
ovaries are very large. But at present I am unable to see
how, on Lamarckian principles, the difference could have been
produced, and the selection principle appears to fail equally
in this case.

Other unisexual characters occur in the Pleuronectidæ.
One of considerable interest exists in the Plaice. In this
species the scales are for the most part reduced and rudimentary, scarcely projecting from the skin, and having no
spines on the posterior edges like the scales of the dab or the
sole. But in the males, when they attain to sexual maturity,
spinules develop in connection with the scales on certain
parts of the body. This spinulation occurs in all individuals,
with few exceptions, on the middle fin-rays of the dorsal and
ventral fins; when developed to a higher degree it occurs on
the head and operculum also, or, in addition, on the upper
side of the body in the region of the interspinous bones, or
over the whole of the upper side, and to a less degree on the
lower side. The higher degrees of the character are not

developed in the plaice of the English Channel, but become more common towards the north, namely, north of the Dogger Bank and on the south coast of Iceland. In the Baltic the spinulation is very strongly developed.

In Arctic waters there occurs a species which must be considered as the geographical representative of the Plaice, and the latter is absent from the same waters except where the ranges of the two forms meet one another. This is the form originally described as *Pleuronectes glacialis* by Pallas. It is distinguished from the Plaice chiefly by the fact that there are no prominent tubercles on the lateral ridge of the head behind the eyes; the ridge is rough and nearly continuous. Pallas' specimens came from the Kara Sea and the mouth of the river Obi, and he did not mention any sexual differences; the upper side had rough scales. On the east coast of the United States, where the Plaice is absent, occurs a species considered to be identical with the *glacialis* of Pallas, in which the American ichthyologists have found that the males have spinulated or ctenoid scales, while in the females the scales on the upper side are smooth, with the edges entire. On the coast of Alaska specimens have been taken referable to the same species, but the females were spinulated. We have no information concerning sexual differences in specimens obtained from the north coasts of Europe, Asia, and America. It is certain, therefore, that a sexual difference similar to that existing in the Plaice occurs in the *Pl. glacialis* of the east coast of North America, while in specimens of the same form from more northern localities and from the coast of Alaska, the spinulation appears to occur in the females as well as in the males.

Special developments of spinulation have not been observed to occur in the males in other species of Pleuronectidæ, and there seems therefore little reason for supposing that in the Plaice the character is a mere expression or result of constitutional conditions associated with maturity in the male sex. We might suppose that the spines have no special function and confer no advantage, but that the degeneration of the scales has proceeded further in the female than in the male, just as it seems that the loss of hair on the body is more complete in the female than in the male of the human species. On this view it is difficult to understand why the spines are absent in the young males, and only appear at sexual maturity. This, again, is paralleled by the history of the beard and moustache in man.

At present we do not know that the spinulation of the scales in the male plaice performs any function in the relations of the sexes or in the life of the male, and therefore it is impossible to suggest any kind of irritation or stimulation which might be regarded as the cause of the character. Observations have been made on the spawning of soles in the aquarium of the Laboratory of the Marine Biological Association at Plymouth, but they did not support the supposition that there is any definite apposition of the bodies of male and female in the process of spawning. Mr. Butler, who watched the spawning soles, states [1] that the eggs appeared to be shed one at a time, each after a particular movement, the fish raising its head and bringing it down again with force on the sand. It seemed that this movement wafted the egg towards the tail, because a single egg commonly appeared above the tail of a fish after its performance. The actual exit of either ovum or milt was never observed. The soles lay about on the sand indiscriminately. One of them would from time to time move leisurely to another place, and in passing by or over a companion would take notice of it by feeling it with the lower side of its head, where the tactile filaments are situated, but this never led to anything of the nature of pairing, the fish would again move on and continue

[1] *Journal Mar. Biol. Assoc.*, vol. iv. No. 1, p. 5.

the spawning process elsewhere, apparently regardless of the exact position of the others. Fertilisation, therefore, in this case, seems to occur quite independently of any special position or action of male and female in relation to one another, and to be due to mere proximity or congregation. The actual spawning took place, not at night, but between 12 noon and 4 P.M. In this respect the sole differs from the plaice, the spawn of which is shed, in the Dunbar hatchery, according to Mr. Harald Dannevig, the manager of the establishment, usually between dusk and midnight.

There are other species in which the scales have degenerated, and in which no differences in their condition occur in the two sexes. This is the case in the Turbot, and also in the Flounder. In the Turbot one scale here and there has become enlarged into a bony tubercle, with a projecting point, while all the rest of the scales have vanished. In the Flounder, at least in the more southern part of its habitat, the scales over the greater part of the body are much reduced, while along the bases of the marginal fins and along the lateral line they have been enlarged into thorny tubercles, each provided with several points.

In the genus *Arnoglossus* the males are distinguished from the females by several differences, of which the most definite and conspicuous is the elongation of certain of the fin-rays. This is true at least for the species *A. laterna*, which has been minutely studied by several naturalists in recent years. As in many other cases, the two sexes were at first described under different names as two distinct species. Specimens in which the secondary sexual characters are not developed had long been described among British fishes under the name *A. laterna*. The characters of this form are seen in Fig. 20 A, drawn from a specimen 4 inches in length. The fish in this form is frequently taken in the trawl on our south-west coasts, and is a small left-sided flat-fish of no value in the market, commonly known as the Scald-fish or Scald-back, from the

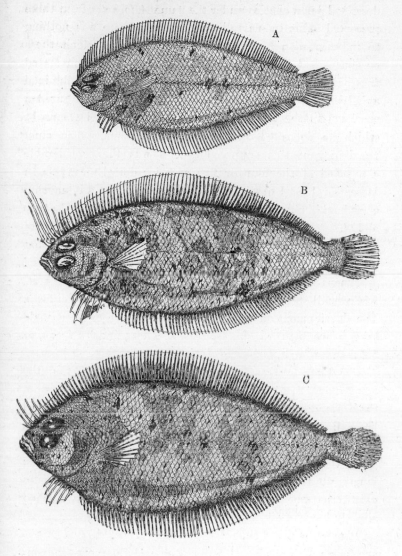

FIG. 20.—*Arnoglossus laterna*, A, immature, B, mature male; C, mature female.

fact that the skin is so delicate that it is usually torn or

partially removed during capture. In 1862[1] Dr. Günther
described a new species under the name *A. lophotes,* from three
preserved skins in Yarrell's collection. There was nothing
to indicate with certainty the locality from which these
specimens had been obtained, but in 1864 J. Couch stated
that he had examined a specimen of the same form obtained
at Plymouth, and in 1882 Professor Moseley captured a
specimen in the trawl off Lundy Island (Bristol Channel),
which he deposited in the British Museum. The chief
peculiarity of this supposed species was the considerable
elongation of the four or five anterior dorsal fin-rays. In
December 1889 I obtained from the trawlers at Plymouth a
considerable number of mature specimens both of *A. lophotes*
and *A. laterna,* and was struck with the great similarity of
the two forms in most of their characters. I soon found that
all typical specimens of the *lophotes* form were male, and all
specimens above a certain size of the *laterna* form were female,
while small specimens of both sexes were of the *laterna* form.
The development of the peculiarities of the mature male
takes place between the lengths 13·2 cm. and 14·7 cm., or
5·2 inches to 5·8 inches.

The other differences between the *lophotes* form and the
laterna, on which Dr. Günther relied, were the greater size of
the eye and the shorter maxillary bone in the former, and
these differences were found to exist in the specimens which
I compared.

In the larger female specimens, more than 13·2 cm. in
length, an incipient development of the male peculiarities
exists, the second, third, fourth, and fifth dorsal rays being
slightly longer than the sixth.

It must be noted that the reason for concluding that the
specimens with elongated rays are older and larger specimens
of the species *A. laterna,* is not that specimens without the

[1] *Catalogue of Fishes,* iv. p. 417.

elongation of the rays never exceed 5·2 inches in length, but that no specimens of either sex with the elongated rays have ever been found which are under that limit of length. If *A. lophotes* were a distinct species therefore, it would be a species of which no young specimens existed, an obvious *reductio ad absurdum.*

Mr. E. W. L. Holt[1] has recently found that sexual maturity occurs in specimens which are still in the undifferentiated condition, that is to say, specimens in which the anterior dorsal rays were not elongated were found to be sexually mature, both males and females. In June, in Teignmouth Bay and Tor Bay, Mr. Holt obtained ripe ova and milt from five females 5½ to 6½ inches long, and three males 5 to 5¼ inches long. The ova were artificially fertilised, and went through the process of segmentation. They died, however, before the embryo was formed, which may possibly be an indication that the ova and milt were not perfectly mature. Later, in July, the same naturalist obtained ova and milt from "differentiated" specimens over 6 inches long. The eggs are pelagic, and have an oil globule, and the few that were measured showed that the eggs of the smaller females were smaller than those of the larger. It is known, however, that smaller female fish of a species may have slightly smaller eggs than the larger, and the measurements were not numerous enough to show that the difference in the size of the oil globule was constant. That the males should be mature, or should at least produce milt before the secondary peculiarities are fully developed, is by no means an exceptional occurrence; in fact, it has been observed in many other cases, among birds, for example, and it is also true in many mammals. It is a general truth that unisexual male characters do not attain their full development till after puberty, and that they only begin to develop at puberty.

[1] *Jour. Mar. Biol. Assoc.,* vol. v. No. 1.

A more remarkable suggestion made by Mr. Holt in reference to this subject is the following: *A. laterna* may confidently be considered to exist in the Mediterranean, being in all probability identical with the *A. conspersus* of the Mediterranean ichthyologists. It is certain that a specimen of the *lophotes* form was sent to Dr. Günther from Palermo. Specimens of the *laterna* form have been taken on the south-west coast of Norway, but none of the *lophotes* form have been mentioned from that region. Mr. Holt suggests, therefore, that the differentiated or *lophotes* form is never developed on the coast of Norway, but that the fish remains permanently, and reproduces, in the *laterna* form. This conclusion rests only on negative evidence, and is, in my own opinion, improbable. The *lophotes* form appeared for many years to be a rarity in British waters, and, considering how little the trawl is used in Norwegian waters, it would seem more probable that specimens in this condition could be captured off the Norwegian coast if sufficient endeavours were made to obtain them. It will probably be found, if an opportunity ever occurs of observing the habits of the fish when spawning, that the elongation of the anterior dorsal fin-rays is associated with habitual erection or vibration of these rays during sexual excitement, as in the Dragonet.

An elongation of certain fin-rays occurs as a unisexual male character also in *Pseudorhombus ocellatus*, as described by Dr. Günther in his *Report on the Shore Fishes of the Challenger Expedition* (vol. i., 1880). The description is as follows: " The dorsal fin commences above the nostrils, is not scaly, and terminates close to the caudal, its anterior rays being shorter than the middle ones. In the male the thirteenth to nineteenth rays of the dorsal and the seven anterior of the anal are prolonged into long filaments." The specimens were obtained outside Nares Harbour, in the Admiralty Islands, at a depth of 152 fathoms. It is curious in this case that, although the elongated rays in the anal (or ventral) fin are the most anterior, the rays of the dorsal which are elongated are not the most anterior, but are situated some distance behind the commencement of the fin, and opposite to the elongated rays of the ventral. This fact tends to support the view that the elongation is due to some special stimulation of the particular fin-rays, not to a general tendency in the most anterior rays to elongation. In this case we know nothing of the habits of the fish, or of the way in which it moves its rays. But if there is some special stimulation which in this case has acted on the thirteenth to nineteenth dorsal rays, and in other cases on the anterior dorsal rays, the observed condition is explained, whereas we cannot believe that selection from among the variations which occur in the dorsal fin of other flat fishes—for instance, Sole, Plaice, or Flounder—could have produced such a modification.

Elongated fin-rays occur in two other species described in the same report, but do not appear to be confined to one sex. One of these is *Rhomboidichthys angustifrons*. In the single specimen obtained the anterior dorsal rays were produced, and were nearly detached from the adjacent rays. The sex of the specimen is not mentioned; it was obtained at 30 fathoms in the Arafura Sea. In *Lophonectes gallus* the five anterior dorsal rays are prolonged in both sexes, but the adult males were distinguished by another character, namely, the presence of pointed tubercles on the snout, two on the sides, one at the mandibular symphysis. Specimens of this species were obtained off Port Jackson in the Bass Straits, at a depth of 30 fathoms.

SUB - ORDER ACANTHOPTERYGII. — *Sparidæ.* — There are many families in this Order in which no conspicuous sexual differences are present. *Cantharus lineatus*, the Black Sea-bream, requires to be considered, because its behaviour during the breeding season has been observed by

Saville Kent,[1] and is mentioned by Darwin. " Before the breeding season both sexes were of a delicate silvery blue, varied by irregular lines of pale yellow, a hue scarcely in harmony with the popular name of ' Black Bream.' The light colours disappeared in the breeding condition, or rather were replaced by a prevailing shade of deep leaden black, deepest on the back, but spreading over the whole surface of the fish, except a few transverse lighter bands in the region of the abdomen. The males in particular are most conspicuous for this change, and these retiring from the remainder of the shoal select certain separate and prescribed areas at the bottom of the tank, where they commence excavating considerable hollows in the sand or shingle by the rapid and powerful action of the tail and lower portion of the body. A depression of suitable size having been produced, each male now mounts vigilant guard over his respective hollow, and vigorously attacks and drives away any other fish of the same sex. Towards his companions of the opposite sex his conduct is far different. Many of the latter are now distended with spawn, and these he endeavours, by all the means in his power, to lure singly to his prepared hollow, and there to deposit the myriad ova with which they are laden, which he then protects and guards with the greatest care. Whether the aggregated produce of a large number of females is thus consigned to one bed, and whether the ova are guarded by the male until the young fish make their appearance, are points which, while awaiting confirmation, may be almost confidently inferred, reasoning from the very analogous nest-forming habits of the Gasterosteidæ." Raffaele, on the contrary, although he did not separately identify the eggs of *Cantharus lineatus*, believes that those of this species, and probably of all the species in the family, are pelagic. If this be correct, the behaviour described by Saville Kent was only

[1] *Nature*, May 1873.

directed to the fertilisation of the eggs, and not to the subsequent protection of them by the male. It might be asked, if the views maintained by me are correct, why have not the actions of the male *Cantharus* produced corresponding structural modifications similar to those described below in *Callionymus lyra*. In reply to this, it may be pointed out that the male *Cantharus* is not stated to perform such definite and vigorous gestures of courtship as the *Callionymus*. The change of colour which takes place in the former is to be attributed, as in the latter, to the increased production of pigment in the skin under the influence of the nervous excitement associated with the sexual instinct.

Scorpænidæ-Sebastes norvegicus, sometimes known as the Norway Haddock, is a strongly spined species belonging to the Scorpænidæ. Specimens have occasionally been taken on the east coasts of Scotland and England. This species is viviparous, the female producing about a thousand living young. Fertilisation must consequently be internal, but no secondary sexual differences appear to have been described, nor has the process of fertilisation been observed. This case appears, therefore, to be an illustration of the fact, sufficiently obvious in many mammals and birds, that internal fertilisation does not necessarily involve sexual dimorphism.

Gobiidæ.—The Dragonet, *Callionymus lyra*, is usually placed in the family Gobiidæ. The fact that it has pelagic ova, while those of the species of *Gobius* are adhesive, is in itself no objection to this classification; as in other families, *e.g.* Clupeidæ, some species have adhesive ova and others pelagic. The adult male dragonet differs so much in appearance from the adult female that it was at one time described as a distinct species, under the name *C. lyra*, the female being named *C. dracunculus*. The peculiarities of the male consist chiefly in its vivid colouring and the great elongation of the first dorsal fin. The second dorsal and the ventral (anal) fins are

also elongated to a less extent posteriorly. The male is
larger than the female. We might infer by analogy that the
male in this species practises definite habits and gestures of
courtship, and Mr. Saville Kent proved that this was the case
by observations, of which he gave a description in *Nature* in
1873 (vol. viii. p. 264). His remarks are quoted by Darwin
in his *Descent of Man, etc.*, p. 336. Mr. Saville Kent also
describes the process of pairing of these fishes in one of the
Handbooks of the International Fisheries Exhibition (vol. i.,
1883, p. 128). The account there given is as follows :—

" The male, resplendent in his bridal livery, swims leisurely
round the female, who is reclining quietly on the sand, his
opercula distended, his glittering dorsal fins erect, and his every
effort being concentrated upon the endeavour to attract the
attention and fascinate the affections of his mate. . . . The
female, at first indifferent, becomes at length evidently dazzled
by his resplendent attire and the persistency of his wooing.
She rises to meet him, the pair—so far as is practicable with
fishes—rush into each other's arms, and with their ventral
areas closely applied ascend perpendicularly towards the
surface of the water. In connection with these manœuvres,
it may be safely predicted that the ova are extruded and
fertilised, but in the limited depth of water of an aquarium
tank the matrimonial tour cannot apparently be sufficiently
prolonged to ensure the consummation of this act, the fish,
after reaching the surface, being projected by their previously-
gained impetus slightly above it, when, falling apart, they
sink slowly to the bottom, and the process, after short intervals, is repeated."

My friend, Mr. E. W. L. Holt, has recently been able to
make a careful investigation of the phenomena in the Marine
Biological Laboratory at Plymouth, and has published an
excellent account of his observations in *Proc. Zool. Soc.* of
April 19, 1898. From Mr. Holt's paper I take the facts

of the case, but for the interpretations I offer I am alone
responsible.

In the female, throughout life, the first dorsal fin is very
short in a vertical direction. The second dorsal and the
ventral fins are of moderate proportions, their posterior rays,
when depressed, not extending to the caudal fin. The borders
of the genital aperture are not produced into an elongated
papilla. The colours of the dorsal surface are brown or
reddish-brown, barred and mottled with lighter and darker
markings, and assimilating in tint to the ground on which
the fish may be resting. In young specimens on bright gravel
the general colour may be diversified with purple, green, and
crimson. The ventral surface is white.

The young male and young female resemble the adult
female. The male, when it becomes mature, undergoes marked
changes in several of its characters. The snout becomes more
elongated. The first dorsal fin is much prolonged vertically,
the first ray longest, the posterior successively shorter. The
second dorsal and the ventral fins increase in size, the posterior
rays especially elongating, till, when depressed, they reach
beyond the base of the caudal fin. There is a distinct
genital papilla, visible even in specimens only 2 inches in
length, but longest in mature fish. The metamorphosis takes
place gradually, and its completion is not constantly related
to a particular size, nor to the attainment of sexual maturity;
that is to say, as in many other cases, male specimens are
often sexually mature before the secondary characters have
attained their maximum development. A striking change in
coloration also occurs. While the back retains the marbled
brown markings, the front and sides of the head, the sides of
the body, and the pelvic, dorsal, and caudal fins become
decorated with bands of bright blue and yellow. The eye,
reddish-brown or cupreous in females and young males,
becomes, in large breeding males, of a brilliant metallic blue-

green. On the ventral surface, the throat, the lower side of the pelvics, and the ventral fin acquire some black pigment, the ventral occasionally showing a bluish tinge in addition. The colour change in the eye seems to be limited to the breeding season. The other colours are more permanent, but their brilliance, especially that of the yellow, is much more intense during the breeding season. It was found that the special coloration of the male was much more directly connected with the maturity of the genital organs than the structural differentiation. The smallest sexually mature male was $6\frac{1}{4}$ inches long, and had the blue and yellow coloration well, though not completely, developed, and the structural peculiarities well marked. A larger but sexually immature male, $7\frac{3}{16}$ inches long, although its dorsal fin was much elongated, showed none of the special coloration. The male is distinctly larger than the female, being stated to reach a length of 1 foot (30 cm.), while the female does not reach 10 inches (25 cm.). The difference in size is partly due to the greater length of the snout and caudal fin in the male.

Mr. Holt's observations were made upon specimens living in a glass-fronted tank, of which the bottom was covered with fine light-coloured gravel. A number of females and small undifferentiated males were living in this tank in the winter of 1897-98, and two fine fully developed males were introduced in January 1898. Until February 11, all the dragonets were quiet in their movements, and the adult males were not observed to display their dorsal fins. On the date mentioned, and every following day till February 19, the pairing repeatedly occurred. When it was going on all the dragonets gave signs of unusual excitement, but the chief actors were the two adult males. These kept darting along the bottom of the tank at short intervals, at the same time displaying their special characters. The dorsal fins were erected sometimes before the fish made its rush, oftener at the moment of starting, and at the same time the jaws were protruded to the utmost, the gill-covers were expanded, and the pelvic fins held rigidly forward and outward. The fish in this movement scarcely left the ground, the anal fins being depressed and invisible. The movement was produced by the pectoral and caudal fins, sometimes by a stroke of the whole tail. The yellow bands were more brilliant than before the commencement of sexual activity, but did not change with the erection of the dorsal fins, and became less brilliant after the first few days. The blue bands on the sides flashed out with intense brilliance as the fins were erected, but became paler again before they were lowered; these bands also became less vivid after the first few days.

The rushes of the male fish were sometimes not directed to a special object; sometimes, if females or young males were near, the adult male darted at them, and they fled away from him. Occasionally the two males met in full display, and then one lowered his fins and swam hastily away. Only one female at first was breeding; she was 6¾ inches long. She showed no signs of great excitement. When one of the males approached her, he seemed to recognise her sex and condition, gliding past her or circling in front of her, or sometimes resting still in front of her with all his finery displayed.

The behaviour described was evidently an invitation to the female; when she was willing she swam to the side of the male, who immediately lowered his fins and retracted his jaws and gill-covers. The two swam slowly side by side along the ground, the male raised the fore-part of his body by the action of his pectorals, and the female placed one of her pelvics on that of the male, and pressed as close as possible into the hollow between his gill-cover and lateral fins. The hinder part of the second dorsal and ventral fins in the male were erected, and the whole of these fins in the female. The male then slowly raised himself and his partner into a vertical position, and the two ascended towards the surface of the water. In this movement the male used chiefly his pectorals, aided by the caudal and the hinder parts of the second dorsal and the ventral. The first dorsal of the male was now depressed, and lay extended along the back. The female moved her pectorals slightly, and occasionally her caudal, but the male appeared actually to carry the female up through the water.

As the pair ascended, their ventral surfaces were slightly inclined to each other, so that the edges of their anal fins were in contact for some distance. The elongated genital papilla of the male was turned towards the female, and the ova were probably discharged through the space bo tween the ventral fins, and fertilised by the milt which was emitted in the same direction. The discharge of the ova and milt could not be actually seen, the ova are very small and transparent, and milt would not necessarily be seen in small quantities. It is certain that ova were emitted and fertilised in the tank during the period when the observations were made, as they were obtained by placing a fine net at the overflow of the tank, and were hatched in separate jars.

The ascent of the pair of fish was very slow. When they reached the surface the male and female sometimes separated at once, but more often continued together for a time, with their snouts bobbing out of the water. Sooner or later the two separated, and then darted rapidly to the bottom. Occasionally the male or the female ascended to the surface alone, but not often. The female in pairing sometimes took the right, sometimes the left side of the male.

During the first period reproductive activity lasted only eight days, and only one female was engaged. Pairing took place between 9 A.M. and noon, after which the males ceased to sport, and usually buried themselves in the gravel. At about 4 P.M. activity recommenced, but in a much less degree,

and no pairing was observed in the evening, at night, or early
in the morning.

Mr. Holt obtained additional specimens of the fish, and these
were placed in the same tank, from which all other kinds of
fish were removed to facilitate observation. The new females
obtained, however, seemed all to die. On March 8, sexual
activity again commenced. Only one female was engaged at
this period also, and if not the same individual which was
watched on the previous occasions, was of about the same size.
Besides the two males which paired in the previous month,
there were now three others with fully developed sexual
characters. None of the five were in very brilliant colour,
and one in particular, believed to belong to the original stock,
had lost nearly all the bright yellow of the bands on the body.

Mr. Holt watched the behaviour of these five males and
one female, to ascertain what evidence of selection on the
part of the female could be observed. Of the five males,
1 and 2 were large, 3 and 4 rather smaller, but as well
developed in colour and characters of the fins, 5 was large
but dull in colour. The last of these made no demonstrations,
he swam away from the others which approached him, and at
last buried himself in the gravel. The fourth was not seen
near the female. There were thus three males left which
showed sexual excitement. 1 was seen to ascend with the
female, they then descended to the ground near 2. The latter
displayed several times before the female, while 1 lay still,
breathing rapidly and taking no notice ; he was evidently
fatigued. The second male and the female took hold of each
other and began to ascend, when the first set up his fins and
darted under them, brushing their ventral surfaces with his
long first dorsal. But this had no effect on them, and they
made the ascent in the usual manner.

After this the first male was about to ascend with the
female again, when the third approached and displayed. The

first left his partner and erected his fins, etc., at the third. After a few demonstrations the first darted above the third, striking the first dorsal of the latter, which then fled, although no injury whatever was inflicted. A similar attack was observed on another occasion, but the defeat of the third male did not prevent him pairing successfully with the female alternately with his conqueror. It is thus evident enough that the peculiarities of the male cannot be ascribed to the selection of those individuals which possess them in greatest perfection. It is true that the observer in this case does not mention any difference in the special characters among the three males concerned, but he does note that the third male, which was smaller than 1 and 2, was equally successful in pairing. Mr. Holt "imagines" that the demonstrations of large, fully differentiated males would have the effect of driving off sexually mature specimens which were not so large, and whose insignia were not so fully developed. But he has no observations to support this belief, and if it were correct it would only be a case of *seniores priores*, the smaller specimens would become fully developed and pair with the females when their time came.

Males in the mature condition appear to be much more abundant than females. In one case Mr. Holt found that of the whole number of dragonets caught by a trawler, 95 were males and 21 females, and he has observed an excess of males in the course of his own trawling operations. This fact is worth noting in comparison with the numerical relations between the sexes in polygamous birds and other animals. In one case superiority in size, and special adornment, both of colour and structure, is found when each male has several wives; in the other, when there are several males to one female. The fact that is common to both cases is, that the male habitually makes particular gestures and movements under the influence of sexual excitement.

It is worth while to consider whether we can discover any special reason why the definite co-operation of male and female should be necessary for the fertilisation of the small buoyant ova of the Dragonet, while in other cases, such as that of the Cod, no such special pairing takes place. It seems evident from Mr. Holt's observations, and from the fact that the males are more numerous, that the milt of several males is required to fertilise the ova produced by one female. Each male, therefore, probably produces a very small quantity of milt at a time. But this is also the case in the Common Sole, in which Mr. Butler was unable to detect any signs of definite pairing during spawning in the aquarium. One explanation that suggests itself is, that dragonets have not the habit of congregation, but live scattered about at considerable intervals on the sea-bottom. In that case, the quantity of eggs and milt being very small in comparison to the quantity of sea-water in which a number of the fish are living, the eggs would escape fertilisation unless the milt and eggs were brought into close proximity. Whether this is the only explanation or not, the important fact in relation to the subject of the present work is, that the male actually exhibits a sexual excitement, under the influence of which he performs certain observed movements in order to invite and attract the female, and that these movements are not performed by the female.

With regard to the structural peculiarities of the male, the careful observations of Mr. Holt show that each one of them corresponds to a particular muscular movement regularly and frequently repeated in courtship and pairing. The two dorsal fins are erected, especially the front one, which is so greatly elongated. This habit of erecting the fins is not practised under the same circumstances by the female. It is a logical inference that the special activity has been the cause of the hypertrophy of the fins in the male. I do not pretend to know why the muscular exertion of erecting the fin should increase the length of the fin-rays. It might be urged that it would only increase the size of the muscles concerned. But the muscles are attached to the fin-rays, and the erection of the fin causes a constant stretching and folding of the fin-membrane. The movement is, therefore, an irritation of the tissues of both fin-rays and membrane, and, in my opinion, we are forced to conclude that the increased size which exists has been the result of this irritation. Again, in the copulatory vertical ascent to the surface of the water, the motion is principally due to the vibration of the caudal-fin and of the hinder parts of the second dorsal and ventral fins of the male, and it is just these parts which are larger in the male than in the female. Again, in the display with which the male invites the female, the jaws and gill-covers are protruded, and corresponding to this movement there is a hypertrophy, at any rate of the snout region, in the male as compared with the female. Lastly, the greater size and strength of the male, as a whole, corresponds to the greater activity and exertion he exhibits in the process of courtship and copulation.

Mr. Holt points out that the male dragonet makes the gestures observed in courtship also, to a certain extent, under other circumstances. He erects his dorsal fins when rushing to seize a worm, and if young males are present they flee before him. He also raises his fins and increases the brightness of his blue bands when chased about the tank with a net, and was observed to do the same when alarmed by a turbot introduced into the tank. He does not, however, under these circumstances assume the full courting attitude, and sometimes preferred to remain still in order to escape observation. The gesture by no means prevented males from being seized and devoured by predaceous fish, and may best be regarded as the involuntary result of excitement. The elongated fins may alarm small and timid specimens of the same species, merely as any sudden movement will alarm and frighten them away, but it is obvious that these fins are not in themselves formidable. All dragonets possess weapons of some importance in the three-spined projection on their opercula, which can be thrust out from the sides of the head at will. These seem to be used for defence, and are not specially associated with the peculiarities of the adult male.

We have now to bestow some consideration on the peculiarities of coloration in the mature male. In the case of the dragonet, as in most, if not all other cases, the difference in the colour of male and female is a quantitative, not a qualitative difference. That is to say, the same pigments are present in both sexes, but in different amounts. These pigments are a yellow, probably of the kind known to physiological chemists as lipochromes, and a black, known as melanin. The colour of this and other fishes does not, however, depend on pigments alone, but partly on a reflecting substance disposed in various ways, and found to consist chemically of a substance called, from its presence in guano, guanin. The pigments are largely contained in definite bodies known as chromatophores, which consist of branching processes radiating from a common central disc. The chromatophores are of microscopic size, and under nervous influence in the living fish are capable of extending or contracting their processes, changes which have a marked effect on the temporary coloration.

The young male and female are identical in coloration, so that the peculiarities of the adult male are due to changes that take place in the coloration elements of the young male. In the latter the second dorsal fin is marked by horizontal *brown* bands, alternating with bands of opaque

14

white with colourless margins. In the adult the brown bands are bright yellow, the white bands blue with gray margins. The brown bands in the young are found, on microscopic examination, to derive their colour from numerous yellow and black chromatophores, lying immediately beneath the epidermis, which is colourless. Besides definite black chromatophores there is a network of strands of granular matter, brown by transmitted light, pale yellow by reflected light, and evidently of the same nature as the pigment of the black chromatophores. Mr. Holt describes aggregations of this brownish substance as degenerate chromatophores, from which I infer that the reticular strands contain melanin in very thin lines, the lighter coloration being merely due to the smaller quantity of the pigment present at any one spot. The general brown colour of the bands is, therefore, due to a mingling of brown and yellow dots. In the adult male these brown bands become bright yellow in consequence of the reduction in number or entire loss of the black chromatophores, and the excessive development of the yellow pigment. The latter appears diffuse and continuous, until some of it is removed from a piece of skin by a reagent, and then separate yellow stellate chromatophores are visible. The black chromatophores present in the younger stage are represented by a complete network of granular matter, the colour of which is too feeble to affect that of the abundant yellow pigment.

The white bands in the young contain a few black chromatophores, but their whiteness is due to a granular reflecting matter, arranged in an irregular network. In the adult the white bands become blue, and in them are a few contracted black chromatophores. The brilliant blue colour is due to a dense network of bundles of small bean-shaped bodies. These are yellow by transmitted light, but intensely blue by reflected light over a black background, such as that afforded by a black chromatophore. It seems probable, although Mr. Holt does not say so, that these bean-shaped, or, as he calls them, "prismatic bodies," are developed from the network of granular matter present in the white bands of the young. Each prismatic body consists of a number of minute rod-like crystals. Probably the blue colour is due to the interference of the light rays reflected from the prismatic bodies, the red and yellow rays of light being extinguished. It is impossible, however, with our present knowledge, to go into this question. The important point is, that the blue colour appears to be produced by a deposition of guanin in particles of a certain shape.

On the first dorsal fin in the adult male there are no blue bands, but white ones corresponding to them. The white appearance is due to a network of reflecting matter similar to that of the blue in the second dorsal, but the prismatic bodies are considerably smaller, and there are few black chromatophores. This shows clearly that the blue colour is due to the special state of aggregation of the guanin and the presence of black chromatophores. Physiologically, therefore, the blue in the adult male is produced by the deposition of guanin at the surface of the skin.

The blue and yellow of the sides of the body are produced in the same way as in the dorsal fins, but there are slight differences. In the blue bands black chromatophores are often abundant, and in the same plane, to some extent superficial to the chromatophores, is a layer of prismatic bodies, more abundant, and therefore less reticulate in arrangement than in the second dorsal fin. In addition, there is another layer of black chromatophores and prismatic bodies at the inner surface of the skin near the flesh, the latter overlying and between the former. The blue bands on the body are capable of sudden intensification, and Mr. Holt considers this is due to the expansion of the black chromato-

phores under nervous influence. Beneath the colouring
elements mentioned is a layer of reflecting tissue, forming
a more or less continuous "argenteum" underlying the
skin. The yellow bands of the sides of the body in
the adult are, of course, due, like those in the fins, to
an excessive development of yellow pigment. After the
breeding season the brilliant coloration of the males fades
considerably. The yellow bands fade to a golden-brown, and
the blue bands become less intense. Examination shows that
the diffuse yellow pigment is reduced in quantity. In the
blue parts are noticed aggregations of brownish-yellow
matter, apparently derived from the degeneration of black
chromatophores. A reduction of the black chromatophores would, of course, result in a diminution of the blue
colour, since the prismatic bodies are blue only when backed
by black.

What explanation can be offered of the evolution of this
development of colour in the breeding males? Mr. Holt
considers the colour characters as due to some form of
sexual selection, but reasons that the behaviour of the
female does not strongly support the view of an æsthetic
selection. He concludes that the enlarged dorsals and
brilliant colours of the male are probably nothing else than
a conspicuous advertisement of his presence. He believes
that the male cannot see the female unless she is quite
close to him, and that the female would not see the male
unless he were conspicuously coloured. But from my point
of view it matters little whether the colours are necessary or
advantageous, either in attracting the female or rendering
the male conspicuous. The colours are due to a change in
the male which does not occur in the female, and therefore
I hold there must be some conditions which produce the
colours in the male and do not act on the female. As both
sexes are equally exposed to light in the copulatory ascent

through the water, we can scarcely attribute the colour change in the male to special influences of light. Mr. Holt mentions the suggestion which has been made in many cases, that the pigment and guanin are due to an adventitious excretory process connected with genital activity. But this suggestion is difficult to reconcile with the fact that a similar excessive excretion does not occur in so many other male fishes whose genital activity is, at least, equally great. We are thus driven to the hypothesis, however improbable it may seem, that the production of pigment and guanin in the male is due to his sexual excitement, which appears to be the only condition in which he differs greatly from the female, and from other male fishes which do not change colour in a similar way. By sexual excitement I mean here the nervous excitement which is a recognised physiological state, and of which the male dragonet affords conspicuous evidence at the time of his courtship. Physio logical processes are known to be governed largely by nervous impulses, and not merely the circulation, but the excretory activity of the skin, are known to be influenced by nervous action. Pigment and guanin are produced in the skin by the secretory or excretory activity of the living cells. That the marked excitement of the male dragonet's brain should cause increased nervous stimulation of the skin is not an extravagant supposition, and it is definitely supported by the fact that the blue bands, if not the yellow, are flashed out in more intense brilliance as the fins are raised in his amatory rushes. When the question is regarded physiologically, instead of merely from the selectionist's point of view, the significance of such reasoning as I have used cannot be ignored.

Such an explanation covers not only the development of the coloration, but its partial diminution after the period of sexual excitement is passed. Mr. Holt found that the yellow pigment was not given off from the skin perceptibly during life, but very soon after death it could be dissolved out readily in fresh water and in sea-water, as well as in alcohol and various other reagents commonly used for preserving specimens. The colour of the solution was destroyed by acids, and bleached very rapidly in light. He considers that its diminution in the living fish after the breeding season is more probably due to its diffusion into the water than to its bleaching *in situ*, though no evidence of its presence in the water was obtained. Indications of the degeneration of black chromatophores causing the fading of the blue colour after the breeding season were mentioned above. Whatever becomes of the pigments and guanin in the skins of fishes, whether they are excreted or reabsorbed, we have reason to believe that they are not entirely permanent. Reabsorption by the blood probably enough takes place. If they are not permanent a diminution of secretory activity in their production would naturally lead to a diminution in the quantities present in the skin, and thus we can understand why the brilliant coloration of the male dragonet fades after his sexual excitement has ceased for the season. It is scarcely necessary to point out that this suggestion applies to numerous other analogous cases.

Before quitting the subject it may be mentioned that Mr. Holt found the solution of the yellow pigment to have an odour resembling that of an acrid cucumber, and a subacid taste not particularly disagreeable, but causing a prolonged irritation of the human salivary glands. He found that the pigment was distasteful to several fishes, but neither distasteful nor terrifying to young dragonets. It was unpalatable to at least one predaceous fish, the pollack, but even fully-coloured male dragonets were greedily eaten by the turbot.

In most of the species of *Gobius* the male takes care of the eggs. *Gobius minutus* scoops out the sand from beneath a shell, the female lays her eggs on the lower surface of the shell, and the male then guards them and keeps up a circulation of water by the motion of his pectoral fins. Sexual differences, both of structure and colour, exist in these species, but to a much less degree than in *Callionymus*. In the male *Gobius minutus* the colours of the male are brighter and more intense than those of the female, at least in the breeding season. The breeding habits of these species have been minutely studied by a French naturalist, Guitel.[1] The males of *G. minutus* were found to fight for the possession of the females, and the fights were serious, the females being left to the victors.

Aphia pellucida and *Crystallogobius Nilssonii* are two small species of the Goby family, which are believed to spawn only once and then die. In both, sexual differences of structure are rather strongly developed. In *Aphia*, in both females and immature males, the teeth are small, of uniform size, in a single row. In mature males these teeth are replaced by another row of longer pointed ones, and the dorsal and ventral fins become higher, especially in the hinder part. The whole head becomes thicker and the body plumper. The fish does not exceed 1½ inch in length. It is taken in depths of 1 to 15 fathoms, on the British and Norwegian coasts.

In *Crystallogobius* the females are slender with pointed heads and toothless jaws. Their first dorsal and pelvic fins are rudimentary. In the young males the head is somewhat pointed, but contains teeth. In the mature male the snout becomes short, the extremity of the mandibles is curved upwards and received into a notch in the upper jaw. At each angle of the projection of the mandible is a long tooth. The first dorsal consists of two rays, and the second dorsal and ventral (anal) are broader than in the female. The fish, like

---

[1] *Arch. de Zool. Expérimentale*, 1892 and 1895.

Aphia, is very transparent; *Aphia* has scales, but *Crystallo-gobius* is scaleless. The males are much less numerous than the females, and also considerably larger, although they themselves do not exceed 2 inches in length. The species has lately been proved to be fairly abundant at depths of 30 fathoms around the British and Irish coasts.

The behaviour of these fish during life has not yet been observed, but we may infer by analogy that the males fight together for the company of the females, using their teeth as weapons. This would account for the special development of the teeth, while the greater activity and use of the fins would explain the larger size of the body and greater development of the fins in the male sex.

The sexual differences in the Lumpsucker are well and widely known, the fish being large and very common on our more northern coasts. The male is much smaller than the female, and more brightly coloured. The colour of the female is a dull blue, while the male is blue on the back and red on the sides and ventral surface. The spawn of this fish is adhesive and the eggs rather large. Large masses of the spawn are frequently seen attached to weed, rocks, or piles between tide marks at low-water springs, and the male is said to be usually found guarding such a mass. The males are much more numerous than the females. Common as the fish are, their behaviour in courtship and in the fertilisation of the eggs does not seem to have been studied, nor has any minute investigation been made of the elements of the coloration in the two sexes. Saville Kent states that he observed the brilliant colours of the male to disappear " after his paternal duties had been discharged." It is highly probable, therefore, that the change of colour is due to the same cause as that which occurs in *Callionymus*, namely, nervous excitement affecting the secretion of pigment. It is noteworthy that the male of *Callionymus* is larger than the female, while in

Cyclopterus lumpus the relative sizes are reversed. In *Callionymus* we have seen that the male has to make greater exertions in the breeding process, and if it is true that the male *Cyclopterus* remains attached, by means of his ventral sucker, beside the spawn he has fertilised, this sedentary duty may well be the cause of his diminished proportions. The female has the sucker equally well developed, but as she does not assist in guarding the spawn, she is probably more active, and also probably obtains more food.

The nest-building habits of the Sticklebacks have often been observed and described, and these fishes seem to afford a case in which the relation between habits and sexual dimorphism can easily be studied. Considering that the male alone builds the nest, courts the female, and keeps guard over the nest and eggs, driving off intruders with great vigour and courage, it might be expected that he would show striking differences from the female in some of his structural characters. But, so far as I can discover, this is not the case. The characters of the fresh-water form, *Gasterosteus,* are very variable, so that several varieties have been described, and, by some naturalists, distinguished as species, but it does not appear that these differences are sexual. The chief distinction of the male in the breeding season is the assumption of a bright pink or red colour on the lower part of the head and the ventral surface of the body. The females are rather dull coloured.

What then exactly are the habits and behaviour of the fish ? The males are described as very pugnacious. In fighting they swim round each other like boxers or swordsmen, and then one dashes at the other and tries to strike him with his spines. Of these it has two to four on the back, representing the anterior rays of the dorsal fin, and one on each side representing the pelvic fin. These spines are firmly hinged to bony plates in the body, and the sides of the body are protected by bony plates, probably representing scales. Yet the spines and armour are not described as confined to, or more developed in the males. The fighting, however, appears certainly not to be confined to adult or breeding males, but to be practised by both sexes at various ages.

The building of the nest consists merely in gathering together bits of weed and rubbish at the bottom of the water, felting it together to some extent, and arranging it into a round form with a hole in the top. This work the fish performs with his snout, and it is not of a kind likely to lead to any special modifications of structure. The courting of the female consists in the male swimming in little jerks about her, occasionally pushing her with his mouth, until she follows him to the nest, swimming just above him as he leads the way. When the eggs are deposited and fertilised the male takes care of the nest, usually hovering over it, so that the motion of his pectoral fins produces a current of water over the eggs. In all this there is no definite action or gesture which is exclusively confined to the male. If it is true that the fighting habits are not confined to the male, and that the arms and armour are equally developed in both sexes, then it is not inconsistent with my views that the only constant difference between the sexes is that of the colour, which is chiefly developed in the breeding season, and which is to be explained as in other cases already discussed. On the other hand, Darwin quotes a statement by one observer of sticklebacks that " the females are quite pacific," and if this is correct it is difficult to harmonise it with an equal structural development in the sexes, unless it could be shown that the parts used for fighting in the male are exercised for some other purpose in the female.

Of *Gasterosteus pungitius*, which has nine or ten short spines in front of the dorsal fin, Day found specimens in

Ireland in which the pelvic spines were absent altogether. He does not state whether these were females.

In the Sea - Stickleback, *Gasterosteus spinachia*, sexual differences of colour and structure have not been emphasised in descriptions, but the male has the peculiarity of binding together the weeds of which his nest consists by means of a whitish thread spun from his own body. It has been recently proved that this thread is secreted by the kidneys, and is only produced in the breeding season. It must be admitted that it is difficult to indicate any special stimulation that could have caused the kidneys to secrete a tenacious thread in the male only. Yet it is most probable that the use of this thread for securing the nest arose quite unconsciously on the part of the fish. If he were swimming about the nest to arrange it, and a tenacious secretion escaped from his kidneys, it would necessarily become a binding thread. All we have to explain, therefore, is the apparently abnormal and unique secretion. According to Prof. Mobius, as quoted by Geddes and Thomson, the enlargement of the testes, producing a mechanical pressure upon the kidneys, is the cause of the secretion. The pressure, if this view is correct, sets up a pathological condition or inflammation in the kidneys, which results in the secretion of a mucous product, and a somewhat similar product is formed in certain diseases of the kidneys in the human subject.

Labridæ. — Among the British species of the family Labridæ, sexual dimorphism is most strongly marked in *Labrus mixtus,* Fries and Ekstrom. The difference between the male and female appears to be confined to the coloration. The male has a gorgeous appearance, being clothed in bright orange, red, and blue, like some of the saints in pictures by the old masters. The red colour is on the back and sides. Five or six bands of blue radiate backwards from the eye, one being generally continued along the body, below the lateral line to the caudal fin, while a similar but less marked blue band is situated above the lateral line. The fins are yellow or orange and blue. The female is reddish on the back, but the colour is not so brilliant, and the blue bands are wanting. There are three deep black blotches on the back in the posterior half of the body. The young males are coloured in the same way as the females. Mr. W. Saville Kent observed the courtship of the male of this species in the aquarium of the Crystal Palace, and his description of it, contained in a letter to *Nature*, is quoted by Darwin.[1] The male had formed " a deep hollow in the sand of its tank, and was endeavouring in the most persuasive manner to induce a female of the same species to share it with him, swimming backwards and for-wards between her and the completed nest, and plainly exhibiting the greatest anxiety for her to follow. The normal brilliancy of this fish was supplemented by a light opaque patch that extended over a considerable portion of the back and shoulders, while the tints of the remaining portion of the body were more than ordinarily deepened." The eggs of some species in this family are adhesive, for instance, *Labrus maculatus*, the commonest British species, while those of others are free. According to Raffaele[2] the eggs of those species of *Labrus* and *Crenilabrus*, which are not adhesive, are heavier than the sea-water, while those of other genera are buoyant. Probably, then, the eggs of *Labrus mixtus* are heavy and free, and possibly the male keeps guard over them in the hollow which he makes. Saville Kent's observations prove that the male fish develops nervous sexual excitement in his invitations to the female, and this is associated with a peculiarity of coloration, as in the Dragonet. The elements of the coloration are similar to those of the latter fish, an

---

[1] *Descent of Man, etc.*, p. 341.
[2] "Uova galleggianti e le larve dei Teleostei nel Golfo di Napoli," *Mitt. Zool. Staz., Neapel*, Bd. 8, 1888.

excess of a lipochrome giving a reddish colour, and *blue bands*, doubtless due, as in the Dragonet, to special aggregations of reflecting substance or guanin. This case would form an interesting subject for renewed investigation. As the young males are stated to have the three dorsal black blotches seen in the female, we may surmise that their disappearance is due to the excessive production of the orange or red pigment. In this case, as in that of the Dragonet, our present knowledge shows no difference in conditions of life between male and female, except the nervous excitement of the male at the breeding time, and so far it may be considered to afford support to the explanation offered above of the special development of colour in the male. As in the Dragonet, Saville Kent's evidence shows that the colours lose their brilliancy after the breeding season.

In *Coris julis*, Günther, another species of the family Labridæ or Wrasses, there is, besides a marked difference in coloration between the sexes, a slight structural difference of the same kind which occurs in several other species of various families. The three first spines in the male are slightly elongated, being nearly equal to half the vertical height of the body. The colours of the two sexes are thus described by Day.

Male.—Purplish or bluish brown along the upper *half* of the body, and silvery white below. Along the upper half runs a broad yellowish white and generally indented line, which commences behind the eye and is continued to the base of the caudal fin. Dorsal fin, yellowish, with a purple or orange outer edge, and a large oval black or bluish spot on the anterior portion.

Female.—Upper *third* of the body purplish, with a light yellow band extending from the eye to the base of the tail. Lower two-thirds of the body silvery, with one or more yellow longitudinal bands. A dark spot in the axil of the pectoral fin, and another behind the opercle, as in the male.

Steindachner (*Ich. Span. u. Port.*, 1868, p. 35) seems to have been the first to assert that the *Julis mediterranea*, and *J. giofredi* of Risso, described by Dr. Günther (*Cat. Brit. Mus.*) under the names *Coris julis* and *Coris giofredi*, were the two

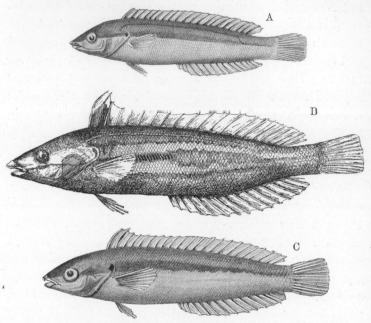

Fig. 21.—*Coris julis*, a Mediterranean fish. *A*, immature; *B*, mature male; *C*, mature female.

sexes of one species. M. P. Gourret has recently, in the *Ann. du Musée de Marseille*, very explicitly opposed Steindachner's conclusion. My friend Mr. E. W. L. Holt, during a stay at Marseilles, had opportunities of studying the fish, and has very kindly supplied me with the results of his observations. The figures of the two mature forms and the young male (Fig. 21, A, B, C) have been delineated from specimens of his under his supervision.

The two forms are commonly distinguished at Marseilles as the *Girelle royale* and the *Girelle de Geoffroi*. Mr. Holt states that the former, in which the three first dorsal spines are elongated, has a brilliant coloration of linear bands of green, blue, orange, red, etc. Also that it has on the side a large blackish spot, more or less pronounced, and on the dorsal fin a black spot bordered with red. That the *Girelle de Geoffroi* has a more subdued coloration. The back, red or brownish, is bordered below by a sombre medio-lateral band; on the ventral flank is a yellow band. He finds that the most distinctive colour-marks of the *royale* are the medio-lateral orange band with indented outline bordered above and below with blue, and the large blackish spot on the side. Day, as I have mentioned above, states that there is a black spot in the axil of the pectoral fin in both forms, but the figures illustrating the present discussion show plainly enough the exclusive presence of the elongated dark lateral mark in the *royale*.

Gourret's opposition to the view which regards the two forms as constituting a sexually dimorphic species appears to be founded on two pieces of evidence : (1) That a naturalist named Sarato found *male* specimens of *Coris giofredi* in full sexual maturity; (2) that he has himself seen two specimens of *C. julis* which were of the female sex. But the fact that he expressly mentions the comparative scarcity of males in the one form, and of females in the other, is enough to deprive his arguments of nearly all their force. The evidence on which he relies affords no proof whatever of his conclusion. Mr. Holt confirms the fact that males with the characters of *giofredi* are frequently mature, but this is merely an instance of the general truth that unisexual characters are not fully developed until after puberty. As for the two specimens of *Coris julis* which were female, if he were not mistaken in their sex, they may well have been two female specimens in

which, as often happens, the male peculiarities were to some
degree developed. Mr. Holt found that the largest females
generally presented a slight elongation of the anterior rays,
accompanied by the black spot bordered with red, and we
know that such a modification of the female in advanced age
is common enough in dimorphic species. The female *Coris*
in which this was observed were from 11·5 to 14 cm. long.
The male or *royale* form attains to a length of 16 cm.

But of course the real reason for regarding these two
forms as belonging to one species is that the characters to
which the controversy refers only occur in specimens above
a certain size. Mature males of both forms occur, but small
immature males of the more conspicuous form do not. Mr.
Holt states that no specimens of the *royale* have been seen less
than 9 cm. long.

We are forced to conclude that males of the one form are
transformed into the other, and that a certain amount of
modification may occur in the females. The assumption of
the adult characters may not occur in all specimens at the
same size, both because the rate of growth varies, and because
puberty may not always occur at the same age. But there
can be no reasonable doubt that the two forms of *Coris* are
the males and females of one species, the young closely
resembling the adult female. The more specialised form is
produced by the modification of the other, not from a distinct
parentage.

Of the habits of the fish nothing seems to have been
recorded which could be regarded as physiologically related
to the evolution of the unisexual characters of the male.
Day quotes the observation of Birchell (*Zool.* 1876) that the
fish are accustomed in an aquarium to hide in a bed of shingle.
It is probable enough that, when breeding, fishes of this species
practise a courtship similar to that observed by Saville Kent
in *Labrus mixtus*. In this case the sexual excitement of the

male may be the real cause of its modification. The elongation or hypertrophy of the anterior rays of the dorsal fin may be caused by the frequent agitation of these rays under the influence of sexual excitement, and the heightened activity of the nervous system in that condition may account for the greater development of coloration in the skin.

A sexual difference of colour is stated by Darwin, on the authority of A. Agassiz, to occur commonly in the species of the Chromidæ, which are fresh-water fishes allied to the Labridæ or Wrasses. It appears that the males are more brightly coloured, whether they guard the eggs, as some do, or not. Some of the males in this family, like the North American *Pomatis*, build nests for the eggs and keep guard over them, while some which occur in the Sea of Galilee are said to carry the eggs in their mouths, like *Arius* among the Siluridæ. Probably, however, the guarding of the eggs has nothing to do with the brighter colour of the males, which is most likely, as in *Callionymus*, entirely due to the nervous excitement of the male in his endeavours to effect fertilisation. The *Geophagus*, mentioned by Darwin as a species in which the male carries the ova in his mouth, and develops a protuberance on his forehead during the breeding season, is one of the Chromidæ, and in all probability, if the behaviour of the fish were known, the two facts are connected together, the protuberance being probably due to some friction caused by the action of the male in getting the ova into his mouth.

Another family allied to the Wrasses is that of the Embiotocidæ or surf-perches of the coast of California. The females of these are all viviparous, but I have not yet found any sexual differences described in them except that of size, the females being much larger than the males. That this is not the necessary consequence of the viviparous habit is shown by the case of mammals, in which the males are usually the larger.

SUB-ORDER LOPHOBRANCHII.—The chief secondary difference between the sexes. in this Order is the pouch which is commonly present in the males for holding the eggs during their development. The pouch, however, is not present in all the genera, nor when present has it in all cases the same structure. In *Nerophis*, the snake pipe-fishes, in which the body is smooth and rounded, the eggs are attached to the skin of the abdomen of the male in front of the anus, and not covered by any cutaneous folds, but exposed. In *Syngnathus* and in *Siphonostoma* the eggs are contained in a pouch situated beneath the tail behind the anus, and formed of two longitudinal flaps which meet in the middle line but are not united at their edges. In *Hippocampus* the pouch is formed of similar folds united together by their edges, an opening being left only in front. It is reasonable enough to suppose that at the beginning of the evolution of these forms the eggs were adhesive and became attached to the ventral surface of the tail, except in *Nerophis*, where the tail being very slender and prehensile the eggs were received on the abdomen. In *Syngnathus* and *Siphonostoma* the tail is square in section and its ventral surface is flat. It is probable that the fish would exert itself by muscular effort to form the lower surface of its tail into a groove in order to retain the eggs. Such an effort might well be excited by the tactile stimulation due to the presence of the eggs, and would probably lead to the depression of the central part and the increased growth of the skin at the edges of the ventral surface of the tail. Granting that growth took place in this case, as in other cases, in the directions in which straining of the skin and muscles was habitually set up, the evolution of the longitudinal folds is, on Lamarckian principles, explained. The fusion of the edges of the folds in *Hippocampus* may be attributed to the edges being pressed together with greater force. We have no reason to believe that incipient outgrowths of the ventral edges of the tail occurred apart from the presence of the eggs, and such incipient outgrowths must have occurred on the selection theory. We do not find such incipient outgrowths even in the females of the same species, and the theory of selection makes no attempt to explain the origin of the outgrowths.

In the genus *Solenostoma*, which occurs on the east coast of Africa and in the East Indies, according to Günther, the pouch for containing the eggs is in the female instead of in the male. We have thus in this order a striking illustration of the truth that special growths are due not to any general properties of male or female constitution, but to special mechanical stimulations. Such stimulations act on the nerves and give rise to habitual reflex actions in muscles; the strains produced by such habitual exertions of the muscles result in growth in particular directions of the parts affected. It would be desirable to investigate in detail, from the point of view here indicated, the structure and development of the egg-pouch in these fishes.

According to Günther, as quoted by Darwin, the female *Solenostoma* is more vividly coloured and spotted than the male, although a difference of colour between the sexes is not generally characteristic of the Lophobranchii. It is probable that in this case the female is in the habit of courting the male to induce him to fertilise her eggs, in which case her more brilliant colouring, as in the males of other species, might well be the result of nervous excitement.

CHAPTER V

INSECTS

LEPIDOPTERA—*Mimicry.*—The subject of mimicry is connected with the subject of sexual dimorphism very intimately by the fact that in a certain number of cases the difference between the sexes in Lepidoptera is that one sex mimics some species of a remote group, while the other preserves the usual characteristics of its family. This fact is mentioned and discussed by Darwin. He remarks that in such cases it is obvious that the successive variations by which one sex, *e.g.* the female, has been modified have been transmitted to her alone. He suggests that some of the variations have been at times transmitted to males, but that such males have been eliminated by being thus rendered less attractive to the females. He supposes, that is to say, that the females while undergoing modifications of colour themselves, in a certain direction, would have nothing to do with males that varied in the same direction. In support of this suggestion he quotes some sentences from Mr. Belt concerning the retention, in the males of some species of mimicking Leptalides, of an original or Leptalid character which is wanting in the female. In one case such a character is a white patch on the wing, which Belt imagines to be exhibited to the females in courtship to gratify "their deep-seated preference for the normal colour of the Order to which the Leptalides belong." It is scarcely necessary to criticise this suggestion seriously. It obviously affords no explanation, and we have no reason to believe in the existence of the deep-seated preference, which, if it existed, has in some cases preserved the males entirely unchanged, and in others has allowed them to adopt the same mimicking appearance as the females. We have at present no evidence that the sense of sight plays any important part in the pairing of butterflies.

To refer to an example. In the hall of the Natural History Museum at South Kensington there are displayed some specimens illustrating mimicry among Indian butterflies. The Euplœinæ are generally uneatable, and a genus *Salatura* is illustrated with certain species of *Elymnias* which mimic it. *Elymnias cottonis* occurs in the Andaman Islands, where *Salatura* is unknown, and there the two sexes of the *Elymnias* are nearly alike and unmodified, that is to say, they have the usual characters of the Satyrides, the family to which *Elymnias* belongs. But in Northern India *Elymnias cottonis* is replaced by *E. undularis*, the female of which resembles the distasteful *Salatura genestia*, but the male is not disguised.

In this case the habits of the two sexes are not mentioned on the explanatory labels. It is very commonly stated, in the original memoirs in which cases of mimicry are described, that the mimicking forms are found *in company with* the mimicked. Usually the pattern forms are conspicuous, numerous, and fly openly in flocks. When a number are collected by the entomologist he finds on subsequent study of his specimens that among them in small proportion are specimens of the mimicking or disguised species. This is the fact which I desire to emphasise, that the disguised forms are captured in the company of those they imitate. This fact is not considered of much importance by those who have endeavoured to explain mimicry by selection, and when both sexes are alike its importance is not so evident. But when the two sexes are remarkably different, its importance is easy to perceive. For, supposing similar variations occurred in the two sexes, then there is no reason why the selection in the two cases should not be the same. A variation tending to disguise would confer the same protection wherever it was found.

It may be suggested that in one sex survival depended on a different character, which conferred an advantage in the habits of that sex, but not in the conditions of life of the other. For instance, this suggestion is made in reference to another case of mimicry among the Indian butterflies from Col. Swinhoe's collection in the hall of the Museum at South Kensington. This case is as follows :—*Lærtes pammon* has two forms of female, one mimicking *Menelaides aristolochæ*, the other *M. hector*. The male of *Lærtes pammon*, which differs from the females and is not mimetic, is stated to be very active and thus able to "protect itself," an expression which evidently means to escape from its enemies. This male is also stated to be eagerly devoured by birds, lizards, etc., when caught. *Menelaides aristolochæ* and its allies are stated to be distasteful and not generally devoured. A curious fact about this case is that all the species mentioned belong to the same family, the Papilioninæ.

Now in spite of the activity of the male of *Lærtes pammon*, it is evident that variations of it approximating to the distasteful species would have a still better chance of survival than those individuals which were only active and not modified. Thus if selection were the only factor, some modification of the male would be produced. We must conclude therefore that the required variations only occurred in the female, and not in the male. That being the case, we must inquire the reason for their occurrence. On the theory that the similarity of habits between the female and the mimicked species was the cause of the mimicry, the facts at once become intelligible; on the theory of selection they do not.

To pursue the investigation further we ought to inquire what in detail are the habits of the female and mimicked species on the one hand, of the male on the other. It is certain that since the males and females copulate they must be in company for a time. But nevertheless they are probably only in company for a brief portion of their lives, and have different habits, as for example in the case of species in which the females are wingless and stationary while the males are winged and active. As to the direct causes of the modifications so far as colour is concerned, I attribute it chiefly to the quality of the light to which the insect is exposed. Light rays of different quality are reflected from different surroundings, and these falling upon the surface of the wings of butterflies most probably produce modifications of colour. That such modifications are produced by the particular exposures of caterpillar and chrysalis, has been sufficiently proved by the experiments of Prof. Poulton.[1]

It follows, of course, that in my opinion all cases of mimicry are simply examples of the similar effect of similar conditions. If the mimicking species were in any instance constantly found to live in situations quite different from those inhabited by the species imitated, this would be a serious objection to my theory. But so far as I can ascertain this is never the case; disguise and association always go together, and it is therefore reasonable to hold that the association is the cause of the disguise.

Bates, in his original memoir,[2] considers the question

---

[1] *The Colours of Animals,* International Scientific Series, 1890.
[2] *Trans. Linn. Soc.,* vol. xxiii., 1862.

whether the mutual resemblance between protected and mimicking species can be due to the "coincident adaptation of the two analogues to similar physical conditions." He rejects the conclusion as an explanation of definite mimicry, but thinks that facts of similar variation in two already nearly allied forms do sometimes show that they have been affected in a similar way by similar conditions.

The genus *Hypolimnas* affords an excellent example of unisexual mimicry.[1] In *Hypolimnas bolina* there is comparatively little difference between the sexes, in *H. misippus* there is a great deal. In both species there are varieties, but the males do not differ much from one another. The male of *H. misippus* is similar to that of *H. bolina*, of which figures of both sexes are given. These figures are taken from specimens from Palawan in the Philippine Islands. The male of *H. misippus* is smaller, and the white spot on the upper side of the hind wing is larger and rounder.

The commonest form of the female of *H. misippus* mimics the commonest of all the Danainæ, viz. *Danais chrysippus*, and they both occur in India, the Malay Archipelago, Aden, and South Africa. *Danais chrysippus* is of a brownish yellow colour over the greater part of the wings, with a patch of black and white on the apex of the fore wing, and a black border with white spots on the hind wing.

In Africa[2] another form of *Danais* occurs which differs from *D. chrysippus* in the fact that the yellow of the hind wings is replaced by white except at the border. This form was formerly described as a distinct species under the name *D. alcippus*. It occurs in West Africa, Central Africa, and Abyssinia, where *chrysippus* is absent, and in South Africa close to, if not actually in the range of, *chrysippus*. A variety of *Hypolimnas*, which we may call *alcippoides*, mimics *D.*

---

[1] See Colonel C. Swinhoe, *Journ. Linn. Soc. Zool.*, vol. xxv. 1896, p. 339.
[2] Arthur G. Butler, *Proc. Zool. Soc.*, 1884, p. 478.

FIG. 22.—A. *Hypolimnas bolina*, male, B. ditto. female, from Palawan, Philippine Islands;
C. *H. misippus*, female, East Africa; D. *Danais chrysippus*, female, East Africa; E.
Hypolimnas misippus, female, var. *alcippoides*, from R. Niger, West Africa; F. *Danais chrysippus*, female, var. *alcippus*, from Lagos, West Africa.

alcippus, and occurs also in West Africa, but it is by no means a perfect imitation of *Danais alcippus,* the white not being so much developed. Specimens of this form in the British Museum collection are few in number, and the majority of specimens of *Hypolimnas* from Sierra Leone are of the ordinary form, with only a slight tinge of white on the hind wings. Here then the mimicry is by no means so exact as the paper of Colonel Swinhoe would suggest. In Central Africa (Victoria Nyanza) and at Massowah also, the form *Hypolimnas alcippoides* occurs.

Specimens with *some* white on the hind wings also occur occasionally in India.

Another form of *Danais* occurring in Africa differs from *chrysippus* only in the absence of the black and white patch on the apex of the fore wing, so that nearly the whole upper surface is brownish yellow. This form is named by Dr. Butler *Klugii.* It occurs, though not abundantly, in India at Bombay, Karachi, and the Punjab; in Africa in the upper part of the valley of the Nile, and about the great lakes of the Nile. A variety of *Hypolimnas* resembles or mimics this form of *Danais,* and occurs in India more commonly than the form it resembles.

A fourth form of *Danais* is like the last, but with white on the hind wings. This form is named *D. dorippus,* and occurs in Nubia and along the shores of the Red Sea. A variety of the female *Hypolimnas misippus* resembling this has been taken at Aden, but I do not know if it occurs commonly along with *dorippus* in Nubia. I have seen a specimen of *misippus* resembling *D. klugii* with a tinge of white on the hind wings from Sierra Leone.

The whole story then comes to this, that there are four varieties of one species, *Danais chrysippus.* These four are made up of combinations of three characters, namely (1) a general brownish-yellow colour, (2) a black and white apex to the fore wing, (3) a white central region on the hind wing. The commonest form is the combination of (1) and (2). The second form combines (1), (2), and (3)—*alcippus.* Take away (2) and (3) and we have the form which is brownish yellow nearly all over the wings—*Klugii.* Add to this the white on the hind wing and we have the combination of (1) and (3)— *dorippus.* Or, to put the matter in another way, we have in the first place two forms of *D. chrysippus*, one which is brownish yellow with a black and white patch at the apex of the fore wing, one which is brownish yellow without the black and white patch. Each of these forms also occurs with white on the hind wings, and thus we get the *four* varieties. The female of *Hypolimnas misippus* presents similar variations.

Of the four varieties of *Danais chrysippus* only two occur in India, namely, the two without the white on the hind wings, the typical form, and var. *Klugii.* In Africa all four forms occur, each one being characteristic of a different region. At Aden all four forms occur *together*, and interbreeding. At Aden also all four forms occur in the females of *Hypolimnas misippus ;* in India the two varieties of this occur corresponding to the two forms of the *Danais.* In Africa there is evidence that each form of the *Danais* is not accompanied in its own region exclusively by the corresponding form of the *Hypolimnas*, but rather that the ordinary form of the latter merely shows in some specimens approximations to the variety of the *Danais.*

Now we have to consider the evidence concerning habits and conditions, which in this case is by no means sufficient for my purpose. The authorities do not give a detailed account of the habits of the various forms, and I can only refer to casual remarks which suggest that important differences really exist. Colonel Swinhoe states that the male of *H. misippus* is far more active on the wing than the female, and is most pugnacious, perching on the tops of bushes, and darting forward to attack any other butterfly that may fly past. Trimen states that this species is a bold and active insect, frequenting flowers in gardens and open spots, and that the habit of settling on the ground is more practised *by the male*. *Danais chrysippus*, the imitated form, appears to frequent open plains, the larva feeding on Asclepiad plants, which are of no great size. Marshall [1] says that in India the species is common everywhere, but the dry hot plains of Northern India seem to suit it, and there it is almost the only butterfly which flourishes in the dust and glare. There is thus a general similarity of habits between the female *H. misippus* and *D. chrysippus*, but there is little at present to show that the male of the former species has habits which correspond to the difference of his coloration from that of the female. It must be remembered, however, that the habits and conditions have not been carefully observed and described, because collectors and specialists have not yet realised their importance.

The general distribution of the varieties suggests that climate has something to do with the variations. Thus the form *D. alcippus* is characteristic of the humid forest region of West Africa.

The adherents of the theory of mimicry maintain that in the West Indies and South America *H. misippus* is an introduced species, because the pattern form *D. chrysippus* does not occur in America. But the facts offer two obstacles to their views, which they do not discuss. The first is—How is it that one species has been introduced without the other, considering that in Asia and Africa the two species occur together? The second difficulty is—How is it that the species which owes its existence in the Old World to the protection afforded by mimicry, flourishes when introduced

[1] *Butterflies of India, Burmah, and Ceylon.*

into the New World where the pattern form does not exist? For the basis of the theory of mimicry is that the enemies of the insect are acquainted with every detail of the appearance of the pattern form.

The case of *Papilio cenea* is discussed by Prof. Poulton in his book on the *Colours of Animals* (International Scientific Series) as a particularly convincing illustration of the theory of utility as the explanation of mimicry. The facts, according to the researches of Mr. Roland Trimen, are as follows :—The male of *Papilio cenea* in Africa has the usual characters of a swallow-tail, possessing the special " tails " on the hinder wings, and black, yellow, and brown markings. The *female* of *Papilio cenea* occurs in three different varieties, each of these being stated to mimic a different species of Danaid belonging to its district. One of these female varieties is distinguished as *P. cenea* proper, and resembles *Amauris echeria*, both occurring in South Africa. The resemblance is certainly remarkable ; the female *P. cenea* does not possess the "tails," it is much smaller than the male, and it has a great deal of black or dark colour like *Amauris echeria*. A second form of the female of *P. cenea*, called *hippocoon*, resembles *Danais niavius* in South Africa, and both the mimic and the mimicking forms are slightly different in Natal. Both are black and white. A third form of the female of *P. cenea* resembles *Danais chrysippus* in Cape Colony.

It is further pointed out that in three regions, namely, Madagascar, the island of Grand Comoro, and in Abyssinia, three species of *Papilio* occur closely allied to *P. cenea*, but having both sexes almost alike, and exhibiting no mimicry.

Now, remarkable as these facts are, it is necessary to observe that the male *P. cenea* is distinctly more conspicuous than the Danaid species which the females resemble. If then the male requires no protection from disguise, why should the female require it? The females evidently, so far as danger is concerned, would clearly have been quite as well off if they had mimicked their mates instead of imitating species with which they had nothing to do. All the species of *Danais* above mentioned are mimicked by other species as well as by the varieties of *Papilio cenea*, and, further, the latter varieties are connected by intermediate forms. Even supposing that we admit the utility of the existing mimicry, the question in regard to its origin is whether the individual variations in the two sexes of *P. cenea* were originally the same, that is, whether the survival of particular individuals was the determining factor. This essential point is entirely ignored in the theory of selection as the explanation of the mimicry, or rather we may say that the original similarity of variation tendencies and directions is assumed. But in support of this very important assumption we have no evidence whatever. On the other hand, if the original variations were not similar, if the male has never varied in the direction of the disguise which the females have assumed, then selection or survival is no explanation. The explanation lies in the difference of variation in definite directions. Even if we had no evidence to show that the females are subjected to different conditions from the males, conditions which might have determined the direction in which they have been modified, at least it is certain that the selection theory in this case is founded on an unsupported assumption, and as it is probable that the habits and conditions of life of the sexes are different, and that those of the females are similar to those of the species they mimic, we have good reason to hold it probable that in this case particular conditions have caused variations in definite directions in one sex, and not in the other.

But it so happens that we have very distinct evidence of the subjection of the two sexes to different conditions, evidence recorded by Sir Roland Trimen, F.R.S., the original discoverer of this case of mimicry.[1] He says that the species is confined to wooded districts, but the female is much less frequently seen on the wing than the male. The latter is exceedingly conspicuous in flight, only occasionally halting at flowers. It returns repeatedly over the same ground in the neighbourhood of a female who remains settled *in some shady spot among the weeds and bushes.* As the afternoon draws on the female leaves her retirement and flutters slowly about. She is always much slower on the wing than the male, and stays much longer at the flowers she visits. Trimen noticed that she was especially fond of the white flowers of a low-growing labiate. On the other hand, the brown and yellow ochre colouring of the under side of the wings in the male serves well to protect him from observation when at rest among withered foliage. Thus we have the pale yellow of the upper side of the wings in the male developed under bright sunlight, the duller browner colours of the lower side in the neighbourhood of withered foliage, the sombre-tinted female in shady spots among bushes. The wings of the female have degenerated in size and power in comparison with those of the male, as a result of the activity of the latter and the inactivity of the former.

The argument would be still stronger if it could be shown that the imitated species of the Danaidæ had habits similar to the female *P. cenea,* and different from those of the male of that species. To a certain extent this can be shown. The first form of *P. cenea,* female, is the commonest, and the following is the account given by Trimen and Bowker of the habits of *Amauris echeria,* the Danaid which it mimics. This butterfly is rather gregarious, is strictly confined to woods and copses, its flight is remarkably graceful and leisurely, it is fond of floating across open spots in the woods,

---

[1] Trimen and Bowker, *South African Butterflies,* London 1889, vol. iii. p. 254.

flapping its wings once or twice, and then settling on some projecting twig and remaining for some time motionless, usually with the wings closed, and hanging downwards. It is clear, therefore, that the pattern form and the mimic spend much of their time settled among bushes.

From an observation by Mr. Mansel Weale quoted by Trimen and Bowker, it would appear that all three forms of the female of *P. cenea* may arise from the same parents in one locality. The former gentleman reared all three forms from a number of larvæ found together, and therefore it may be inferred that the three forms are the dominant types in a wide range of variation in the females of a single species. In other words the female is trimorphic, although the three imitated forms of *Danais* are distinct species. To speculate on the causes of this state of things is perhaps not very profitable without further evidence, but it may be pointed out that it does not necessarily imply selection. It is possible that each form of the *Papilio* is related to particular conditions, or they may be merely the three main types which variability, once set up by conditions, tends to produce. In either case crossing of the forms occurs through the males, a male which is the offspring of one form mating with either of the others, and then the progeny resembling either the mother or grandmother, but not uniting the characters of both. If each variety is related to special conditions, then (as in the case of the primrose) probably an individual which develops a particular variation-type places itself under the same conditions which produced the variation, and so develops it still further. If this is not the case then we must conclude that the permanent distinctness of the three forms, in spite of intercrossing, is due to physiological obstacles to the combination of the characters in the same individual.

It has been tacitly assumed by those who invented and those who have adopted the theory of mimicry that the

mimicking forms are edible, and that they escape destruction
by deceiving the enemies which would devour them if they
were not disguised. Yet strange to say this assumption has
never been tested. It may be perfectly true that mimicking
forms often belong to edible and much persecuted families,
but it is by no means certain that a form which has acquired
the dark or conspicuous colours of another inedible species
owes its safety entirely to its deceptive *appearance.* Inedible
forms, such as the Heliconidæ, the gooseberry caterpillar, and
others are distasteful largely in consequence of the presence
of the pigments which make them conspicuous. Therefore
when a mimicking form acquires similar pigments it probably
likewise ceases to be palatable to insect eaters, and would be
equally unmolested even if it possessed no particular resemblance to a species of another family. The theory of specific
mimicry involves assumptions that have not been sufficiently
realised. It assumes that birds or other enemies of butterflies are as precise in entomological discrimination as the
human specialist. Consider, for example, the cases in which
special varieties of the imitating form are associated with
special varieties of the imitated in different localities. The
differences between the varieties require careful examination
to be perceived, even an entomologist would not distinguish
them as varieties if he studied them only alive in their
natural conditions. Suppose that the mimicking edible form
had only one variety in both localities, and the pattern form
had two. Is it conceivable that a bird or lizard would
perceive the slight discrepancy in the second locality, and
would pick off the individuals of the edible form which had
not a sufficiently exact resemblance to the markings of the
second variety of the inedible form? If we are to suppose
that this takes place we have also to suppose that the bird
or lizard knows a particular variety of an inedible species
and does not molest it, but attacks the individuals of an

16

edible species which resemble *the other variety* of the inedible species. This supposition is so manifestly absurd and impossible that no one who has realised it can continue to regard natural selection alone as a sufficient explanation of the refinements of mimicry to which I have alluded.

That external conditions, whether of climate, food, or light, have had an important influence in determining the characters of the Heliconidæ in South America, which are there the forms imitated by other species, is indicated by the statement of Bates that these species are peculiarly creatures of the tropical forests, like the Platyrhine monkeys, the arboreal Gallinacei (Penolopidœ and Cracidæ), the sloths, and other animals of the same region. The Heliconidæ are most numerous where the forests are most extensive and the climate most sultry and humid. Since the Heliconidæ are accompanied in their gregarious flocks by the imitating forms, the latter have as a matter of fact been subjected to the same influences. Where the sexes are dimorphic in the imitating forms, the difference of conditions appears to consist, as in the cases mentioned below, in the fact that the males resort to sunny places in the daytime, and seek the females only in the evening.

The sexes of many butterflies and moths differ considerably, although neither sex is mimetic. Darwin has discussed these cases at some length, but it can scarcely be considered that he has shown it to be very probable that the differences are due to sexual selection. He admits that many serious objections may be urged against this explanation. He points out that in several cases the males and females of the same species of butterfly are known to inhabit different stations, the former commonly basking in the sunshine, the latter haunting gloomy forests.[1] He considers that it is thus

---

[1] The passage to which Darwin refers in Bates' *Naturalist on the Amazons* is worth quoting here :—"It is a singular fact that with very few

possible that the different conditions of life may have acted differently on the two sexes, but that this is improbable because the period of exposure, *i.e.* of the life of the imago, is short and the larvæ are exposed to the same conditions. Now the colours of the imago, it is well known, do not depend directly on those of the larva, and as the imago varies independently there is no reason why its variations should not be influenced by its special conditions. It is very obvious that there is no evidence of real importance to show that female butterflies exert a choice in their sexual relations, or that the brilliant colours of one sex in dimorphic species have any influence in exciting the sexual instincts of the other sex. Indeed, the fact that such a high degree of coloration and ornamentation can exist in one sex only of many species of Lepidoptera affords good reason for rejecting the view that the brilliant plumage of male birds is chiefly due to the choice of the female among competing suitors. On the other hand, if we assume that variations in definite directions are excited by external conditions, in this case principally by light of different colours, the facts become intelligible in general, although it is not possible in the present state of knowledge to explain all particular cases.

On the other hand, Darwin quotes the evidence of Mr. Bates that in the case of the South American genus, *Epicalia,* there is in many species an extreme difference between the sexes, although they haunt the same stations. I can only suggest in this case that the two sexes may be influenced by different conditions in some way of which Mr. Bates was not aware. It must be remembered that, according to the views

exceptions all the individuals of these various species (about 80 in number) thus sporting in sunny places were of the male sex, their partners, which are much more soberly dressed and immensely less numerous than the males, being confined to the shades of the woods. Every afternoon, as the sun was getting low, I used to notice these gaudy, sunshine-loving swains trooping off to the forest, where I suppose they would find their sweethearts and wives."

I am maintaining, external influences only excite variation
and determine its direction, the result of the variation, the
coloration and marking produced may depend very largely
on the physiological processes of growth and the development
of tissues.

It is very interesting and important to notice that in a
large number of instances the difference in coloration between
male and female of the same species is precisely of the same
kind as the difference between the upper and lower surfaces
of the wings in the individual. This is a correspondence
which surely is not without significance. For example,
Darwin quotes the following case from Prof. Weismann
(*Descent of Man*, second edition, p. 312):—"The female of
one of the Lycænæ expands her brown wings when she
settles on the ground, and is then almost invisible; the male,
on the other hand, as if aware of the danger incurred from
the bright blue of the upper surface of his wings, rests with
them closed, and this shows that the blue colour cannot be
in any way protective." Now if the exposure, *i.e.* the light
reflected from habitual surroundings, determines the coloration, then this difference of habit in the two sexes will
explain why the upper side of the wings in the female is
brown, in the male not. It does not exactly explain why
the upper surface in the male should be blue. But, as is
well known, in many butterflies which rest with their wings
vertically raised and the upper surfaces in contact, the
lower side which is thus exposed in the resting insect is
coloured so as to resemble with remarkable exactness the
surrounding surface, while the upper surface, exposed only
during flight, is conspicuously and beautifully coloured.
This is strikingly the case in the famous butterfly *Kallima*,
whose closed wings resemble a dead leaf, while the upper
surface is brilliant with orange and other colours. In moths,
on the other hand, which rest with the wings depressed, the

upper surfaces usually exhibit protective resemblance, and
not the lower.

It might be objected that if the exposure of the upper
sides in butterflies causes bright conspicuous colours, how
can similar exposure cause dull protective colours in moths?
But the exposure is not similar. By exposure I mean the

FIG. 23.—A. *Catocala electa*, a British moth, wings expanded as in flight. The hind wing is
red and black. B. The same with wings closed in the resting position, the brightly
coloured hind wings entirely concealed. C. *Satyrus semele*, a British butterfly showing
the upper surface of the wings as in flight. D. The same, showing the lower surface
of the wings. When the insect settles the *fore wing* is drawn down behind the hind
wing, so as to be entirely concealed.

kind of light to which the surface is exposed, and I believe
that in Lepidoptera the coloration has chiefly been determined by the quality of the light. The upper side of a
butterfly's wings in flight is exposed to bright sunshine or to
the coloured lights reflected from gay flowers. The upper
side of the wings of a resting moth receive dull light in

shady places reflected from the bark of trees or such dull-coloured surroundings.

Darwin mentions the fact that in the Bombycidæ and Noctuidæ when at rest the fore wings overlap and conceal the hind wings, and these are exposed only during flight. In accordance with this the hind wings are often brightly coloured. The yellow under-wing, *Tryphœna pronuba*, is an illustration of this. It often flies about during the day or early evening and its yellow hind wings are bright and conspicuous. Species of Catocala offer other examples of the same condition. The upper surface of the hind wings are coloured red and black, and are therefore very conspicuous, but when the insect settles the hind wings are entirely covered with the fore wings, the dorsal surface of which is protectively coloured with zigzag markings of various shades of gray, so that they are indistinguishable on surfaces of bark or rock. This is shown in the figures of *Catocala electa*.

In some butterflies a similar result is attained by a method exactly opposite. The wings are held vertically when the insect is at rest, and the fore wing is covered by the hind wing : the under surface of the hind wing is then protectively coloured, and the insect at rest is only to be detected with difficulty. An interesting account of this protective resemblance in *Satyrus semele* will be found in Barrett's *Lepidoptera of the British Islands,* vol. i. p. 223. This insect settles habitually on the ground, and the under side of its hinder wings varies in colour in some degree according to the colour of the soil on which it usually rests ! In its usual haunts on heaths and hill-sides this surface of the wings is always dark, like the earth or rock ; in chalky districts the colour is mottled with white, producing in an extraordinary degree the mottled whitish appearance of weathered and stained chalk. The selectionist explains all the above facts by the utility of the different colorations.

But on this view the brilliance of the non-protective coloration has to be explained. It can scarcely be suggested that it is a warning coloration, for warning and protective coloration cannot well exist in the same individual. On the selection view it must be maintained that, on the one hand, those individual butterflies were being selected in which the coloration of the lower surface afforded the most protective resemblance, while on the other those whose upper surfaces were most brilliant and conspicuous were being chosen by the females. But this raises the question—Why did the upper and lower surfaces of the wings vary independently? If the different exposures which undoubtedly exist determined the modifications, we have an answer to this question, while on the other view no attempt is made to consider the laws or causes of variation. Or, to put the matter in another way, the facts point with the utmost clearness to the conclusion that the coloration has been influenced and determined by the different exposures.

On the theory of sexual selection it must be held that selection by the female has been exercised in those cases in which the male is specially adorned, and not in those in which the sexes are equally without adornment. Now in birds this contention may be supported by evidence from the different sexual habits of the various species and families, some being promiscuous, some pairing for life, or for a season, and some being polygamous. But in butterflies and moths the sexual relations do not vary in this way in different species or families. There is no permanent association of male and female, but all the species are equally promiscuous. Other things being equal, therefore, there ought to be the same amount of competition between males, and the same amount of selection in all species. Other things, however, are not necessarily equal, and even if the degree of competition were the same, the method of competition might be different. In some cases the males might be more numerous in proportion to the females than in others. In some cases the males might fight, in others compete by the beauty of their wings, in others again the individuals with the most acute sense of smell might succeed. Male Lepidoptera certainly do not fight very fiercely, and I do not know of any structures possessed by them which are specialised for offence or defence. What evidence is there of the competition in beauty? Is there any reason to believe that the colour or markings of the male serve as in birds to gain the consent of the female. Dr. A. G. Butler[1] some years ago discussed the shaded marginal spots in Brahmæa, one of the Heterocera or moths of West Africa, and suggested that their evolution was due to the same principle as that of the ocelli of the Argus pheasant, according to Darwin. He states that many moths when approaching the female swing up and down with a pendulum motion behind her, so that at each swing the ocelli on the wings of one side would be seen correctly shaded. But it is by no means clear that this movement on the part of the male is intended to exhibit the wings to the female, or indeed that the eyes of the Lepidopterous insect have any appreciation of beauty at all. In birds there is no doubt that males display their specialised plumage, and that the females are sexually excited by the display. But in butterflies I find no reason to believe that anything of the kind takes place. Birds erect their sexual plumes, and in most cases the beauty and the colour are scarcely visible except when the bird is showing off. The beauty of a butterfly's wing is equally visible whenever the insect flies ; there is no special attitude of display exhibited in courtship, nor any evidence of the male inviting the female by showing his beauty. In illustration of this subject I may refer to Skertchly's observation of the courtship and

[1] *Lepidoptera Exotica*, London, 1874, p. 78.

coupling of *Ornithoptera brookiana*.[1] In all the species of this genus the females are larger than the males, and sombre in colouring, while the males are very brilliant. In this particular species the male is mostly black, with green marks on the wings, and a broad collar of crimson. The male seen by Skertchly was sipping the flowers of a tree, vibrating its wings rapidly like a hawk-moth, the vivid green markings flashing out in the sunlight. The female came and "did all the wooing." They circled about in flight with the female above and a little behind, so that she could see the emerald marks of the male. There is no evidence of competition here, although the males are so numerous that one collector caught over a thousand of them, and only fifteen females. The observer remarks: "One would expect the amorous swains to swarm around coy maidens instead of behaving like lepidopterous Josephs." He also writes: "It certainly seemed to me that, being mature, she accepted the first male she met." These observations were made in Borneo.

Moseley,[2] however, in the Aru Islands, saw a dozen males of *Ornithoptera poseidon* fluttering round and mobbing a single female. But it is difficult to believe that a female in such circumstances had the power of choosing the most beautiful male : in the confusion and crowding she could not possibly see which was the brightest. The luckiest and most active male would probably be successful.

The above remarks apply to cases in which the males are more brilliant than the females, and those in which the sexes are similar. There are, however, cases among Lepidoptera, as in birds, in which the female is more brilliant and beautiful than the male. The differences in these cases are not extreme, not nearly so great, for example, as in dimorphic species exhibiting mimicry. In the British species of butter-

[1] *Ann. Mag. Nat. Hist.* (6) iv. 1889, p. 213.
[2] *Naturalist on the Challenger*, p. 373.

flies in which the female is more coloured, e.g. *Colias edusa*, and in *Pieris*, it is stated by Professor Meldola that the females support the males in the marriage flight, and Professor Poulton has observed that in these cases the females were the more ardent wooers, so that the males could exercise a choice. There is, however, no evidence at all that the males are affected by the colour of the females, and when we consider that the difference consists in *Pieris* in the possession by the female of one or two black spots, it is impossible to believe that the male is determined in his affections by slight variations of these. On the other hand, the very fact of the female supporting the male in flight is a difference in her exertions, and it is possible that, as in fishes, greater sexual excitement may affect the secretion of pigment.

There is every reason to believe that the sexual instincts of Lepidoptera, and probably of insects generally, are exerted chiefly through the sense of smell located in the antennæ, and that the sense of sight has little or nothing to do with the matter. Therefore a theory based on ideas of beauty and selection has very little foundation. Moreover, the dimorphism does not always, or even generally, consist in differences of beauty, nor are the most beautiful species generally the most dimorphic. Professor Poulton[1] has maintained that the dependence of bright colours and beauty in male moths on sexual selection is strongly supported by the fact that the more degenerate the female the less brightness and beauty are seen in the males. His evidence for this argument is taken from the Bombyces. In the family Saturniidæ the male Emperor moth is much more beautiful than the female, and is in itself brilliantly coloured. In the Psychidæ, on the other hand, the female is much more degenerate, having neither wings nor legs. In these the males, though well developed and active, are less ornamented. The reason,

---

[1] *Colours of Animals*, Intern. Sci. Series, 1890, p. 294.

according to Poulton, is that the degenerate females are incapable of exercising a choice, and therefore the more beautiful males are not selected.

In answer to this I would urge that the main point to be explained is the sexual dimorphism. If one principle can explain the degeneracy of the females and higher development of the males in the Psychidæ, it can also explain the superior brilliancy of the males in the Saturniidæ. It can scarcely be maintained that the males in the former have preferred the most degenerate females. This has not yet been suggested even by Professor Poulton. It is much more reasonable to suppose that the females in this family have become degenerate through sedentary habits, while the males have not adopted such habits. The dimorphism in this family is much greater than in the Saturniidæ, and if difference of conditions explains the greater difference, a fortiori, it probably explains the smaller. Therefore, though I do not know the habits of male and female in the Emperor moth, it seems to me reasonable to believe that the plainness of the female in that species and the more vivid colouring of the male are due not to the choice exercised by the female, but to the different effects of different habits and conditions.

From the above considerations I conclude that, in the majority of cases, sexual differences in colour and marking in Lepidoptera are related to differences in the conditions of life, not directly to courtship or the union of the sexes. There are, however, a number of sexual differences known which are related to the union of the sexes, and the function of most of these specialisations seems to be to enable the individuals of one sex to find those of the other. In such cases the process of selection need not be denied. It is obvious that an individual that fails to find a mate leaves no progeny, and his defects are therefore eliminated, while the individual which finds a mate most easily has the best chance of leaving progeny. But, as I have repeatedly urged, the point is, Why is the inheritance limited to one sex? and this is explained on the theory that the elaborations of structure are due to stimulations only affecting one sex.

The olfactory sense plays an important part in guiding the male to the female, and this sense resides in the antennæ. These organs are frequently specialised in the males, often to an extreme degree in the Bombyces, especially in the Psychidæ, in which the female is often sedentary. In this case the exercise of the sense and of the organ has evidently been at work throughout the evolution. It is not merely the exercise of the nerves of perception, which must be more stimulated as the search for the female falls more exclusively on the male, but the tissue of the antenna itself is doubtless exercised by various movements and contractions produced by the active efforts of the male to discover the required scent. The acuteness of this sense in certain species is well known. Sir Roland Trimen[1] states that the male of *Lasiocampa Quercus* is attracted by the empty box from which a female has been removed.

In the genus *Mastigophorus*, belonging to the Noctuidæ, and occurring in India and tropical America, there is an extraordinary development of the mandibular palpi in the males. These are elongated and bent so as to be carried over the back ; they are not only much thicker and longer than the antennæ, but actually longer than the body. In the females they are very much smaller. In the males they terminate in fringes or brushes of long hairs. Unfortunately, the function of these organs is not known. The palpi in general are probably organs of touch, but possibly these specialised palpi possess other senses. The fact that the antennæ are not specially developed in most of the Noctuidæ suggests that these enlarged palpi have taken over the

[1] *South African Butterflies*, p. 13.

olfactory function. Whatever their function, there can be little doubt that they are moved about actively when in use, and thus the stimulation to their development has never been wanting. The excessive development has doubtless resulted from excessive use. If they are organs of touch, they may possibly be used in finding the female in the following way : the Noctuidæ generally live on and near the ground, and the males might fly about over the ground or grass with their palpi extended and moving until these organs came in contact with a female.

COLEOPTERA.—In the Longicornia or Cerambycidæ the antennæ are usually much longer in the males. These organs are doubtless employed either for touch or smell, or both, in finding the females, and it is in accordance with the greater use that is made of them that they should be enlarged in the males. In a few species the sexes differ in colour, and although I have no evidence on the point, it is probable that in these cases the habits are different. In any case, it is stated that the bright-coloured species expose themselves in the daytime on flowers and plants, while the dull-coloured forms do not leave their hiding-places until twilight.

In the Lamellicorns occur sexual differences as marked as in any instance in the animal kingdom. The unisexual characters of the males are often horn-like projections from the head and thorax, which in many species exhibit an extraordinary development. Darwin, being unable to find good evidence that these horns were used as fighting weapons, came to the conclusion that they had been acquired as ornaments.

These excrescences are chiefly characteristic of the Dynastides, a sub-family of the Scarabæidæ, among which are found some of the largest insects known. The proportional size of the horns is extraordinary. They project from the dorsal surface of the head and prothorax in such a

way as to be opposed to each other, they are not articulated
but rigidly connected with those parts of the body.   But the
head and prothorax themselves are movable, and thus the
horns can be moved about like the limbs of a pair of tongs.
Entomologists are still unable to assign a definite use to
these excrescences.   It is stated that they are but little used
for fighting.   According to Mr. David Sharp, in the *Cambridge*

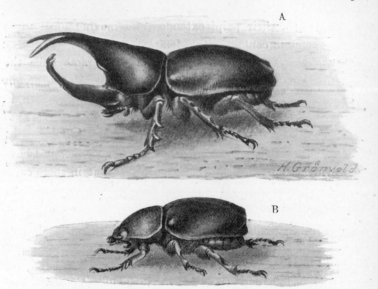

FIG. 24.—*Xylotrupes Gideon* : a common beetle in India and the Malay Archipelago.
A, male ; B, female.

Natural History, Baron von Hügel saw the males of *Xylotrupes
Gideon* in Java sometimes carrying the females by means of
their horns; but Mr. Sharp considers this must be an
exceptional case, because in the majority of species the shape
of the horns makes such an employment of them impossible.
Whether the excrescences are useful or not, it seems to me
that their resemblance to similar unisexual developments in
other families indicates that they have been produced by
mechanical irritation, by blows of some kind ; and as so

little is known of the life-histories of these forms and of their
habits it is premature to conclude that they are inexplicable.

In the Lucanidæ the peculiarity of the males consists in
the enlargement of the true mandibles, which are sometimes
as long as the body and give rise to the popular name of
stag-beetles.   These organs also, according to Mr. Sharp, are
of very little use ; but it is known, as stated by Darwin, that
male stag-beetles fight fiercely with their great mandibles,
and they have often been seen carrying off the females with

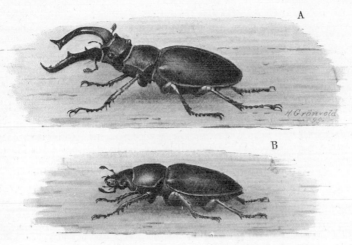

Fig. 25.—*Lucanus cervus* the common Stag-beetle.   A, male ; B female.

them.   Thus I see no difficulty in attributing the great
hypertrophy of the mandibles to the violent use which is
made of them, which on the one hand enlarges the muscles
and the cuticle to which the muscles are attached, and on the
other causes the epidermis to be hypertrophied, so that
the whole appendage grows larger and the cuticle thicker.
Darwin gives striking figures of the male and female of
Chiasognathus Grantii, one of the Lucanidæ found in Chili,
and states from his own observation that the greatly enlarged
mandibles of the male are used as weapons.   He also describes

the habits of another species, *Lethrus cephalotes*, in which the male and female cohabit in the same burrow, and the male, which has enlarged mandibles, gives battle to all intruders. We have therefore in this case, as in others, the evidence that the special modification or hypertrophy of particular parts in one sex is associated with special mechanical stimulation, and we have no reason to believe that the male would have been thus different from the female unless as a consequence of this special stimulation.

Conspicuous as the excrescences of male Coleoptera are in themselves, they are even more extraordinary in their variability within the same species. Secondary sexual characters are often variable, but there are no other animals in which such differences in the degree of their development in the same species are constantly found as in these two families of Coleoptera. In the Dynastides every degree of development may occur, from males which are almost similar to the females in everything except that they are slightly larger, to males with an extreme development of horns, and a size of body much greater than that of the female. In the Lucanidæ very often the degrees of development fall into two or more distinct stages, intermediate conditions being rare or wanting. In this family the mandibles of the females are often of considerable size, and those of the best developed males are not only much larger but of different shape. In one species, for instance, the mandibles in the females are fairly straight and parallel, while those of the males are curved so as to meet only at the ends. Now the least developed form of the males resembles the females not only in the size but in the *shape* of the mandibles, while the intermediate "forms" or states are of course intermediate. Thus the males themselves are polymorphic. No theory based on selection has succeeded in explaining this remarkable state of things. Darwin considered that the great range of variation supported the conclusion that the horns of Dynastides had been acquired as ornaments, because, I suppose, in that case the imperfect development would be of little importance. But whether the structures are ornaments or weapons, if only the best developed are successful, their perfection ought to be transmitted to their offspring, so that on this reasoning either sexual selection does not occur, or it fails of its object.

Now it seems to me that the views I have put forward in the present work are capable of explaining, at least to a certain extent, the extraordinary variability of the sexual attributes of these Coleoptera. The chief principle of my theory is that sexual characters have been developed by stimulations associated with the functional activity of the male sexual organs, and with the nervous excitement corresponding to that functional activity. The sexual instinct gives rise to certain habits of combat or courtship, these habits cause special mechanical irritations of particular parts of the body, and the consequent irritation and hypertrophy take place during the time when the activity of all the organs and tissues is intensified by sexual excitement. Heredity, following the course of the original development, causes the structural modifications only to develop in the individual when the male organs are active and the sexual instincts are excited, or when these conditions are approaching. Now in insects we have evidence that the development of the sexual organs depends largely on the nutrition of the larva. The longer the larval state the more room there is for variations in the nutrition of the larva. Again, when the food of the larva is relatively innutritious, as it is in the case of the Lucanidæ and Dynastides which live on decaying vegetable matter, especially rotten wood, there is a still greater probability that some of the larvæ will be imperfectly fed. It is therefore possible that some of the male individuals

17

when they reach the stage of the imago will be sterile, either absolutely or comparatively. The testes being absent or imperfectly developed, the unisexual excrescences which are correlated with them will be absent or imperfectly developed. When the modification in the male has been the alteration in shape of mandibles already present in the female, the imperfect development of the testes will naturally imply the development of a male similar to the female.

In support of this view it may be pointed out that the variations in the development of horns and mandibles in these male Coleoptera resemble very suggestively the variations produced in the horns of stags by partial or complete castration. Therefore it seems reasonable to conclude that in these insects there is a kind of natural castration or sterility of varying degree. With regard to the influence of food on the generative organs, especially of nitrogenous food, it is now well established that the ovaries of bees are prevented from perfect development, or allowed to take that development, according to the food supplied to the larvæ. The Termites again develop the sexual organs at almost any stage of development by means of special feeding.

The hypothesis that the least differentiated males of these Coleoptera are sterile or neuter has been previously considered, and rejected by Leuthner.[1] He writes: " The idea that the so-called degenerated forms should be regarded as neuters was refuted by an examination of the fully developed, and even comparatively large sexual organs, in which not only the chitinous parts, but also the testes and their contents (the spermatozoa), were found to be well developed in the smallest males." But he adds in a footnote that the spermatozoa could only be observed in the smallest males of *Lucanus cervus*, the European stag-beetle. Probably he only possessed dead and perhaps dried specimens of other species.

---

[1] Monograph of the Odontolabini, *Trans. Zool. Soc. Lond.* vol. xi., 1885.

I do not consider this evidence by any means sufficient; the smallest males may not be completely sterile, just as worker bees are not always perfectly sterile. The question is whether there is *any* constant difference in the size and development of the sexual organs in the well-developed and the ill-developed males. I cannot discover that any one has properly investigated the subject.

Stridulating organs in Coleoptera have been discussed at length by Darwin, and he shows that only in a few species are they confined to one sex. There is no difficulty, once admitting that mechanical stimulation produces a hereditary effect on growth and development, in understanding how special stridulating organs have been evolved. Darwin supposes that "originally various beetles made a shuffling or hissing noise by the rubbing together of any hard and rough parts of their bodies ; and that from the noise thus produced being in some way useful, the rough surfaces were gradually developed into regular stridulating organs." To this conclusion I have no objection to offer, provided that it is understood that the gradual development was the consequence of the friction, and not due to selection from spontaneous variations.

In many Malacodermata we find a sexual dimorphism similar to that which occurs in many moths, the females having lost their wings, and being otherwise degenerate. This occurs in the common glow-worm, *Lampyris noctiluca,* and species allied to it. The males have ample wings under their elytra, and very large eyes. The female has smaller eyes and neither elytra nor wings ; her body is flat, soft, and broad, and in fact resembles the larva from which she is developed, except that she possesses the ordinary femur, tibia, and five-jointed tarsi to the legs, eleven-jointed antennæ, and a broad, flat, semicircular thorax. It is difficult to perceive in what way the degeneracy of the female is to be explained on the principle of sexual selection. It may perhaps be suggested that, the emission of light serving as a guide to the male, the female does not need to fly, and has therefore lost her wings, through the cessation of selection with regard to the wings. But unless the wings were positively disadvantageous the cessation of selection alone could never cause their disappearance in this case, where they have disappeared only in one sex. It would be difficult to prove that the wings became a positive disadvantage to the female. On the view that disuse of the wings in the female only has led directly to their degeneration, the evolution becomes intelligible, and it is noteworthy that apterous females both in Lepidoptera and Coleoptera occur chiefly in nocturnal species, because these are naturally apt to develop to the extreme their retiring and inactive habits. The glow-worms in both sexes, and in both larval and perfect stages, feed on small snails and slugs, which are to be found in damp grass, and the wings are therefore only required by the males in seeking the females. Here again, if the development of organs is as a general principle associated with the sex or the time of life in which functional stimulation of them occurs, we can understand the sexual dimorphism, but on the selection principle there is no reason why a variation occurring and surviving in one sex should not be equally transmitted to the other.

I do not profess to be able to explain the origin of the property of phosphorescence in *Lampyris*, but this, although more developed in the female, has been observed in all the stages, and in both sexes of the insect. The greater size of the eyes in the male indicates that the light of the female is the indication by which he finds her. But apterous females occur also in species which are not phosphorescent, for instance in *Drilus flavescens*, a beetle of the same family.

HYMENOPTERA.—In some species of Bees, according to Darwin, the mandibles of the males are larger than those of the females, and these males fight with one another with their mandibles. Here, therefore, the required mechanical stimulus is present to account for the greater development. In the social bees there are three forms—the perfect fertile females, the perfect males, and the workers which are permanently immature females, *i.e.* adults in which the sexual organs are imperfectly developed. The perfect females of solitary bees usually possess organs specially adapted for food-collecting, which are absent in the males. There is no difficulty in accounting for this structure as the result of stimulations caused by the act of carrying the pollen. A few words of explanation concerning the mode in which I believe such stimulation acts in insects are here necessary. So far as my knowledge goes, the perfect insect does not change its form, or exhibit new growths after its emergence from the pupa. Nevertheless, mechanical irritations applied to a particular spot on the cuticle can affect the growth of the living cells beneath it, and such stimulation may show itself in the imago of the next generation in a changed form of the epidermis and of the cuticle produced from it. I conceive the process to be of the same kind as that which produces an outgrowth of the epidermis and cuticle in Crustacea, for example the outgrowth of the penultimate joint of the pincher claw in the lobster, which I regard as due to the pressure of the last joint biting against the last joint but one.

In the hive bee the pollen-brush on the legs is wanting in the queen, but present in the worker. It seems to me possible to explain this on the view that the organ has disappeared in the queen through disuse, and that nevertheless she transmits it to her female offspring in every generation, because the reduction of it in the queen is associated with the specialisation and increase of the reproductive organs. The latter are not fully developed in the worker, which accordingly inherits the earlier stage of development of the queen.

Slight differences of colour in the sexes of Hymenoptera are of less importance, and are probably associated in all cases with corresponding differences in the conditions of life or development.

ORTHOPTERA.—In this Order the males nearly all possess a stridulating apparatus which is wanting in the female. The structure of the apparatus is different in the different families, but in all cases consists of toothed or ridged surfaces of the cuticle, which are rubbed against other parts. Here the movement of the parts under the influence of sexual excitement, whether originally producing a sound or not, must, if stimulation affects growth at all, have produced a modification of structure, and on the hypothesis that such effects become in time hereditary, the present condition is explained. On the other hand, the selection theory merely assumes that the variations occurred, and survived, but fails to account for the absence of such variations in most cases in the female.

In some species of Orthoptera, as in the *Pneumora* of South Africa mentioned by Darwin, the males are winged and the females wingless, and the same is the case in the common European cockroach. This condition occurring in so many orders of insects may be explained by disuse of the wings in the females in all cases.

In Neuroptera, differences between the sexes in habits' and structure seem to be but slightly developed, although there are often considerable differences in colour.

In the Homoptera, Hemiptera, and Diptera, a few cases of sexual dimorphism are mentioned by Darwin, such as the organ of sound in the male Cicadæ, wingless females in the Hemiptera, and horn-like outgrowths on the head of a species of the Diptera. They all seem to me to be explicable by the views I have maintained, but I am not able to compare in detail the structures and corresponding habits or conditions.

CHAPTER VI

CRUSTACEA

DARWIN states that in surveying the classes of animals from the lower upwards this is the first class in which undoubted secondary sexual characters occur. He has previously mentioned that among the class Annelida, or marine worms, the sexes when separate sometimes differ very greatly, but considers that their differences are not of the kind which can be safely attributed to sexual selection. But if sexual differences of great magnitude can exist where sexual selection does not and cannot occur, what proof is there that other sexual differences are due to sexual selection? Doubtless Darwin's view was that in certain cases where courtship, rivalry, and the choice of the opposite sex did not exist, natural selection acted differently on males and females. But as has been already pointed out, the facts prove that the difference is not merely in the selection but in the variation, in the modifications. In Darwin's treatment of the subject it is merely taken as a fact that variations occur which are limited to one sex, in other words which are transmitted only to individuals of that sex in which they occur. No attempt is made to explain this. On the other hand, on the theory that different conditions cause different modifications, and that such modifications are necessarily associated with the sex or the period of life upon which alone the particular conditions operate, the origin of the modifications is explained, and *all* cases of sexual dimorphism are seen to be special cases of the one general principle.

Darwin refers to the extraordinary differences between the sexes in the lower parasitic species of Crustacea, in which the males are of small size and alone are furnished with perfect swimming legs, antennæ, and sense organs; the females being destitute of these organs, with their bodies often consisting of a mere distorted mass. Concerning these he remarks that they are no doubt related to their widely different habits of life, and consequently do not concern the question of sexual selection. According to the views I am here expressing the differences in the two cases are due to causes of the same kind. Habits and actions of the individual may be concerned in the quest for food, in the escape from enemies, or in the intercourse of male and female. The end achieved by the characters or organs which are associated with certain habits or actions makes no difference whatever in the explanation of the origin or evolution of these characters and organs. The habits or actions set up particular stimulations of particular parts of the body. These stimulations produce certain reactions in the growth and development of the parts.

The following table of the subdivisions of the Crustacea will help to explain the names used in this chapter :—

CLASSIFICATION OF CRUSTACEA.

SUB-CLASSES.

Malacostraca.   Entomostraca.   Gigantostraca.
Thyrostraca (Cirripedia).

MALACOSTRACA.

Orders.

Podophthalma.

|
Sub-orders.
Brachyura ⎫
Macrura ⎬ Decapoda.
Schizopoda.
Stomatopoda.

Edriophthalma.

|
Sub-orders.
Cumacea.
Isopoda.
Amphipoda.

ENTOMOSTRACA.

Orders.

Branchiopoda.

|
Sub-orders.
Phyllocarida.
Phyllopoda.
Cladocera.
Branchiura.

Ostracoda.

|
Sub-orders.
Podocopa.
Myodocopa.
Cladocopa.
Platycopa.

Copepoda

|
Sub-orders.
Gnathostomata.
Pœcilostoma.
Siphonostoma.

GIGANTOSTRACA.

Orders.

Merostomata.   Xiphosura.   Trilobita.

THYROSTRACA (Cirripedia).

Orders.

Thoracica.   Abdominalia.   Apoda.   Rhizocephala.

|
Pedunculata.
Operculata.

PODOPHTHALMA, or STALK-EYED CRUSTACEA.—In the
Brachyura, or crabs, the male is usually much larger than

the female, and his chelæ or pincers especially are larger
than those of the female. Darwin believed that the chief use
of the chelæ was to seize and hold the female, though he subsequently remarks that the chelæ are well adapted for fighting.
In the Brachyura fertilisation is effected by a process of true
copulation. The male grasps the female at first by the back.

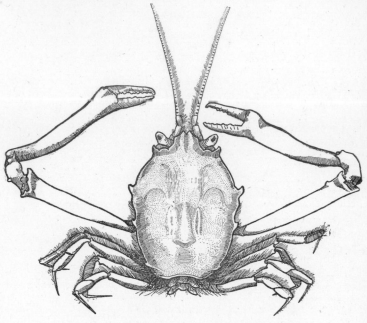

Fig. 26.—*Corystes cassivelaunus*, the Masked Crab, male.

The copulatory organs in the male are the two first pairs of
appendages on the "tail" or abdomen. The apertures of the
seminal ducts are at the base of the fifth pair of walking
legs. The female apertures are on the bases of the third
pair of legs. The intromittent appendages of the male are
inserted into the female apertures, and the milt of the male
is thus introduced. I have not had an opportunity of making
detailed observations with the object of discovering whether

the male exerts his muscular powers in general, and his chelæ in particular, most in holding the female, or in fighting with other males. There can be little doubt, however, that the males struggle with one another, and it is certain that their greater size and strength, and especially the greater development of their chelæ, corresponds to the more active part they play in the relations of the sexes.

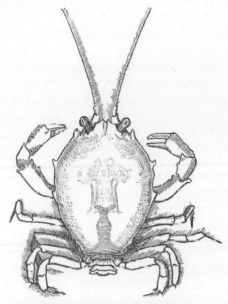

FIG. 27.—*Corystes cassivelaunus*, female.

To illustrate the sexual dimorphism of the Brachyura I have given figures of the male and female in two British species, the Masked Crab, *Corystes cassivelaunus*, and the Angular Crab, *Gonoplax angulatus*. These figures were drawn from average adult specimens, and correctly represent the proportional dimensions of the males and females.

Darwin mentions a Brazilian species of *Gelasimus* in which the male is coloured green and white, while the female is uniformly greyish brown, and states that the male does not acquire his conspicuous colours until he is sexually mature. The chelæ of the male are larger than those of the female, and in some species of the genus, if not in all, the sexes pair and inhabit the same burrow. The colours of the male are liable to change in the course of a few minutes, the white becoming dirty gray, the green losing much of its brilliancy. In this case the elements of coloration are probably the same in kind in the two sexes, though quantitatively they may differ. It is known that the colours of Crustacea are largely due to " chromatophores " which expand and contract under the influence of the nervous system, as in fishes. Thus the only reasonable conclusion concerning this difference of colour is that in principle it is due to the nervous excitement of the male under the influence of the sexual instinct, both in courting the female and defending his possession of her against other males. I believe that the more the phenomena are investigated, the more important will be found the influence of the nervous system in relation to the excitement resulting from sexual relations.

Darwin states that it seems to be a general rule in Crustacea that the unisexual characters of the males are only developed towards the approach of sexual maturity. As in other cases, this is one of the strongest proofs that the characters are the direct result of stimulations which are only set up by the sexual activities.

Sexual dimorphism also occurs in the Macrura. In the fresh-water crayfishes of North America belonging to the genus *Cambarus* it has long been known that two distinct forms of males occur. These were first described by Hagen in his Monograph of the North American Astacidæ.[1] One of the forms is much differentiated from the female, while the other is less divergent and evidently less specialised. These forms differ in the first place in the structure of the

[1] *Ill. Cat. Mus. Harv.* iii., Cambridge, Mass. 1870.

first pair of abdominal legs, which form copulatory organs as in the majority of the stalk-eyed Crustacea. In the first form the tip of this appendage is less membranous than in the second, the hooks on it are horny, the teeth or bifid ends are longer and more separated, the hairiness in those species where hairs occur more profuse. But the first form differs from the second also in other characters. The whole body is more robust and more sculptured, while the claws are longer and broader. Also the hooks on the third joint of the third, or in some species of the third and fourth pairs of walking legs are larger and more developed. The two forms occur in about equal numbers in collections.

Walter Faxon, in his revision of the Astacidae,[1] states that no intermediate condition between the two forms exists, and that there is no constant relation between the special characters and the size of the individual. In the second form the testes are smaller, and the vasa deferentia shorter than in the first, and Faxon at first came to the conclusion that the second form was sterile, although he could offer no explanation of the existence of sterile males. He afterwards found on keeping the first form alive in captivity that after moulting it changed into the second form, and proved thus that the two forms are alternating conditions in the life of the individual, the first form being assumed during the pairing season, the second during the interval between the pairing seasons. It would appear from this that *Cambarus* moults twice in the year, and that this is the reason of the existence of the two forms. Hence it is impossible to avoid the conclusion that the peculiarities of the sexually active form have been determined by the special actions of the breeding male. The peculiarities are precisely those which are related to the relations of the sexes. The copulatory organs are developed and specialised in rela-

[1] *Mem. Mus. Harv.* x. 4, 1885.

tion to their employment in copulation, and the greater size and strength of parts of the body, and especially of the chelæ or pincers, are related to the exertions of the male either in fighting with rivals or obtaining possession of the female. There is clearly no reason why these peculiarities should exist

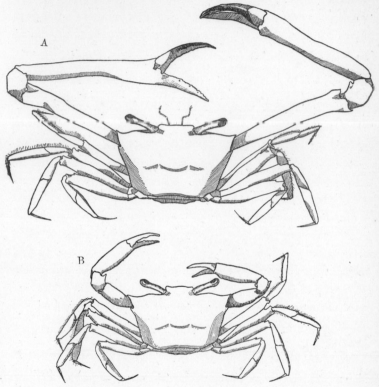

FIG. 28.—*Gonoplax angulatus*, the Angular Crab. A, male; B, female.

only during the breeding season of the year, unless they owed their existence to stimulations whose action was confined to that season.

AMPHIPODA.—These are small sessile-eyed Crustacea which move generally by swimming or jumping. The body is compressed from side to side. The number of thoracic appendages

is the same as in the Decapoda, but the segments corresponding to the posterior seven are distinct from one another.
The first ambulatory appendage thus corresponds to the
second maxilliped of the Decapoda. Of the six appendages
of the abdomen the three first are natatory and similar to
those of the lobster or shrimp, while the hinder three are
short, stiff, and directed backwards ; these function as spring-
ing or jumping limbs, but the force of the jump is due to the
bending and straightening of the abdomen itself.

The apertures of the male generative organs are at the
base of the last pair of thoracic legs, those of the female at
the base of the last pair but two, in both cases in the same
relative positions as in the Decapoda. Special intromittent
organs are wanting, and the exact mode in which fertilisation
is effected is at present unknown to me. But the male is
generally nearly twice as large as the female, and carries her
bodily about between his legs with great persistence. Any
one who turns over fronds of sea-weed or stones on the shore
at low tide will see couples of the common *Gammarus* thus
united. The active part of the male and the passive behaviour
of the female in this stage of the process of reproduction
corresponds to the difference in their dimensions and strength,
and is a sufficient explanation of that difference.

In addition to the general superiority in size the males
possess other unisexual characters. These usually consist in
a greater development of the grasping organs on the anterior
thoracic legs. The differences between the sexes are well
exemplified in the species *Podocerus falcatus* (Mont.). This
species builds tubes for itself out of mud on the surface of
logs or other objects in the water. I have found it extremely
abundant at Falmouth on floating timber just at the level of
the surface of the water. The secondary sexual characters
are so conspicuous that the different forms have been described as three distinct species, namely, the mature male as

P. pulchellus, the immature as *P. falcatus*, and the female as *P. pelagicus*.

Isopoda.—Among the Isopoda, Fam. *Anthuridæ*, there is one genus, *Eisothistos*, in which the difference between male and female is very remarkable. Both are slender and elongated, but the male is not only more slender, but is sinuous and worm-like in shape, and it inhabits the tubes of *Vermilia*, one of the Serpulidæ, annelids which secrete a sinuous cal-

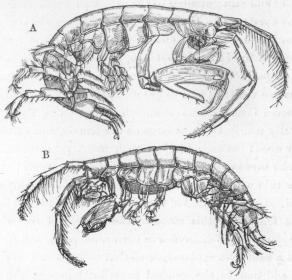

Fig. 29.—*Podocerus falcatus* (Mont.), a British Amphipod.   A, male; B, female.

careous tube attached to stones, shells, or rocks. The whole appearance of the male singularly resembles that of a small *Serpula*, the operculum and branchiæ being imitated by the expanded posterior appendages and telson, and the hairs representing the parapodial setæ. Here the difference between the sexes has nothing to do with sexual intercourse or reproduction, but is only related to the different modes of life. If it were a mere question of selection there is no reason why the selected variations should not be transmitted to the other sex also; the fact that they are not is only intelligible on the view that they are produced by the cramping influence of the tubular habitation, and are therefore correlated with the sex which alone is subjected to that influence.

A great difference between the sexes occurs also in another Isopod, *Gnathia*, Leach, the males having for a long time been distinguished as *Anceus*, and the females as *Praniza*.

There are several species of *Gnathia*, but it is not necessary here to consider the differences between them. It will be sufficient to take one of the commonest, namely *Gnathia maxillaris*, as an example. Sars[1] states that this species occurs abundantly off the coasts of Norway on muddy ground at depths from 20 to 100 fms. The males are more commonly taken than the females, and both are found slowly creeping on the sea-bottom. They are also to be found between tide-marks on the British coasts.

The body of an Isopod is usually described as consisting of three regions—the cephalon, composed of the fused segments which bear the feeding appendages, the pereion, including the segments which bear the crawling legs, and the pleon, composed of the segments which bear the swimming appendages. The differences between the adult male and female *Gnathia* occur only in the cephalon and pereion. In the male (Fig. 30, A, B) the cephalon is broad, flattened, and truncated in front, and from this front edge project a pair of relatively very large strong appendages, usually regarded as the mandibles. Besides these there are visible from the dorsal side two short pairs of antennæ. The oral appendages of a typical Isopod include, besides the mandibles, two pairs of maxillæ, and one pair of maxillipeds or gnathopoda. In the adult male *Gnathia* maxillæ are wanting, but there is a pair of large triangular appendages covering the oral region, and beneath

[1] *Crustacea of Norway*, Bergen, 1897, vol. 1. "Isopoda," p. 51.

these a pair of small jointed appendages.   Dohrn [1] describes

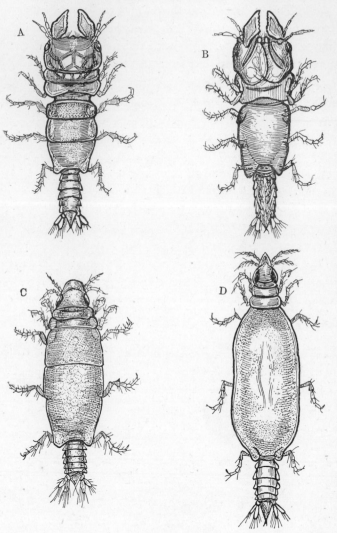

Fig. 30.—*Gnathia maxillaris*, a British Isopod.   A, adult male ; B, adult male, ventral surface ; C, adult female ; D, larva.

these as two distinct pairs of oral appendages, while Sars

[1] *Unters. uber Bau und Entwick. der Arthropoden*, Leipzig, 1870.

describes them as a pair of maxillipeds with palps. Since in *Gnathia* two thoracic segments are united with the head, there must be originally two pairs of maxillipeds, and we may here follow Dohrn's views and consider that in the adult male the maxillæ are wanting and the two pairs of maxillipeds are much reduced. The pereion consists of five free segments, each bearing a pair of walking legs, the two anterior segments being separated from the three posterior by a constriction. There is a sixth rudimentary segment, and a long median penis projecting forwards between the fifth pair of walking legs probably represents the two modified and united appendages of this sixth segment. The " pleon " is considerably narrower than the " pereion," and consists of six free segments each with its pair of short paddle-like appendages.

In the adult female the cephalon is much narrower than in the male, and somewhat pointed in front, and both mandibles and maxillæ are absent. Modified maxillipeds similar to those of the male are present, but smaller. The two first segments of the pereion are free, but the last three are fused together and form a brood-pouch containing the developing eggs. From this pouch the young are produced alive and fully developed.

From the absence of the mouth-parts in the female it may be inferred that she does not feed, the eggs and young developing at the expense of nourishment previously acquired. It is fairly certain also that the male does not use his large mandibles for feeding. According to Bate and Westwood in the adult female there is neither mouth, stomach, nor alimentary canal, but it is not stated that these digestive organs are entirely absent in the male. Unfortunately the act of copulation, so far as I can discover, has not been observed or described, but I think in all probability the enlarged mandibles of the male are used either to hold the female or to fight with other males. Dohrn states that when a small stick of wood is presented to the male he seizes it with these organs and holds on to it so firmly that he can be lifted out of the water by the stick. This suggests that the mandibles are used in fighting. Hesse,[1] on the other hand, states that when a number of the animals were placed in a jar of water, they bit one another indiscriminately, and copulation was not observed. The females could not bite, so that we may perhaps infer from the statement that the males used their jaws on both females and other males, and this suggests that under natural conditions the males fight. In any case, whether the mandibles are used in fighting or simply for seizing the female, we see a reason for their presence in the male and absence in the female, in the fact that the male uses them, while in the female they have disappeared from disuse. It may be added that the female vaginal orifice is said to be placed at the base of the last pair of walking legs, and that the brood-pouch, according to Dohrn, is not the cavity of the body, but is formed between the cuticle and the body. In most other cases the brood-pouch in Isopods is formed outside the body by flattened plates belonging to the appendages.

Now we have to consider the immature *Gnathia* or larvæ. These resemble the female, having narrow heads, and the three posterior segments of the pereion fused and distended. They have mandibles, two pairs of maxillæ and maxillipeds, but all these oral appendages are slender and pointed, forming a piercing and sucking apparatus with which they penetrate the skins of fishes, hanging on to them and devouring their blood. They are not, however, permanently attached. They are active swimmers, and when the fish on which they are feeding is captured they either let go their hold and escape in the water, or drop off soon after the fish

---

[1] "Crustacés Rares ou Nouveaux des Côtes de la France" *Ann. Sci. Naturelles*, tome xix., 1874.

is taken out of the water. They are also frequently captured in the dredge, or on shore, when not attached to fishes.

There is some room for doubt whether the male larvæ are similar to the female. If so, then the larval male has the three posterior pereion segments united and swollen, and then when he casts his cuticle and changes to the adult form these three segments appear free and reduced in breadth. This is stated by Hesse to be actually the case; that observer maintains that all larvæ have the form originally named Praniza. Sars also states that he has witnessed the transformation of the Praniza larva into the adult male or Anceus form.

Bate and Westwood, on the other hand, state that the sexes could be distinguished in the larvæ, though they do not state what the distinction was. When the larvæ leave the brood-pouch all the segments of the pereion are distinct. The mother appears to die after the escape of the young from the pouch.

On the whole, the evidence shows that the difference between males and females, if any, in the larvæ must be very slight, and that both lead the same parasitic but not sedentary existence. The great difference in the adults must therefore be attributed entirely to a difference in habits and functions confined to this stage of life. The fusion and distension of the three posterior segments of the pereion in the larvæ must be attributed to the distension of this part by the blood on which the animal feeds, the mode of life resembling that of a leech. In the adult male these segments return to the original free condition, while in the adult female the same portion of the body is still distended by the mass of large ova which develop there. The shape and size of the cephalon in the male is entirely due to the great muscles which move the enlarged mandibles, and, as was mentioned above, the exertion of these organs must in the male be frequent and energetic. Thus, all we know of the history of this species is in accordance with the view that the sexual dimorphism and the remarkable metamorphosis are directly due to functionally produced modifications, and not to independent variations. The original cause of the divergence from the normal Isopod structure was doubtless the acquisition of the habit of blood-sucking, which led gradually to the postponement of the generative function to the last stage of life, and secondarily, in consequence of the highly nourished condition of the mother, to the viviparous mode of reproduction.

In the parasitic Isopoda forming the family Bopyridæ sexual dimorphism is very strongly marked. In the genus *Bopyrus* the female is five or six times as large as the male, much depressed in form of body and also asymmetrical. The animals live in a stationary condition in the branchial cavity of prawns, *Bopyrus squillarum*, a common British species, being parasitic upon the common prawn, *Palæmon serratus*. The shape of the body is evidently moulded by the shape of the cavity which the animal inhabits, and the asymmetry is due to the permanent bending of the axis of the body. The appendages of the mouth are rudimentary, consisting of a pair of oval flat maxillipeds, and small pointed mandibles. The seven pairs of legs are very short, but strong, and furnished each with a strong claw by which the parasite holds on to its host. Each leg is furnished with large incubatory plates beneath which the young are fostered. The abdomen, or pleon, is narrower and shorter than the pereion, and each of its segments has a pair of appendages in the form of transverse flat plates. The minute male is found fixed among these plates on the ventral side of the female, and not being too large for the space available remains symmetrical in form, though much degenerate. The segments of the pleon in this sex are coalesced, their separate existence being indicated by the incisions at the sides. The antennæ are short and similar to those of the female; the legs are short but strong and clawed. The eyes are very rudimentary in the females, but more developed in the males.

Here we can obviously, in accounting for the difference between the sexes, point to the fact that, whereas the female is parasitic on the prawn, the male is parasitic on the female, The latter, therefore, has a smaller supply of nourishment, and all its functions are in abeyance, except those of holding on to its support and fertilising the ova. In the female, on the other hand, special parts are stimulated, and special muscles are exercised in the support of the eggs and embryos, which exercise, with the abundance of nourishment available, are sufficient to account for her large size. It is somewhat curious that the male, since, so far as we know, it does not migrate from one female to another, should have more developed eyes than the female, and yet it is not improbable that in the act of fertilisation he is to some extent guided by visual sensations, in which case the complete degeneration of the eyes would be prevented.

The young of *Bopyrus*, when they leave the incubatory pouch, are much less degenerate than their parents, being symmetrical and active. The second pair of antennæ are greatly elongated and form the principal organ of locomotion. In the genus *Gyge*, members of which live on *Galathea*, the body of the female is less asymmetrical than in *Bopyrus*, and the male is slightly different in form, but the general relations of male, female, and young are similar.

In *Hemiarthrus* we have a more extraordinary form which occurs in the branchial cavity of *Hippolyte* and *Pandalus*. Towards one side the body is swollen out into a globular mass distended with eggs, and the legs

on this side are obsolete, except the most anterior. The
sides of the body are provided with very large scales,
not arranged in pairs, which fall backwards so as to cover
the body (probably these are the scales of the legs of one
side). The male is extremely minute, and lives partially
immersed between the folds of the posterior part of the body
of the female.

In *Athelges*, although the position of the ovigerous
scales on the dorsal surface of the body is the same,
the body is almost perfectly symmetrical, a fact which is
most likely explained by the other fact that the animal
lives in the branchial cavity of a hermit crab, *Pagurus*,
instead of a shrimp. The carapace of the *Pagurus* is
soft.

The genus *Ione* is parasitic upon *Callianassa*, and although
the male is not very remarkable, and the proportions of the
sexes are as usual, the adult female exhibits peculiar characters in the branched abdominal appendages, and the simple
membranous appendages arising from the six anterior pairs
of legs.

COPEPODA. — The typical Copepoda are minute symmetrical Crustacea, in which the body consists of two obviously
distinct parts, a large anterior portion provided with several
pairs of legs, and an abdomen or tail without appendages.
The anterior portion consists of a cephalothorax and four free
segments. The former bears two pairs of antennæ, a pair of
mandibles, two pairs of maxillæ, and a pair of long appendages similar to those which follow, namely, the four pairs
belonging to the free segments. These appendages are
biramous, and function as swimming legs in those species
which lead an active existence. The narrow cylindrical tail
consists of five segments ending in a fork, and in the female
the two first of these are united, and carry the genital
openings. The Copepoda, like the fabled Cyclops whose

name the common fresh-water representative bears, have but a single central eye.

Secondary sexual differences exist in most of the species, and in some are developed to an extreme degree. The males are generally smaller and more active, and their anterior antennæ, as well as the legs of the last pair, more rarely the posterior antennæ and the second pair of maxillæ, are specially modified to serve as accessory organs of copulation, that is organs for seizing and holding the female, or for attaching the spermatophores to the body of the latter. The females carry the eggs usually in clumps or strings attached to the tail. In these clumps or strings the ova are held together by a hardened secretion produced by the female. In one family (Notodelphyidæ) the ova are carried in a dorsal incubatory pouch. In copulation the male attaches one or several spermatophores to the genital segment of the female. The spermatophores are packets of spermatozoa formed by a gelatinous secretion of the *vas deferens*. In the common fresh-water *Cyclops* the anterior antennæ of the male are thickened and provided with a special hinge-joint, by means of which the male seizes the female by her fourth pair of swimming legs, and then bending up his tail deposits two speramtophores on her genital segment.

In all the Cyclopidæ both of the anterior antennæ are thus modified for purposes of copulation, and the same arrangement occurs in the Harpactidæ.

In the Calanidæ the chief peculiarities of the males, according to Giesbrecht, perhaps the greatest authority on Copepoda, are the following: On the antennæ the æsthetic or perceptive vesicles, which are probably olfactory organs, are more numerous and larger; the fifth pair of feet are modified to form a grasping organ; and thirdly, there are five distinct somites in the abdomen (or tail), the genital aperture being on the left side of the first somite.

These differences are illustrated in Fig. 31, representing the male and female of *Euchœta marina*, which is common in

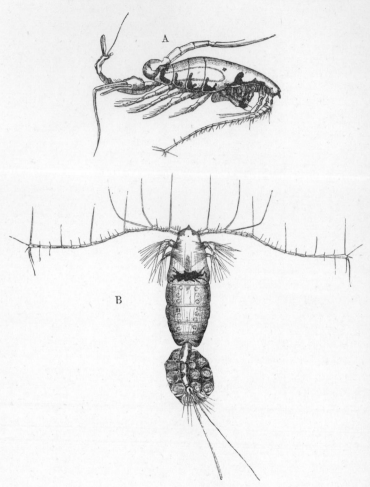

Fig. 31.—*Euchœta marina*, a Mediterranean Copepod magnified.   A, Male; B, Female.   Only a portion of the two long bristles at the end of the body in the female is shown.

the Mediterranean.   The fifth pair of feet, which is wanting in the female, is strongly developed in the male, and equals in length the anterior portion of the body.   Each foot of this

pair has two basal segments, and an inner and outer branch
(endopod and exopod). The second basal segments are large,
the left longer than the right. The endopod of the right
side is a long unjointed styliform appendage, while the left
endopod is reduced to a small stump. The right exopod has
only two segments, the first and second having probably
coalesced. The left exopod is three-jointed, and the structure
of the last segment, with which the male holds its spermatophores in copulation, is very complicated.

In the Pontellidæ only the right anterior antenna and the
right foot of the fifth pair are specialised. In the last
family, Notodelphyidæ, the members of which live within the
branchial cavities of Ascidians, the chief sexual difference
is the presence in the females of a brood-chamber formed by
folding of the skin in the back of the fourth and fifth somites
of the thorax. In this chamber the eggs are carried and
hatched.

On Darwinian principles an explanation of the copulatory
adaptations in this group can be offered with the usual apparent
facility. The males, which are unsuccessful in copulating,
necessarily leave no progeny, while those that have the most
"adapted" grasping organs are the fathers in each generation.
The case does not properly come under sexual selection if we
confine that term to cases of courtship or combat, but on the
other hand, as it is a case of selection with regard to generation and not with regard to the individual life, it belongs
rather to sexual selection than to natural selection in the
ordinary sense. It is, however, of little importance whether
we apply to it the one term or the other. The principle of
selection in any case cannot completely explain the facts,
because it does not explain why the special modifications are
inherited by only one sex. That principle assumes that the
necessary variations occurred without explaining why they
are not evident in the female sex. On Lamarckian principles

the facts offer no difficulties. If special stimulations produce modifications which tend to be inherited only in
relation to those stimulations, it follows that the actions of
the male Copepod in seizing the female would produce
modifications of structure which would be confined in inheritance to the adult period of life in the male, because that is
the only portion of the life-history of the species in which
those particular actions are exerted.

CIRRIPEDIA.—The sexual relations in these sessile and
much degenerate crustaceans are very remarkable. In many
of the typical forms, including all the Balanidæ, which are
without peduncles, there is no sexual dimorphism, since all
the individuals are alike, and all hermaphrodite. We may
consider it most probable, since the sedentary habits of these
animals is evidently secondary, that they are descended
from forms which were bisexual like all other Crustacea.
The hermaphrodites are then probably modified females,
and we have to consider the question how females came to
develop testicular organs and produce spermatozoa. I must
admit that at present I have no suggestions to make concerning
the influence of the conditions of life in developing hermaphroditism. I have been considering the influence of such conditions
on the structure of those parts of the body which are in direct
relation to external conditions, and know nothing of their
influence on the primary generative organs. It is, however,
interesting to note that there are some Cirripides which are
simply bisexual and sexually dimorphic, and which may be
taken to retain the original condition with respect to the
separation of the sexes. Curiously enough hermaphrodite
forms and bisexual forms occur within the same genus,
namely, *Scalpellum*, one of the stalked Cirripedes, and *Ibla*
of the same family. Thus *Scalpellum ornatum* of the coasts
of South Africa has separate sexes, while *Scalpellum vulgare* of
the North Sea and European coasts is hermaphrodite. Where

the sexes are distinct the males are very small and degenerate, and live parasitically within the mantle-cavities of the female. In *Scalpellum ornatum* the males have no mouth; their appendages are rudimentary, and the body contains little but the generative organs. In other species, *e.g.* *Scalpellum vulgare*, a similar male is found within the cavity of an individual possessing female organs, but having testes also. The male is called a complemental male, and it is evident that the female has become hermaphrodite. Here, if anywhere, ought to be found the opportunity of investigating the origin of the hermaphroditism. This condition once developed, the males tend to disappear from existence altogether. This fact is in accordance with the principles I am maintaining. Ova which develop without being fertilised by the spermatozoa from a male can only develop the acquired condition from a more or less distant male ancestor. We do not know what determines the sex of the offspring, but those which become males, as in other cases, will develop the male structures, which in each generation are usually confirmed by the influence of the conditions on the individual. In the case supposed, self-fertilisation occurring with the majority of eggs, this confirmation will be wanting, and thus the inheritance of male characters will become continually weaker. When the hermaphroditism is so perfect that fertilisation by males ceases altogether, the eggs which develop into males will have nothing to inherit, and only the eggs developing in the female direction will give rise to the hermaphrodite adults, as in the majority of Cirripedes.

In the specially modified forms, *Alcippe* and *Cryptophialus*, there is no hermaphroditism; all are of separate sexes, and the males are degenerate and parasitic upon the females.

CHAPTER VII

MOLLUSCA, CHÆTOPODA, AND LOWER SUB-KINGDOMS

MOLLUSCA

IT was Darwin's opinion that in the sub-kingdom, Mollusca, secondary sexual characters, such as he considered in *The Descent of Man*, never occurred. He mentions the special development in male Cephalopoda (cuttle-fishes) of one of the arms, which acts as the carrier of the spermatophores, but thinks that this may be classed as a primary rather than as a secondary sexual character. This conclusion seems to me unjustified. It is evident from hundreds of cases that nothing beyond the ovaries and testes, not even the ducts of these organs, are really primary in the proper sense of the word. I take it that the primary or essential organs are those which are necessarily or invariably required for the function of reproduction, and in Cœlenterata and Sponges reproduction is effected by ova and sperms without the aid of any other specialised organ of the body. It is true that in Mammals and other classes of the higher animals it is customary to consider such characters as horns or plumage as secondary sexual characters, and not to include the actual organs of copulation. But nevertheless the organs of copulation are truly secondary, and are to be explained on the same principles as sexual differences of a more remote kind. Sexual dimorphism, as understood in the present work, includes all differences in the structure or characters of males and females of the same species, except the original differences between the ovaries and testes.

Darwin, with his usual candour, admits freely that there is as much beauty of colour and form in Mollusca as in any other sub-kingdom. This is a sufficient proof that the theory of sexual selection is by no means necessary to explain what to us is beautiful in animals, and also that beauty of form or colour confined to one sex is not completely explained on the hypothesis that it is pleasing to the other sex. The colours in Mollusca, according to Darwin, are probably the direct result of the nature of the tissues and the manner of growth. It is strange that he did not see that this view would harmonise with all the facts of sexual dimorphism, and a great many others, provided it be added that the "manner of growth" is affected in determinate ways by determinate conditions. Whereas on the selection theory we must explain the brilliant colours of a cock pheasant's plumage by the taste of the female, and the equally beautiful colours and markings of a Nudibranch mollusc by the nature of the tissues and the manner of growth, a more rational view regards both as due to the physiological processes of growth and secretion modified by external forms of energy.

Of the Gastropoda some are hermaphrodite, some of separate sexes. The Pulmonata, or air-breathing terrestrial snails, and the Opisthobranchia, are all hermaphrodite, and among these therefore all individuals are alike. The Prosobranchia, on the other hand, of which the Whelk and Periwinkle are typical examples, are of separate sexes. The sexual dimorphism is, however, never very pronounced, and in some species scarcely visible. In some cases the shell is a little smaller or narrower in the males than in the females, in certain species even the teeth of the radula are different in the sexes, but the only conspicuous external difference is the large penis of the males, which is situated in the mantle-cavity, and is not retractile. In the Heteropoda, however, which are free-swimming Prosobranchs with small shells, a typical secondary sexual character occurs. In *Pterotrachea* there is, on the foot of the male only, a sucker which is evidently used for attachment to the female. In other genera, *Atlanta* and *Carinaria*, the sucker occurs in both sexes. Here there is no difficulty in understanding how the special muscular action of the foot could give rise to a special sucker, and as in other cases the development in both sexes in certain cases probably results from the fact that both perform the corresponding muscular contractions.

The Lamellibranchiata are, with few exceptions, such as the scallop and oyster, of separate sexes, but as the fertilisation is automatic, secondary sexual differences are scarcely at all developed. The only instances are in those species in which the female nurses the developing ova within the mantle-cavity, in the folds of the gill-lamellæ. In these species, for example the fresh-water Unionidæ, the shell of the female is more convex, a fact which can only be regarded as the result of the distension caused by the ova and embryos. The shell once formed, is, it is true, not likely to be altered in shape by pressure from within the mantle-cavity, but when the mantle-cavity is distended the edges of the shell will be separated slightly, and the edges of the mantle meeting to cover the gap will secrete additions to the edge of the shell in a steeper curvature than in the case of the male.

In the Cephalopoda the males are, at least when mature, conspicuously distinguished from the females by the modification of one or two of the arms, which are said to be hecto-cotylised. The name hectocotylus was originally given to an elongated cylindrical body, provided with numerous suckers, which was found in the mantle-cavity of the female *Argonauta*,

the well-known Paper Nautilus. This genus belongs to the
order Octopoda. It was afterwards discovered that the hectocotylus was a detached arm of the male *Argonauta*, and that
its function was to convey the spermatophores into the mantle-
cavity of the female. It is now known that the modified arm
of the male is the third of the left side, and that it develops
in a peculiar manner. In the place of an ordinary arm or
tentacle, where the third left arm ought to be, there is found
a pear-shaped membranous capsule, and in the interior of
this is found the arm or tentacle proper, rolled up in a coil.
At the time of sexual maturity the capsule bursts and the
tentacle is released, still, however, attached at its base. The
walls of the capsule are everted and form a receptacle at the
back of the arm, into which the spermatophores are received,
and when the arm charged with the spermatophores is inserted
into the pallial cavity of the female, it becomes detached
and is left in that cavity, where it retains its vitality and
power of motion for some time.

It is evident from this that the so-called capsule in which
the arm develops is formed merely by the concrescence of
membranous outgrowths of the modified arm, with the surface
of the body around the base of the arm. Since the walls of
the capsule after rupture form the receptacle of the spermatophores, it is probable that the peculiar mode of development
is due merely to the precocious development of the membranous sides of this receptacle. Granted such a precocious
development in an arm which originally remained coiled up
until the time for its special function arrived, the membrane
may have been extended by muscular contraction over the
coiled arm with its edges in apposition, until in the course of
evolution concrescence took place.

Supposing the effects of external stimulation do not become
hereditary, we have to form a conception of the evolution of
this hectocotylised arm by the process of indefinite variation

19

and selective survival. We may suppose that the original ancestor had eight arms all alike, and habitually used the third of the left side to convey the spermatophores into the female mantle-cavity. Congenital variations being independent of the effects of function, we must suppose that all sorts of variations occurred in all the arms, the third left among the rest, and that among all these variations some occurred from time to time which, added together, formed the condition now existing. The objections to this view are, firstly, that the other arms show little or no evidence of the variations which must be assumed, and therefore it is more probable that the required variations only occurred in the arm which was specially employed in copulation ; secondly, on this view the development of the arm in a closed capsule is unexplained, for such a mode of development confers no advantage, could not, so far as we can see, give its possessor any advantage in copulation. On the other hand, if we assume that the modification of the arm, now hereditary and congenital, was originally set up by the mode in which it was used, it seems by no means difficult to discover a correspondence between the muscular action of the arm and its existing structure and development. To trace the relation completely would require a renewed study in detail of the action of the arm in the process of copulation. But it is evident that the spermatophores are conveyed in a sac formed partly by the bending of the arm at its base towards its dorsal side, partly by membranous extensions of the skin of the arm on each side towards the back. Granting that the spermatophores were originally held by the muscular contraction of an unmodified arm, the growth stimulated by these contractions might well lead to the formation of a receptacle. Then, as I have suggested above, the precocious development of the walls of this receptacle and the manner in which the arm was held coiled by muscular contraction, might afford the explanation of the peculiar development. It may be asked, why should precocious development occur? To which the reply is that numerous facts point to the induction that generally when the growth of a special part is greatly stimulated by special use or irritation, the development of that part is in the course of generations accelerated. The detachment of the arm, which is now a normal occurrence, would of course be attributed to the mechanical separation of it occasionally occurring in the process of copulation.

In *Argonauta* the peculiarity of the copulatory tentacle is by no means the only difference between male and female. The male is smaller than the female. The latter has a shell, while the former has none. This delicate, beautiful shell, which gives rise to the name Paper Nautilus, is formed, not by the surface of the body or mantle, but by the inner surface of two modified arms. In this case it is the two most dorsal arms which are specialised. Each of these is enlarged into a flat membranous expansion, and one is applied to each side of the body. On the inner sides of these expansions is secreted the thin, delicate shell which encloses the body. The eggs of the female are attached to the shell. It is possible that the support of the eggs was the original purpose for which the dorsal arms were turned back and applied to the sides of the body. In any case it is difficult to conceive of the modification of these arms taking place apart from the special mode in which they are held by the animal. In this instance we see the usual association of specific and hereditary modification with a special use of the organ, confined to one sex. With regard to the secretion of the shell the difficulty is greater. At present I am unable to attribute the secretion of the shell to particular conditions or stimulations involved in the attitude of the arms. It is known that the suckers of the cephalopod arm are often coated with a horny secretion, and the shell may perhaps represent the connected and calcified secretion of a number of suckers. Careful investigation might result in showing that the secretion of the shell is directly caused by the position in which the arms are held.

The peculiar modification of a pair of arms in the female occurs only in *Argonauta*, but the modification of an arm in the male, for the purpose of copulation, is common to all Cephalopods. The degrees of the modification and the particular arm affected are different in different genera. In *Nautilus*, which possesses a large number of arms or tentacles, the modification affects the four interior ventral tentacles on the left side, which coalesce to form a single organ known as the spadix. In *Spirula* the two arms of the fourth pair are hectocotylised. In *Rossia* also the same two arms are modified, but unequally. In other cases only one arm is affected, the fourth on the left side in the Oigopsidæ, a Sub-order of the squids or ten-armed cuttle-fishes ; the third on the right side in *Octopus, Eledone,* and other eight-armed forms ; the second on the right in *Cirroteuthis.*

In *Philonexis* and *Tremoctopus* the modified arm is separated from the male in copulation as in the *Argonauta*, and probably is succeeded by a new arm of the same kind. In other cases no separation takes place. In *Octopus, Eledone,* and others, the modification of the arm is very slight, the extremity merely taking the shape of a spoon. In *Sepia* the suckers are absent at the base of the hectocotylus, while in *Idiosepion* and *Loliolus* they are absent altogether on the whole arm. If each of these different modifications is thoroughly well adapted for its purpose, it follows that the mode or habit of copulation is different in the different genera, and if this is the case the stimulations to which the arm is subjected in the different cases must be very different. The facts in this instance therefore, so far as they are known, are in harmony with the general theory of the influence of external conditions in pro-ducing sexual dimorphism. The degree to which the special arm is exclusively devoted to the copulatory function must profoundly affect its functional activity, and thus in each case there must be great differences in the manner and intensity of the muscular activity of the arm, and in the external irritations to which it is subjected. The suckers are essentially muscular organs, and therefore their disappearance may reasonably be attributed simply to their disuse. A thorough investigation of the relations between the peculiarities of the hectocotylised arm and the mode in which it is used, both in ordinary life and in copulation, would be of great interest, but at present little seems to be known on the subject.

Chætopoda

The two Orders of animals united in the class Chœtopoda, namely, the Oligochæta and the Polychæta, although resembling each other in the essential structure of the chætæ and the regular segmentation or metamerism of the body, differ widely in their reproductive organs and methods. Although it may not be possible in the present state of knowledge to form a plausible theory in detail of the derivation of the terrestrial and fresh-water Oligochætes from the marine Polychætes, we may, nevertheless, reasonably regard the generative adaptations of the Oligochætes as necessarily related to their conditions of life. They are all hermaphrodite, and this character does not appear, it is true, to be necessary for the fertilisation or development of the eggs in animals living in fresh water or in moist earth. But as these hermaphrodites are not self-fertilising some kind of copulation between the reproductive individuals is required to ensure fertilisation, or, to state the matter in more general terms, it is requisite that special means shall be provided to bring the spermatozoa and ova into contact. The means actually employed consist in the emission with the ova of semen received previously from another individual. The accessory generative organs are complicated, the semen being emitted by *vasa deferentia* in one individual and received into special receptacula in another. So far these are the very conditions of structure and method which in other groups of animals are so frequently accompanied with sexual dimorphism, with the presence of secondary differences between the males and females. But the Oligochæta are hermaphrodite, and each individual possesses not only the primary but the accessory generative organs of both sexes. Hence copulation is reciprocal, as in certain Gasteropoda, and there are no individual differences related to reproduction. The girdle or clitellum, a specialised glandular thickening of the skin in a certain part of the body, is an accessory copulatory organ analogous to some which, in the males of many animals, serves for holding the female, and, if present in only one set of individuals, would constitute a sexual dimorphism, but in these hermaphrodite forms the clitellum is present in all mature individuals, and therefore does not give rise to dimorphism. At the same time there is no obvious difficulty in attributing the evolution of the clitellum to the stimulation of the epidermic glands in a particular region, such stimulation resulting, as in other cases, in hereditary hypertrophy. It is noteworthy in this connection that the clitellum, although not differentiating one "form" of individual from another within the species, resembles secondary sexual characters in other cases, in the fact that it is absent in the immature stage of life, and only reaches its full development with the attainment of sexual maturity.

In the marine Polychæta the generative structures and processes are very different. These animals are, with few exceptions, of separate sexes, and fertilisation takes place usually in the water without any special arrangements for its accomplishment. The ova and spermatozoa are set free in the body cavity, and find their way to the exterior either by dehiscence of the body walls, or through the nephridial tubes (so-called segmental organs).

The Polychæta fall naturally into two main divisions, the free and the sessile forms, or Errantia and Sedentaria. In many of the Errantia there are no sexual differences, or indeed any accessory structures related to reproduction. But in certain families, especially the Nereidæ and Syllidæ, very remarkable transformations and differentiations are connected with the reproductive function. These changes of form are typically presented in the genus *Nereis*. In the ordinary form of this genus there are a number of segments all similar, with the exception of a few at the anterior and posterior extremities, and all provided with pairs of similar parapodia. Some species, such as the British form *N. diversicolor*, undergo no change when sexually mature. In other species the posterior segments, throughout more than half of the body length, acquire, in sexually ripe individuals, a different character. Such individuals, consisting of two conspicuously different body-regions, were at one time supposed to belong to a distinct genus, and were described in detail as species of *Heteronereis*. It is now known, however, that the condition is produced by the transformation of individuals of the ordinary *Nereis* form. The change is due (*a*) to an alteration in the shape and size of the parapodia in the posterior part of the body, and (*b*) to a difference in the form and number of the chætæ of these parapodia. With regard to (*a*), the various lobes of the parapodia are much enlarged and flattened antero-posteriorly, while (*b*) the old chætæ are shed and replaced by new, of a different shape, the blade being flattened and paddle-shaped. Both these changes render the parapodia more efficient as organs of propulsion through the water, and as a matter of fact the worms in the *Heteronereis* condition, at any rate when actually discharging their reproductive products, swim about actively in the water instead of crawling on the ground, or lurking under stones and in crevices. The transformation can be studied in the common British form *Nereis pelagica*, the mature or "epitokous" forms of which were originally described as *Heteronereis grandifolia*. The mature form has, in addition to the peculiarities already mentioned, larger eyes and larger cephalic palps than the immature form. So far no differences between the sexes have been mentioned, we have been considering a metamorphosis somewhat analogous with that of the tadpole into the frog. Before proceeding further it may be pointed out that the facts harmonise very completely with the views maintained throughout this work. The ordinary *Nereis* form does, to a certain extent, employ its parapodia as finlets for swimming, and it is not unreasonable to suppose that greater activity in swimming during the actual discharge of the sexual products preceded the evolution of the structural peculiarities of the mature form. The changes in the parapodia are such as might well be produced by merely greater use of them. Greater exercise of them as finlets may well have been the true cause of the hypertrophy of the various lobes. It is perhaps more diffi-cult to understand how mere exertion should have led to the replacement of the original chætæ by a new set of different shape. But it is not impossible that the mechanical action should have had the effect of loosening the old chætæ and stimulating the cells at their base to secrete new, which in their development were subjected to pressures and strains that made them flattened and expanded. Here, as in so many other cases, the most cogent argument is, that the view I maintain explains the relation between the metamorphosis and the change of habits. There is no special reason why mere reproductive maturity should be accompanied by this remarkable change in the structure of the parapodia and the other changes described. It is obvious that the metamorphosis is essentially a somewhat sudden adaptation for active swimming during the reproductive period. The theory of selection among mere indefinite individual variations does not satisfactorily explain the definite metamorphosis. That theory must assume that the variations selected consisted in changes in the individual occurring at a late period of life. It gives no reason why these changes in the indvidual occurred. The changes are actually associated with a definite and important change in the habits and activities of the individual, and the only reasonable conclusion is that the change in the activities was the cause of the transformation of structure which is now hereditary.

But in addition to the difference between the immature and the mature individual, there is also a difference between the male and female in the mature state. The secondary sexual characters give rise to a sexual dimorphism. According to Ehlers, the alterations taking place at sexual maturity are usually more pronounced, of greater degree, in the male than in the female. The number of unmodified segments in the anterior part of the body is characteristic for the species, but there is often in this respect a sexual difference, the number of unaltered segments being smaller in the male. The modification also is usually complete in the first modified segment in the male, while in the female there are several transitional segments. These differences would naturally result if the males were more active than the females. I know of no direct evidence on this point, but it is reasonable to suppose that the males, as in other cases, actively seek the females.

The history of one species of Nereis, *N. dumerilii*, according to the investigations hitherto made, presents remarkable peculiarities, which are very difficult to explain on any

theory. Up to a length of 15 mm. the worms of this species
are all similar, of the ordinary form, and sexually immature.
From these immature young worms develop several different
mature forms. Some individuals become sexually mature
without changing their form, only growing larger. Such
individuals are 15 to 30 mm. long. They live in tubes
formed by excretion from the skin, and in the tubes fertilised
eggs were found. At Messina Von Westinghausen found
these eggs from April to the end of July, at Naples from
December onwards. Other individuals, without growing
much larger, are transformed into what is called the small
Heteronereis form, which appear in an active pelagic condition
in February and March, and are sexually mature. These
Heteronereids are from 20 to 40 mm. in length, and have
65 to 75 segments. The eggs in the two cases are quite
different, and there is a corresponding difference in the
development. The eggs of the mature *Nereis* form have
more yolk and develop directly without metamorphosis,
those of the *Heteronereis* are laid in gelatinous clumps at
the surface of the water, contain little yolk, and give rise to
a trochophore larva which by metamorphosis develops into
the young worm. Again, a third set of the immature
individuals grows to from 55 to 65 mm. long without
becoming sexually mature, and then are transformed into
the large *Heteronereis* form which is found sexually mature
in August. One of the most remarkable facts in this
complicated history is, that the large *Heteronereis* form
is not pelagic, but lays eggs with a small quantity of yolk,
in its tubes. The development of an immature individual
may thus take either of three distinct courses : it may
become mature without metamorphosis, it may be transformed
into a pelagic *Heteronereis* and produce pelagic ova, or it may
be transformed at a much larger size into a non-pelagic
Heteronereis, which produces non-pelagic ova. It is entirely

unknown whether each of the three mature forms is distinct and hereditary, or whether the progeny of one pair of parents may take one of the three different courses according to the conditions of life. In the former case the three forms would be separate varieties of one species if not three distinct species. If the second alternative is correct it is very difficult to suggest any explanation without more complete knowledge of the influence of various conditions of life on the sexual maturity of the worms. It seems probable that the problem in this special case is the same as the general problem why certain species are pelagic and differentiated in the mature condition, while others reproduce without any change of habits or structure. We can scarcely avoid the assumption that the latter is the more primitive condition, and thus we are led to suppose that something in the conditions of life in certain species caused them to produce eggs with less yolk, and to swim about while shedding these eggs. According to my views, this change produced directly the structural metamorphosis in the parents. In *Nereis dumerilii* such conditions of life, whatever they are, may be supposed to occur occasionally, but not uniformly, acting on some individuals, but not on all. In that case the peculiarities in the ova and in the structure of the parents may have become hereditary, but only in association with the special conditions of life, just as in the case of the Axolotl. Every individual may be held to have inherited the tendency to metamorphosis in its own structure associated with the production of pelagic ova, but actually to exhibit these phenomena only when a particular stimulation calls them forth. In a precisely similar way every sterile female in polymorphic ants, bees, or termites inherits the power of developing into a perfect fertile female, and we know that this is so from the fact that under the proper conditions the development always actually takes place.

The case of the Axolotl seems very similar. In certain localities the transformation of the Axolotl form into the pulmonate form takes place in all individuals, in other localities the larvæ of the same species never undergo the metamorphosis, but breed in the branchiate condition, and die in that condition. Artificially such Axolotls can be made to pass through the metamorphosis, and it is quite possible that with further knowledge the conditions which determine whether a young *Nereis dumerilii* shall reproduce in one of the three states or the other might be artificially controlled.

In the family Syllidæ, which consists of small slender worms, the process of metamorphosis is complicated by another, namely, the tendency of the modified hinder region of the worm to separate and form a distinct sexual zooid, while the anterior asexual portion continues to live and grow. We thus have a combination of multiplication by fission and sexual reproduction. The degrees of complication form a graduated series, and the explanation of the phenomena is best attempted after the salient facts have been described.

In the typical Polychæta each parapodium or lateral finlet consists of two parts, a dorsal and ventral, each part having corresponding structures. These structures are a cylindrical process or "cirrus," a bundle of bristles or chætæ, and a more or less prominent projecting lamina bearing the bristles. The relative position of the parts is reversed in the dorsal and ventral portion of the parapodium, so that the dorsal cirrus is the most dorsal structure, the ventral cirrus the most ventral. In other words, there is a dorso-ventral symmetry in the parapodium.

In the Syllidæ the parapodia are degenerate, or to some extent rudimentary. Each parapodium in the immature form consists of a dorsal cirrus and the ventral portion of the parapodium (the neuropodium), with sometimes a ventral cirrus also. The dorsal portion or notopodium, except the cirrus, is wanting. The chief modification in the sexually mature condition is the appearance of the dorsal bundle of bristles, which are very long and serve as natatory organs. The ventral cirrus is absent in one division of the family, the Autolytinæ, in which, therefore, the parapodium is most rudimentary.

The above does not apply to the cephalic segment, and one behind this called the tentacular segment. These two bear no parapodia.

The appendages of the cephalic segment are five in number : two antero-inferior palps, two lateral antennæ, and one median antenna. The tentacular segment bears usually two pairs of tentacular cirri, sometimes only a single pair.

The forms possessing ventral cirri are divided into three sub-families, according to the freedom or fusion or partial fusion of the cephalic palps. We thus have four sub-families classified as follows :—

	present	fused	throughout	. . . .	Exogoninæ
Ventral	Palps		at base only	. . . .	Eusyllidinæ
Cirri			not fused	. . . .	Syllidinæ
	absent .	. . . .	. . . .	. . . .	Autolytinæ

It is necessary to give these characteristics in order to refer to the degrees of asexual multiplication which occur.

In all the species of the first sub-family, Exogoninæ, the sexual reproduction is direct. No fission occurs, the animals present the same phenomena as the Nereidæ, that is to say, the posterior segments become modified when the sexual products are mature, the modification consisting in the development of the bundle of elongated dorsal bristles. The same condition obtains in the Eusyllidinæ. In the Syllidinæ, however, fission occurs, the posterior modified set of segments separating from the rest, and thus forming a " reproductive zooid." This portion alone produces the ova or spermatozoa.

Here we come upon another phenomenon. It is well known that segmented worms, like many other animals, have the power of producing again parts that have been removed naturally or artificially. This process is usually called regeneration, but as the word generation is associated with the idea of the production of new individuals or offspring, I prefer to call the process recrescence, which more exactly expresses its nature. Thus when the hinder part of a Syllis separates, the anterior portion may produce new posterior segments, and the separate hinder portion may produce a head. The perfection with which the recrescence of cephalic segments takes place in the sexual zooid after its separation differs in different species, and the different forms were originally, before their derivation from the asexual zooid was known, described as distinct species.

In some species the sexual zooid produces eggs or spermatozoa (the sexes are distinct) without the recrescence of a head at all. This is the acephalous zooid.

In others no antennæ or palps are produced, but a more or less perfect cephalic segment is developed with one or two pairs of eyes. Here we get the first indication of sexual dimorphism in the sexual zooids.

In others two rudimentary antennæ or one pair are developed in addition to the eyes.

In others there are two pairs of antennæ in addition to the eyes.

Finally, in others again the median antennæ is added, so that there are five in all. These probably correspond to the five appendages of the original asexual form, though they do not exactly resemble them, none of the five in the sexual form being quite similar to the palps of the asexual.

In the Autolytinæ, separation of the hinder portion of the body as a sexual zooid always occurs, but the process is further complicated by the recrescence of new hinder segments before the asexual zooid is entirely separated. This process being repeated leads to the formation of chains of sexual zooids attached to the original asexual stock, the youngest member of the chain being that next to the proliferating stock. Naturally all the zooids of one chain are of the same sex. The formation of the cephalic appendages of the sexual zooid is complete, but they are not exactly similar to those of the asexual stock, nor are those of the males quite similar to those of the females.

Thus we have, in the Autolytinæ, sexual dimorphism, which is exhibited in a slight degree in the Syllidinæ, distinctly developed in the sexual zooids. Sexual dimorphism is here associated with alternation of generations, or, as it is technically termed, metagenesis, but, as I have explained above, the latter phenomenon is easily explained as resulting from the familiar process of recrescence, or new growth of lost parts. I have now to describe the sexual dimorphism in some detail in certain examples.

As in many other cases of sexual polymorphism, the three forms in the Autolytinæ were originally described as distinct genera. The asexual form was *Autolytus,* the male sexual zooid *Polybostrichus,* and the female *Sacconereis.* In all the Syllidæ the embryos are carried by the female attached to the skin, and in many cases, as in the Autolytinæ, they are contained in a sort of oval pouch attached to the ventral side of the mother. This ovigerous sac is stated to be formed by the secretion of epidermic mucous glands.

The connection of the three forms was first proved by Alexander Agassiz in 1863,[1] who studied a species on the American coast named *Autolytus cornutus.* In the asexual stock the head has three tentacles, the median being the longest (palps are rudimentary in the sub-family). The segment next the head has two pairs of cirri, one long and one

[1] *Boston Journ. Nat. Hist.,* 1863, "The Embryology of *Autolytus cornutus.*"

short. In the female sexual zooid the tentacles of the head are similar, and there are two eyes, each with two lenses, as in the asexual stock. Behind the head is a segment bearing tentacular cirri. Behind this come six segments, which have no dorsal bristles, and resemble those of the asexual stock. The segments behind these bear, in addition, the characteristic bundle of long dorsal bristles.

In the male zooid the chief differences are in the head. There are three tentacles as in the female, the median being very long and the two lateral very small. In front of these are two long bifid palps, to which there is nothing corresponding in the female. The segment behind the head, which is without bristles, bears two pairs of cirri.

There is also a constant difference between the sexes in the position of the generative organs. In the male the testes are confined to the anterior unmodified segments, which do not possess the long natatory bristles, while in the female there are ova, and probably ovaries, in every segment.

I have given illustrations of the three forms in a worm called *Myrianida*, in which the dorsal cirri are foliaceous. In this genus the hinder segments are not modified into the sexual form after they are fully formed, but a large number of new segments of small size are formed in front of the last segment of the asexual stock; heads are formed at intervals in this series of segments, and the zooids thus indicated proceed to develop into the sexual forms. This means merely that the course of development which occurs in *Autolytus* is hastened, and the future destiny of the posterior segments is indicated at a very early stage.

There is good reason to believe that all the differences above described correspond to differences in the conditions under which the three forms are developed. This fact is evident enough in the original paper of Agassiz, for he states that the asexual stock forms a case attached to the stems of the fixed

Hydroid *Campanularia*, while the sexual forms do not build cases or tubes, but swim about actively in the water, and so energetic are their motions that they frequently lose many of their natatory bundles of bristles. The asexual stock is, there-fore, a sedentary, or at times crawling worm, while the sexual

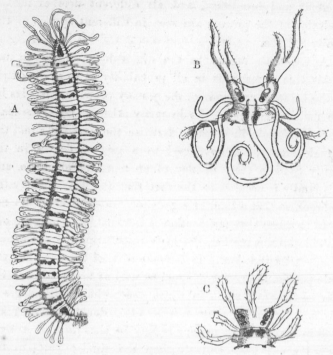

Fig. 32.—Myrianida, a marine Polychæte worm of the family Syllidæ. A, the asexual zooid, which produces at the posterior end the sexual zooids. B, the head of the male sexual zooid. C, the head of the female sexual zooid.

zooids are active swimming creatures. Thus we can under-stand how the present condition has been derived from that which occurs in other sub-families, namely, a modification of the posterior segments without separation. The worms being slender and delicate, the active motion of the hinder segments which, as was described above, occurs in the Nereidæ, caused from time to time this portion of the body to break off. The

20

formation of the head in the separated hinder portion, and
the growth of new hinder segments in the original front
portion, are simply processes of recrescence such as occur in
almost any segmented worm if it is artificially divided. The
processes being repeated in every generation have become
constant and hereditary, and all different degrees in the
evolution of the process are seen in different species of the
family Syllidæ.

Again, with regard to the dimorphism of the sexual
zooids, this corresponds in all probability to some difference
in the habitual use made of the sensory cephalic tentacles by
the male and female. As in many other animals, the male
seeks the female in order to fertilise the ova. We find the
sexual dimorphism developed to a greater degree in the
family Syllidæ than in any other marine Polychæta, and
this family is peculiar in the fact that the females carry the
embryos, so that a kind of copulation takes place. I do not
mean to assert that fertilisation is internal, but since the ova
never leave the mother, the male must approach the female
to effect fertilisation. It is possible that the palps of the
male possess the power of smell as well as touch. Whatever
may be the exact mode in which the cephalic appendages of
the male are used, there can be little doubt that they are
used in seeking the female. It may be that they are merely
moved about more actively than the similar parts in the
female or asexual stock. The sexual relations imply some
stimulation to the sensory organs of the head in the male
zooid. The tendency originally was merely to develop by
recrescence in both male and female zooid parts of the head
similar to those of the asexual stock. It is the conditions
which have modified the developments. These conditions
being associated with sexual maturity, the resulting modification is inherited only in association with sexual maturity, and
thus we have a complete explanation of the evolution of this

complicated history, which cannot be satisfactorily explained on any other view.

GEPHYREA.—These are worm-like marine animals which burrow in sand or mud, or live in holes and crevices in rocks. Though the number of species is small, their organisation is so peculiar that they cannot well be included in any of the larger sub-kingdoms, and must therefore be considered as forming a sub-kingdom by themselves. They are unsegmented animals, without lateral appendages, and the skin is soft and naked. Some of them possess bristles which resemble those of the Chætopoda. Sexual dimorphism does not appear to be exhibited by any of the Gephyrea except one, namely, *Bonellia*, but in this genus it is carried to an extreme degree.

Bonellia is a greenish-looking, sausage-shaped creature, at the anterior end of which is a long, flexible, fleshy tentacle, divided into two branches at the extremity. The body is an inch or two in length, the tentacle longer. This description applies only to the female. The male is only about one-hundredth the size, and lives parasitically, actually within the oviduct of the female. In the small male the tentacle is wanting.

The degenerate condition of the male in this case as in others, and as in both sexes of many parasitic animals, may be attributed to the direct effect of the parasitic mode of life. On the principle which I have enunciated in this work of the heredity of acquired characters in association with the conditions under which they were acquired, we can understand why the effects of the parasitic habit have been transmitted only to the males. The development of both sexes of *Bonellia* has been investigated. At a very early stage after hatching the male embryos attach themselves to the tentacle of an adult female. Up to this time they move by means of the minute vibrating processes known as cilia, but these are now lost. No mouth or anus is formed, but the

testes and ducts are developed. The immature males make
their way next into the gullet of the female, and there live
for some time, probably until they are mature or nearly so,
then they migrate to the oviduct.

The exact steps by which such a condition of things was
derived from the doubtless original condition in which the
males were similar to the females and independent, can only
be inferred from analogy and the possibilities of the conditions of life. The young of both sexes abandon the free
swimming condition at an early stage, and creep about on the
ground. Where the adults are abundant there are probably
numerous larvæ, and these would have plenty of opportunities
to creep over the tentacles of adults, and feed at their expense.
The young females would soon abandon such incipient para-
sitism, while young males, as soon as their development was
advanced enough, would possess the instinct of remaining
with the female. The eggs of an adult female would thus be
generally fertilised by a male producing sperms for the first
time, and the males of the progeny would tend to inherit the
immaturity of the father. In some such way it may have
happened that the males in successive generations became
more precocious and more parasitic, until the present condition was attained.

In the Echinodermata, including star-fishes, sea-urchins,
sea-cucumbers and feather-stars, although the sexes are with
very few exceptions in separate individuals, external sexual
differences, or sexual dimorphism, is generally absent. The
reason of this is plainly in accordance with Lamarckian
principles, for in this sub-kingdom there is not only no
copulation, but no relations between the sexes, and no
difference in the conditions under which males and females
live. Where one individual of a species can live, others are
generally in the neighbourhood, and the male and female
reproductive elements, eggs and sperms, are merely discharged

into the sea-water automatically. One great cause of the absence of special habits or instincts, is the rudimentary state of the nervous system. There are distinct strands of nervous tissue, but no differentiated ganglia, the muscular system and sensory organs are very slightly developed, and sexual instincts, for the development of which sensory organs and developed nervous centres are necessarily required, accordingly do not exist.

There ·are cases, however, among the Echinodermata in which the eggs are kept during development in some kind of external brood-pouch, and this structure, when confined to the females, constitutes a secondary difference between the sexes. The common brittle-star *Amphiura squamata* is viviparous, but here the brood pouch is a portion of the genital apparatus which occurs in both sexes. In some Holothurians, however (*Psolus ophippiger*), there is a brood-pouch on the back of the females only, a condition similar to that which occurs in certain Amphibia. The receptacle is formed by calcareous plates supported by rods projecting from the skin. In this case the special structure is a modification of parts originally existing, and unmodified in the male. The modification is evidently dependent on the stimulation produced by the presence of the eggs and embryos, without which stimulation the "variations" required to give rise to the modification would not have occurred.

COELENTERATA.—In this sub-kingdom, including jelly-fishes, polyps, corals, and sea-anemones, secondary sexual differences are generally absent, and for the same reasons as in the Echinodermata. Here also, however, occasional cases occur in which some slight difference in the female are developed in association with protection of the eggs or larvæ. In the commonest jelly-fish of our coasts, *Aurelia aurita*, the female differs slightly from the male. The difference consists in the form and length of the arms or tentacles surrounding the mouth. In the female the ova undergo the earliest stages of development in small pockets formed on the external surface of the arms, so that here again the modification is associated with the special stimulation due to the presence of the ova and larvæ, and therefore not applied to the arms of the male.

In the Hydrozoa generally, there is a very marked polymorphism associated in many cases with reproduction, though different in its relations from sexual dimorphism. I refer to that difference of the forms of individuals which constitutes what is generally called the alternation of generations. The usual history is that the egg gives rise to a polyp form having a cylindrical body with a terminal mouth surrounded with tentacles. This form of zooid does not usually produce ova but proliferates by buds, which grow into similar zooids connected with the original stock, so that a branching plant-like compound structure is produced. This hydroid stock is attached to the sea-bottom. When it is mature, however, some of the zooids produced develop into the Medusa or jelly-fish form, which become detached and swim away independently. The Medusæ produce eggs and sperms, and are of separate sexes. It is difficult to decide what was the original form of the zooid in these cases, whether the Medusa or the polyp, but it is at least obvious that the difference of structure corresponds to the difference of the conditions of life. The characteristic organ of the Medusa is the bell-shaped expansion, which is essentially a swimming organ, and constantly performs muscular contractions. Here again, therefore, we find the general principal holds, that structural evolution is controlled by functional activities dependent on the stimulations involved in the conditions of life.

INDEX

THE END

Printed by R. & R. CLARK, LIMITED, *Edinburgh.*

THE LAST LINK

OUR PRESENT KNOWLEDGE OF THE DESCENT OF MAN

BY

ERNST HAECKEL

(JENA)

WITH NOTES, BIOGRAPHICAL SKETCHES AND GLOSSARY

BY

HANS GADOW, F.R.S.

(CAMBRIDGE)

SECOND EDITION

PUBLISHED BY A. & C. BLACK, SOHO SQUARE, LONDON.

I

A

CLASSIFICATION
OF VERTEBRATA

RECENT AND EXTINCT

WITH DIAGNOSES AND DEFINITIONS, A CHAPTER

ON GEOGRAPHICAL DISTRIBUTION, AND

AN ETYMOLOGICAL INDEX

BY

HANS GADOW, M.A. Ph.D., F.R.S.

CAMBRIDGE

PUBLISHED BY A. & C. BLACK, SOHO SQUARE, LONDON.

A
DICTIONARY OF BIRDS

BY

ALFRED NEWTON, M.A., F.R.S.

Professor of Zoology and Comparative Anatomy in the University
of Cambridge

Assisted by HANS GADOW, F.R.S.; with contributions from RICHARD
LYDEKKER, B.A., F.R.S.; CHARLES S. ROY, M.A., F.R.S.; and ROBERT
W. SHUFELDT, M.D.

Specimen Illustration.

The appearance of a general work on birds by an ornithologist of the
long experience of Professor Newton may well be regarded as marking an
epoch in the science of which it treats. It is the best book of its kind which
has yet appeared."—*Natural Science.*
  "Will probably be the most useful and accurate compendium of the subject in any language."—*Nature Notes.*

Containing 340 Illustrations and a Map.

PUBLISHED BY A. & C. BLACK, SOHO SQUARE, LONDON.

*New Issue in one handy volume, demy 8vo,
720 pages.   Price 12s. 6d.*

AN INTRODUCTION

TO THE

STUDY OF FISHES

BY

ALBERT C. L. G. GÜNTHER

M.A., M.D., Ph.D., F.R.S.

KEEPER OF THE ZOOLOGICAL DEPARTMENT IN THE BRITISH MUSEUM

Specimen Illustration.

Containing 321 Illustrations

PUBLISHED BY A. & C. BLACK, SOHO SQUARE, LONDON

New Issue in one handy volume, demy 8vo, Cloth,
779 pages. Price 12s. 6d.

AN INTRODUCTION

TO THE STUDY OF

MAMMALS
LIVING AND EXTINCT

BY

WILLIAM HENRY FLOWER
C.B., F.R.S., D.C.L., LL.D., P.Z.S., F.L.S., F.G.S., &c.
LATE DIRECTOR OF THE NATURAL HISTORY DEPARTMENTS, BRITISH MUSEUM

AND

RICHARD LYDEKKER
B.A., F.G.S., F.Z.S., &c.

Specimen Illustration.

"There has been nothing resembling it—alike so exhaustive and so popular—since the time of Buffon."—*Academy.*

"A mine of valuable information well up to date."—*Nature.*

Containing 357 illustrations.

PUBLISHED BY A. & C. BLACK, SOHO SQUARE, LONDON.

5

In one volume, demy 8vo, cloth, 450 pages.
Price 18s. net

ZOOLOGY

OF

THE INVERTEBRATA

A TEXT-BOOK FOR STUDENTS

BY

ARTHUR E. SHIPLEY, M.A.

FELLOW AND ASSISTANT TUTOR OF CHRIST'S COLLEGE AND DEMONSTRATOR OF
COMPARATIVE ANATOMY IN THE UNIVERSITY OF CAMBRIDGE

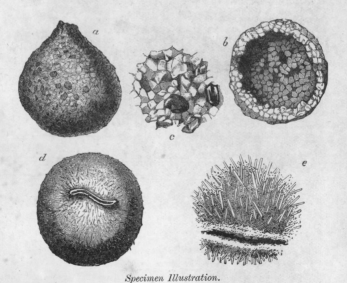

Specimen Illustration.

Containing 263 Illustrations

PUBLISHED BY A. & C. BLACK, SOHO SQUARE, LONDON

6